COMPREHENSIVE BIOCHEMISTRY

SOLE DISTRIBUTORS FOR THE UNITED STATES AND CANADA:
AMERICAN ELSEVIER PUBLISHING COMPANY, INC.
52 Vanderbilt Avenue, New York 17, N.Y.

Library of Congress Catalog Card Number 62–10359

With 103 illustrations and 17 tables

PRINTED IN THE NETHERLANDS BY
DRUKKERIJ MEIJER – WORMERVEER AND AMSTERDAM

COMPREHENSIVE BIOCHEMISTRY

COMPREHENSIVE BIOCHEMISTRY

SECTION I (VOLUMES 1–4)

PHYSICO-CHEMICAL AND ORGANIC ASPECTS OF BIOCHEMISTRY

SECTION II (VOLUMES 5–11)

CHEMISTRY OF BIOLOGICAL COMPOUNDS

SECTION III

BIOCHEMICAL REACTION MECHANISMS

SECTION IV

METABOLISM

SECTION V

CHEMICAL BIOLOGY

GENERAL INDEX

COMPREHENSIVE BIOCHEMISTRY

EDITED BY

MARCEL FLORKIN

Professor of Biochemistry, University of Liège (Belgium)

AND

ELMER H. STOTZ

Professor of Biochemistry, University of Rochester, School of Medicine and Dentistry, Rochester, N.Y. (U.S.A.)

VOLUME 3

METHODS FOR THE STUDY OF MOLECULES

ELSEVIER PUBLISHING COMPANY

AMSTERDAM · NEW YORK

1962

CONTRIBUTORS TO THIS VOLUME

L. J. BELLAMY

Explosives Research and Development Establishment, Ministry of Aviation, Waltham Abbey, Essex (Great Britain)

G. J. BULLEN, B.Sc., Ph.D., A.R.I.C.

Crystallography Laboratory, Department of Physics, Birkbeck College, University of London, W.C.1 (Great Britain)

MICHEL DAUNE

Maître de Conférences à la Faculté des Sciences de Strasbourg, Centre de Recherches sur les Macromolécules, 6, rue Boussingault, Strasbourg (France)

ANDERS EHRENBERG

Biochemical Department, Karolinska Institutet, Stockholm (Sweden)

CHRISTINE D. JARDETZKY, Ph.D.

Biological Laboratories, Harvard University, Cambridge 38, Mass. (U.S.A.)

OLEG JARDETZKY, M.D., Ph.D.

Department of Pharmacology, Harvard Medical School, Boston 15, Mass. (U.S.A.)

RICHARD ALAN MORTON, Ph.D., D.Sc., F.R.I.C., F.R.S.

Johnston Professor of Biochemistry, Department of Biochemistry, The University, Liverpool 3 (Great Britain)

NORMAN H. NACHTRIEB, Ph.D.

Department of Chemistry and Institute for the Study of Metals, University of Chicago, 5640 Ellis Avenue, Chicago 37, Ill. (U.S.A.)

CHARLES SADRON

Professeur à la Faculté des Sciences de Strasbourg, Directeur du Centre de Recherches sur les Macromolécules, 6, rue Boussingault, Strasbourg (France)

HUGO THEORELL

Biochemical Department, Karolinska Institutet, Stockholm (Sweden)

S. I. WEISSMAN, Ph.D.

Department of Chemistry, Washington University, Saint Louis 30, Mo. (U.S.A.)

GENERAL PREFACE

The Editors are keenly aware that the literature of Biochemistry is already very large, in fact so widespread that it is increasingly difficult to assemble the most pertinent material in a given area. Beyond the ordinary textbook the subject matter of the rapidly expanding knowledge of biochemistry is spread among innumerable journals, monographs, and series of reviews. The Editors believe that there is a real place for an advanced treatise in biochemistry which assembles the principal areas of the subject in a single set of books.

It would be ideal if an individual or small group of biochemists could produce such an advanced treatise, and within the time to keep reasonably abreast of rapid advances, but this is at least difficult if not impossible. Instead, the Editors with the advice of the Advisory Board, have assembled what they consider the best possible sequence of chapters written by competent authors; they must take the responsibility for inevitable gaps of subject matter and duplication which may result from this procedure.

Most evident to the modern biochemist, apart from the body of knowledge of the chemistry and metabolism of biological substances, is the extent to which he must draw from recent concepts of physical and organic chemistry, and in turn project into the vast field of biology. Thus in the organization of Comprehensive Biochemistry, the middle three sections, Chemistry of Biological Compounds, Biochemical Reaction Mechanisms, and Metabolism may be considered classical biochemistry, while the first and last sections provide selected material on the origins and projections of the subject.

It is hoped that sub-division of the sections into bound volumes will not only be convenient, but will find favour among students concerned with specialized areas, and will permit easier future revisions of the individual volumes. Toward the latter end particularly, the Editors will welcome all comments in their effort to produce a useful and efficient source of biochemical knowledge.

Liège/Rochester
July 1962

M. FLORKIN
E. H. STOTZ

PREFACE TO SECTION I

(VOLUMES 1–4)

Students and teachers of Biochemistry would not deny the importance of a sound understanding of at least certain areas of organic and physical chemistry in the comprehension of modern biochemistry. Toward this end the Editors have constituted the first section of Comprehensive Biochemistry. This section is intended neither as a textbook of organic nor of physical chemistry, but rather as a collection of chapters which seem generally pertinent in the interpretation of biochemical techniques and in the understanding of the chemistry of biological compounds and reaction mechanisms. Certain areas of organic and physical chemistry have been reserved for later presentation in context with specific biochemical topics, but the material of Section I seems to the authors to underlie all of modern biochemistry. The choice of material for Section I may well not agree with that of individual readers, and comments toward the construction of future volumes will be appreciated.

Section I has been subdivided into groups of topics designated as Atomic and Molecular Structure (Volume 1), Organic and Physical Chemistry (Volume 2), Methods for the Study of Molecules (Volume 3), and Separation Methods (Volume 4). It is hoped that all may find general favour, and that the individual volumes will find a special place on the shelf of the specialist.

Liège/Rochester
July 1962

M. FLORKIN
E. H. STOTZ

CONTENTS

VOLUME 3

METHODS FOR THE STUDY OF MOLECULES

Chapter I. Crystallography

by G. J. Bullen

Chapter II. X-Ray Diffraction

by G. J. Bullen

Chapter III. Analysis by Emission Spectroscopy

by N. H. NACHTRIEB

Chapter IV. Spectrophotometry in the Ultraviolet and Visible Regions

by R. A. MORTON

Chapter V. Infrared Spectra of Compounds of Biological Interest

by L. J. Bellamy

Chapter VI. Fluorescence

by A. Ehrenberg and H. Theorell

Chapter VII. Electronic Paramagnetic Resonance

by S. I. Weissman

Chapter VIII. Nuclear Magnetic Resonance

by C. D. Jardetzky and O. Jardetzky

Chapter IX. Determination of Mass, Form and Dimensions of Large Particles in Solution

by CH. SADRON AND M. DAUNE

The other Volumes of Section I contain the following chapters:

Volume 1. *Atomic and Molecular Structure*

Chapter I. Atomic Structure by W. PARKER ALFORD (Rochester, N.Y.)
Chapter II. Electronic Theory of Organic Molecules by H. H. JAFFÉ (Cincinnati, Ohio)
Chapter III. The Structure of Molecules by J. D. BERNAL (London)
Chapter IV. Stereoisomerism by KURT MISLOW (New York)

Volume 2. *Organic and Physical Chemistry*

Chapter I. Mechanisms of Organic Reactions by M. L. BENDER AND R. BRESLOW (Evanston, Ill. and New York, N.Y.)
Chapter II. Behaviour of Molecules in Solution by W. D. STEIN (Cambridge, Great Britain)
Chapter III. Diffusion and Osmosis by W. D. STEIN (Cambridge, Great Britain)

Volume 4. *Separation Methods*

Chapter I. Countercurrent Distribution by LYMAN C. CRAIG (New York)
Chapter II. Chromatography by E. LEDERER AND M. LEDERER (Paris and Rome)
Chapter III. Gas Chromatography by P. CHOVIN (Paris)

COMPREHENSIVE BIOCHEMISTRY

SECTION II

Chemistry of Biological Compounds

Volume 9. *Pyrrol pigments, isoprenoid compounds and phenolic plant constituents*

Chapter I. Porphyrins and metalloporphyrins
Chapter II. Physico-chemical properties of porphyrins
Chapter III. Chlorophyll
Chapter IV. The bile pigments
Chapter V. Isoprenoid compounds
Chapter VI. Vitamin A
Chapter VII. Vitamins E
Chapter VIII. Vitamins K
Chapter IX. Quinones
Chapter X. Flavonoid compounds, tannins, lignins and related compounds

Volume 10. *Sterols, bile acids and steroids*

Chapter I. Sterols
Chapter II. Bile salts
Chapter III. Steroids

Volume 11. *Water-soluble vitamins, hormones and antibiotics*

Chapter I. Thiamine
Chapter II. Riboflavin and closely related flavins
Chapter III. Niacin
Chapter IV. Vitamin B_6
Chapter V. Pantothenic acid
Chapter VI. Biotin
Chapter VII. Folic acid and pteridines
Chapter VIII. Vitamin B_{12}
Chapter IX. Plant hormones
Chapter X. Insect hormones
Chapter XI. Antibiotics

Chapter I

Crystallography

G. J. BULLEN

Birkbeck College, Crystallography Laboratory, University of London (Great Britain)

1. Introduction

The aim of the two chapters *Crystallography* and *X-ray Diffraction* is to acquaint the reader with the information, useful to him as a biochemist, that can be obtained from crystallographic studies. The former chapter deals with the crystal lattice and the terminology used to describe it and with methods of determining crystal structures from the diffraction data; in the latter are discussed the principles of X-ray diffraction and the experimental techniques used to record the diffraction pattern. We shall be concerned not only with deriving a detailed picture of the atomic and molecular arrangement from this pattern but also with the briefer measurements of unit cell dimensions and optical and other physical properties which can provide useful information quickly.

The fact that crystals diffract X-rays (and also electron and neutron beams) shows that they are made up of a regular three-dimensional arrangement of atoms or molecules in which a motif containing a relatively small number of molecules is repeated parallel to itself many thousands of times. It is this regularity of structure which is responsible for the regular external shape of the crystal though the latter is not the most characteristic manifestation of the structural regularity. Of more importance is anisotropy of properties. A crystal is homogeneous, *i.e.* it has identical properties at all points within it, but it is, in general, anisotropic; directed properties such as thermal conductivity or the speed of propagation of light depend upon direction in the crystal. The external regularity may be removed, *e.g.* by unequal growth of faces or by dissolving faces away, but the anisotropy remains.

References p. 32

2. The crystal lattice

As the internal structure of a crystal is periodic it can be discussed in terms of a lattice, which is an array of points in three dimensions such that the surroundings of each point are identical. We can choose any point in the motif as a lattice point; the array of similarly situated points in all other motifs then constitutes the lattice. The size and shape of a lattice are specified by

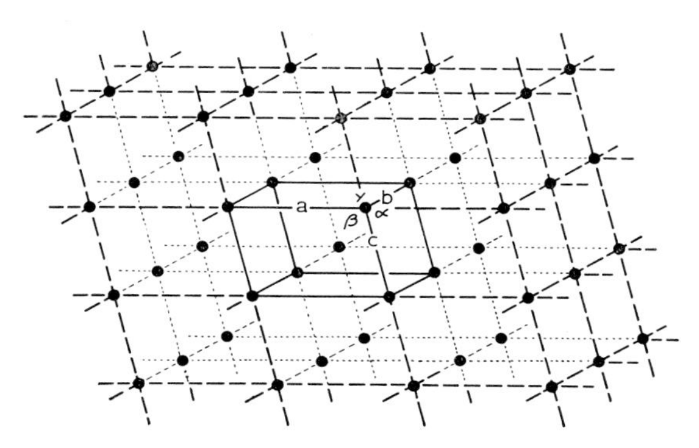

Fig. 1. A crystal lattice with one unit cell outlined. (Courtesy of K. LONSDALE, *The Centennial Review*, II (1958) 275.)

six parameters, the three primitive translations a, b and c (Fig. 1) and the three angles between them α, β and γ. The parallelepiped with sides a, b, and c, which may be taken as the motif that is repeated to form the crystal, is called the *unit cell*. The translations a, b and c are the axes of a co-ordinate system (not necessarily Cartesian) used to describe the geometry of the molecular arrangement.

If the molecules in the unit cell are arranged symmetrically, *i.e.* related in position and orientation by symmetry operations, the lattice will also possess symmetry. It is the symmetry of internal structure that is responsible for the external symmetry of the crystal faces. Crystal symmetry is described using the following symmetry elements:

(a) Rotation axes which may be 2-, 3-, 4-, or 6-fold

A figure is said to possess an X-fold rotation axis if it is brought into self-coincidence by a rotation of 360°/X about that axis. The regular tetrahedron (Fig. 2a), for example, has a 3-fold axis passing through each vertex perpendicular to the opposite face. When the tetrahedron has been rotated through 120° about one of these axes it presents the same appearance to the observer as it did before. The rotation axes are also termed diad, triad, tetrad, and hexad respectively. A 1-fold axis is equivalent to no symmetry at all, *i.e.* to identity. Lattices do not exhibit 5-fold axes or axes of order higher than 6.

(b) Rotation–inversion axes

The operation of an X-fold rotation–inversion, symbol $\bar{X}$, is one of rotation through 360°/X about the axis followed by inversion through a centre (X = 1, 2, 3, 4, or 6). The regular tetrahedron has $\bar{4}$ axes passing through the mid-points of opposite edges. The methane molecule (Fig. 2b) has tetrahedral symmetry, containing $\bar{4}$ and triad axes. The description of

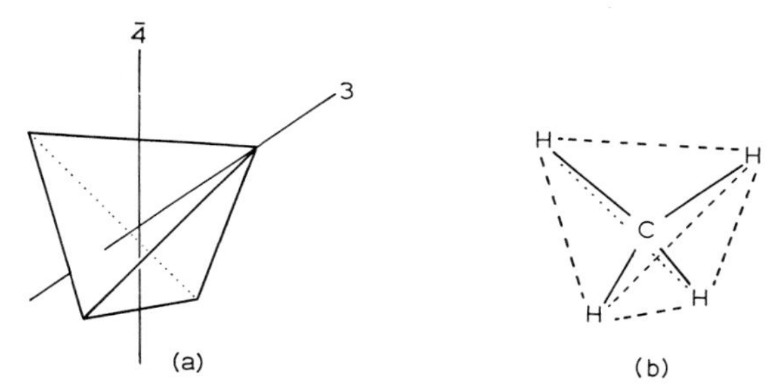

Fig. 2. (a) Symmetry axes of the regular tetrahedron; (b) The methane molecule.

all symmetry elements as either rotation axes or rotation–inversion axes has the merit of being systematic, although some rotation–inversion axes are equivalent to more familiar concepts. Thus the $\bar{1}$ axis is equivalent to a centre of symmetry, $\bar{2}$ to a mirror plane placed perpendicular to the $\bar{2}$ axis, and $\bar{6}$ to a triad axis together with a mirror plane perpendicular to it.

A given crystal may exhibit several symmetry elements passing in different directions. One in the shape of a regular tetrahedron, for example, has three $\bar{4}$ axes like that shown in Fig. 2a, four triad axes through the four vertices, and six mirror planes ($\equiv \bar{2}$) each containing an edge and bisecting the opposite edge. A combination of symmetry elements like this is called a *point group*; thirty-two point groups can be constructed using the symmetry elements described above and crystals are accordingly classified as belonging to one of thirty-two *crystal classes*. Two systems of symbols are used for point groups. In the Hermann–Mauguin system, usually preferred by crystallographers, the symbol comprises the symmetry elements required to specify the point group. For example the symbol for the symmetry of the tetrahedron is $\bar{4}3m$. The basic notation is

References p. 32

Rotation axis X, Inversion axis $\bar{X}$

Rotation axis with mirror plane normal to it X/m

Rotation (inversion) axis with mirror plane parallel to it Xm ($\bar{X}$m)

Rotation (inversion) axis with diad axis normal to it X2 ($\bar{X}$2)

Rotation axis with mirror planes both normal and parallel to it X/mm

Examples: 4/m, 4mm (two sets of mirror planes parallel to 4), $\bar{4}$2m, 4/mmm.

For a full explanation of point-group symbols the reader should consult Volume I of *International Tables for X-ray Crystallography*[1].

The shape of the lattice, *i.e.* the relative lengths of a, b and c, and the values of the interaxial angles, depends upon the symmetry of the arrangement of the molecules in the unit cell. For example, if the point group of the crystal is one containing a tetrad axis, the lattice must have a square cross-section, *i.e.* $a = b$ (taking c parallel to the tetrad) and $\alpha = \beta = \gamma = 90°$. The crystal classes are arranged in seven systems each characterized by the possession of a certain minimum symmetry and a consequent shape of lattice. The systems are listed in Table I with the minimum symmetry required for each and the corresponding relations between the axial parameters.

TABLE I

CRYSTAL SYSTEMS

System	*Minimum symmetry*	*Axial and angular relationships*
Triclinic	None *or* centre of symmetry only	$a \neq b \neq c$ $\alpha \neq \beta \neq \gamma \neq 90°$
Monoclinic	One 2-fold axis (rotation or inversion) usually placed parallel to b	$a \neq b \neq c$ $\alpha = \gamma = 90°, \beta \neq 90°$
Orthorhombic	Three mutually perpendicular 2-fold axes (rotation or inversion) parallel to a, b, c	$a \neq b \neq c$ $\alpha = \beta = \gamma = 90°$
Tetragonal	One 4-fold axis (rotation or inversion) placed parallel to c	$a = b \neq c$ $\alpha = \beta = \gamma = 90°$
Hexagonal	One 6-fold axis (rotation or inversion) placed parallel to c	$a = b \neq c$ $\alpha = \beta = 90°, \gamma = 120°$
Trigonal	One 3-fold axis (rotation or inversion) parallel to c (using hexagonal axes) or to [111] (using rhombohedral axes)	Hexagonal axes: $a = b \neq c$ $\alpha = \beta = 90°, \gamma = 120°$ Rhombohedral axes: $a = b = c$ $\alpha = \beta = \gamma < 120° \neq 90°$
Cubic	Four 3-fold axes each inclined at 54°44′ to the crystallographic axes	$a = b = c$ $\alpha = \beta = \gamma = 90°$

Note: The sign $\neq$ is used to mean "is not necessarily equal to"; equality may occur accidentally, though not as a consequence of symmetry.

A lattice may be primitive (symbol P), with only one lattice point in each unit cell (as in Fig. 1), or centred, with 2, 3 or 4 lattice points to each cell. For example Fig. 3 shows the cubic lattices. Besides the P lattice we can have a body-centred (I) lattice with a lattice point at the centre of the unit cell as well as at each corner, or an all-face-centred (F) lattice where the mid-points of the faces are lattice points (4 points per cell). In systems with lower symmetry there may be centring of only one pair of opposite faces of the cell (A, B, or C depending on which faces are centred). As trigonal and hexagonal lattices have the same shape, one system of axes (called hexagonal) is used for both. In the trigonal system the unit cell based on hexagonal axes can contain three lattice points, spaced equally along a

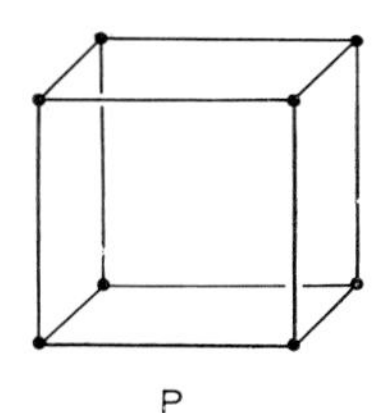

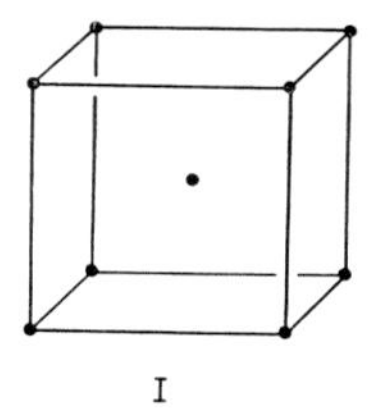

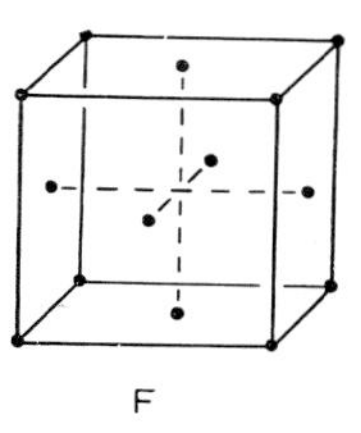

Fig. 3. The three cubic lattices.

body diagonal of the cell. The lattice is known as rhombohedral (R) because it can be described using the alternative system of rhombohedral axes. Note that the lattice becomes primitive if rhombohedral axes are used, but is centred when described in terms of hexagonal axes. In other words the rhombohedral unit cell has one-third the volume of the corresponding hexagonal cell and has lattice points only at its corners. The lattice symbol is R whichever system of axes is used. There are also trigonal crystals which have a unit cell based on hexagonal axes which is primitive. They have a P lattice and can in no circumstances be described using rhombohedral axes. In all there are 14 different lattices, known as Bravais lattices, distributed among the 7 systems.

For the purpose of interpreting X-ray diffraction by means of the Bragg equation (see Chapter II, p. 35) lattice points are considered as lying on sets of equidistant parallel planes (see Fig. 4 for a two-dimensional example). The orientation and spacing of a set of planes are specified by three indices h, k, l (called Miller indices) derived from the intercepts a/h, b/k, c/l, made on the crystallographic (lattice) axes by that plane in the set which is closest to but does not pass through the origin. As a consequence of the planes being drawn through lattice points, these intercepts will always be simple sub-multiples of a, b, c, so that the Miller indices will be positive or negative integers (except that when a plane is parallel to an axis, the intercept will

References p. 32

be infinite and the index zero). Defined in this way h, k, l cannot contain a common factor (but see Chapter II, p. 35 for a modification). The symbol (hkl) is used to denote the complete set of parallel planes. The distance between any two adjacent parallel planes or interplanar spacing d can be evaluated in terms of the Miller indices (the expression depends on the shape of the lattice, *e.g.* for an orthorhombic lattice, $1/d^2 = h^2/a^2 + k^2/b^2 + l^2/c^2$). In general as h, k, l increase, d decreases, *i.e.* the planes become closer together. Widely spaced planes such as (11) in Fig. 4 (two indices only are used for this two-dimensional example) are populated by many lattice points while planes with higher indices such as (23) contain fewer points. It is a fact of observation, expressed as the Law of Rational Indices, that the

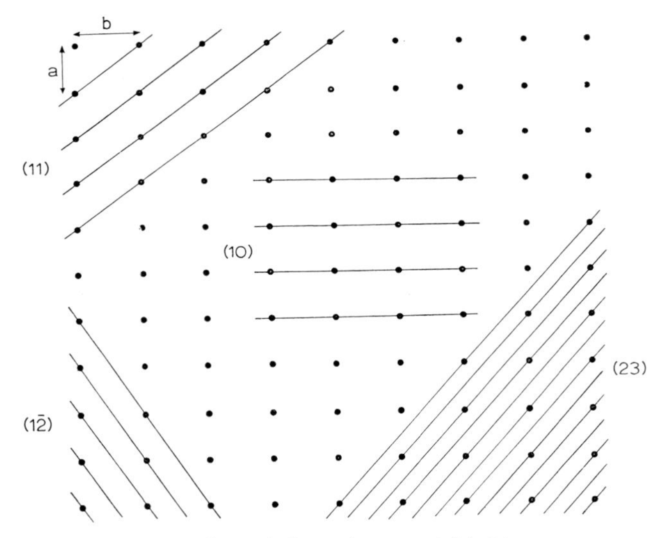

Fig. 4. Sets of planes in a crystal lattice.

external faces of a crystal are parallel to lattice planes with low indices (rarely greater than 3), *i.e.* planes clos ly populated by lattice points.

When a number of different lattice planes are parallel to a common direction, that direction, parallel to a row of lattice points, is called a zone axis. The most obvious zone axes are the crystallographic axes; for example, all $(hk0)$ planes will intersect in a zone axis parallel to c. If the co-ordinates of the first lattice point from the origin on the row of points parallel to a zone axis are ua, vb, wc (u, v, w being integers) the zone axis is given the symbol $[uvw]$. Co-ordinates of points in the unit cell are expressed as fractions of the cell edges a, b, c, *e.g.* the point (x, y, z) has actual co-ordinates (in Å say)

xa, yb, zc. Thus ($\frac{1}{2}$, $\frac{1}{2}$, $\frac{1}{2}$) is the centre of the cell, ($\frac{1}{2}$, $\frac{1}{2}$, 0) the mid-point of the c face (the face parallel to a and b).

There are two further types of symmetry element which can occur in a crystal structure based on an infinite lattice but which cannot express the symmetry of a finite body such as a single crystal or a molecule. These are the screw axis and the glide plane. The operation of a screw axis X_n ($n < X$) is one of rotation through 360°/X followed by translation parallel to the axis by a fraction n/X of the lattice translation in that direction. A 2_1 screw, for example, involves rotation through 180° and translation by one half the lattice translation (Fig. 5) so that by two consecutive operations an atom is transferred to a similarly situated point in the next unit cell. Further operations produce a screw motion through the lattice. It is obvious that the incorporation of translation prevents one applying this symmetry to a finite body. There are no inversion screw axes.

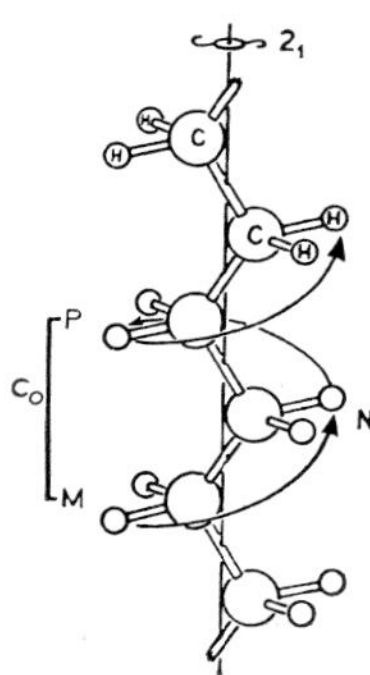

Fig. 5. A 2_1 screw axis relating the CH_2 groups of the polyethylene chain. Group M is brought successively to positions N, P, and so on, by rotation through 180° followed by translation along the axis by $\frac{1}{2}c_0$ (c_0 is the lattice translation). It is not necessary that, as here, the units (CH_2 groups) related by the screw be part of the same chemical molecule. Each could as well be an isolated molecule. (Courtesy of C. W. Bunn, *Chemical Crystallography*, Oxford University Press, 1945, p. 230.)

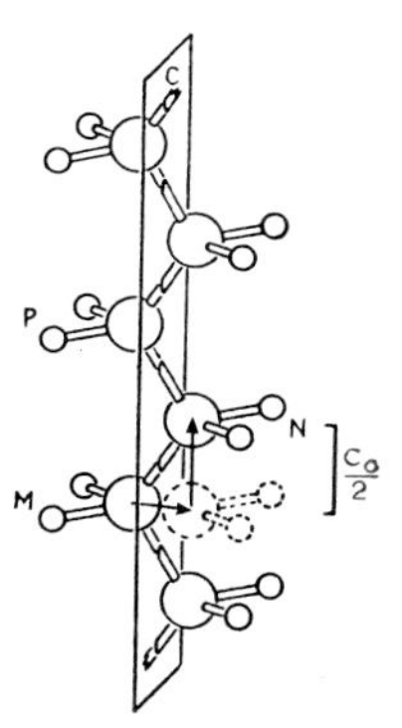

Fig. 6. Use of a c glide plane to relate the CH_2 groups of the polyethylene chain. Group M is moved to N by reflection in the plane followed by a translation of $\frac{1}{2}c_0$, and so on. (Courtesy of C. W. Bunn, *Chemical Crystallography*, Oxford University Press, 1945, p. 230.)

Glide planes a, b, c, n involve the operation of reflexion followed by a translation (parallel to the symmetry plane) of half a cell dimension (lattice translation) in the a, b, c or diagonal directions respectively (Fig. 6). When the lattice is non-primitive it is possible to have a d glide plane for which the translation is by one quarter of the diagonal.

A complete description of the symmetry of the atomic arrangement, *i.e.* of the space group, requires specification of the Bravais lattice and of the

References p. 32

combination of symmetry elements present, which can include screw axes and glide planes in addition to the simple elements occurring in point groups. There are 230 space groups, each designated by a Bravais lattice symbol followed by a symbol of point-group type but where appropriate including translational elements, *e.g.* P4/m, $I4_1$/a, I4mm, $P4_2$cm. Information about the space group can be gained from the X-ray diffraction pattern since the occurrence of lattice centring, glide planes or screw axes causes certain systematic restrictions on the values of h, k, l of the X-ray reflexions. For example, an I lattice requires that only those reflexions occur which have $(h + k + l)$ even whereas a P lattice permits all values of h, k, l. Glide planes and screw axes affect only limited groups of reflexions, *e.g.* a glide plane parallel to (001) with translation component $b/2$ restricts the $(hk0)$ reflexions to those with $k = 2n$, n being integral; it does not affect other groups of reflexions. A screw axis parallel to c requires $(00l)$ reflexions to have $l = 2n$ if it is a 2_1 axis, $l = 3n$ if 3_1, etc. These restrictions are called systematic absences of X-ray reflexions. For a full list of them see *International Tables for X-ray Crystallography*[2]. Unfortunately systematic absences will not always determine the space group uniquely. They would do so (except in a very few cases) provided the crystal class were known. The system can be deduced from the shape and symmetry of the reciprocal lattice as shown in the X-ray photographs but the crystal class cannot because the X-ray pattern is always centrosymmetric even when the crystal class is not. Thus in the monoclinic system, crystals of the non-centrosymmetric classes 2 and m show the same reciprocal lattice symmetry as those of the centrosymmetric class 2/m. It is thus impossible to distinguish space group $P2_1$ from space group $P2_1$/m, or Pa from P2/a, because within each pair both space groups cause the same systematic absences. The classical method of determining crystal class from the external symmetry of the crystal is not reliable because the faces are often not properly developed, so that the apparent symmetry is higher than the true symmetry. There are other methods (not always successful), such as tests for piezoelectricity, statistical surveys of intensities and so on, which are used to choose the correct space group from those indicated by the systematic absences, but these are beyond the scope of this brief survey.

(c) General and special positions

The space group shows the symmetry relations between the molecules in the unit cell just as the point group shows the symmetry of the external crystal faces. Each space group implies, in general, a certain grouping and therefore a certain number of molecules in the unit cell. A crystal with, for example, space group Pm may have two molecules in the unit cell, one placed on each side of the mirror plane. Similarly in P2 there can be two molecules related by the diad axis. If we have both the diad axis and the mirror plane present, as in P2/m, then four molecules are required to satisfy the symmetry. As there is freedom of choice as to the actual positions of the molecules provided they are arranged symmetrically with respect to the symmetry elements, the molecules are said to occupy *general positions* in the unit cell.

If the molecule itself can contain symmetry then it may occupy a position on one of the crystallographic symmetry elements. A molecule possessing a plane of symmetry, for example, may lie on the m plane in Pm so that two half-molecules are related by the mirror symmetry. It is possible then to have a unit cell containing only one molecule, which occupies a special position, *i.e.* a position on a symmetry element. In P2/m there are three possible types of special positions (*i*) on the m plane, (*ii*) on the diad axis, (*iii*) on both the diad and the m plane, *i.e.* at their intersection, the molecule then having symmetry 2/m. Some space groups contain no special positions because they involve only screw axes or glide planes, and finite molecules cannot contain these translational symmetry elements. Examples are $P2_1$, Pc, $P2_12_12_1$. Note, however, that there are special positions in $P2_1/c$. Although it appears from the symbol that this space group contains only a screw axis and a glide plane, there are also centres of symmetry which molecules may occupy. Such centres are always produced by the combination of a 2-fold axis (whether 2 or 2_1) with a symmetry plane (whether m or glide) normal to it. In space groups $P2_1$ and Pc, there must then be at least two molecules in the unit cell (there may be a multiple of 2), and in $P2_12_12_1$ at least four. These restrictions on the number of molecules in the unit cell may be useful for molecular weight determination (see p. 15).

3. Optical properties of crystals

The behaviour of light passing through an isotropic medium such as a liquid is independent of the direction of travel and is described solely by the refractive index of the medium (excluding the phenomenon of rotation of the plane of polarization). Crystals, apart from those of the cubic system, are anisotropic, the refractive index depending on the direction of propagation. This is because the speed of light depends upon the sequence of atoms encountered and since the sequence is different in different directions in a crystal the refractive index is not constant. In cubic crystals the sequence is the same along all three axial directions. It is a consequence of this that the speed of light is the same not only in these three directions but in all other directions so that the crystals are isotropic. Since the crystal structure of each solid substance is unique, every crystal will have unique optical properties which are invaluable as a means of identification of the substance.

References p. 32

In addition, as it is the regular atomic and molecular arrangement that is responsible for the anisotropy of optical properties, a study of these properties should provide information about the way the molecules are packed together.

Light passing through an anisotropic crystal undergoes double refraction, *i.e.* a ray of light entering the crystal is divided into two rays polarized in planes at right angles to one another which travel with different speeds in the crystal. Let us consider first crystals of the hexagonal, trigonal and tetragonal systems. One ray, the ordinary ray, travels with the same speed in all directions, the wave surface being a sphere and the refractive index constant. For the other ray, the extraordinary ray, the wave surface is an ellipsoid of revolution so that the speed of propagation and the refractive index are different in different directions. The axis of revolution coincides

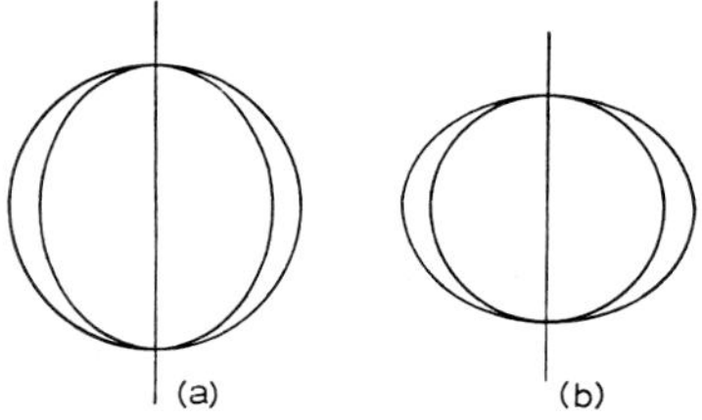

Fig. 7. Wave surfaces in a uniaxial crystal: (a) positive crystal, (b) negative crystal.

with the unique axis of the crystal (hexad, triad, or tetrad, as the case may be). Along this one axis the extraordinary and ordinary rays travel with the same speed so that the ellipsoid and sphere touch at two opposite points, the ellipsoid lying either wholly within the sphere (optically positive crystals) or wholly outside it (optically negative) (Fig. 7). Light travelling in this direction, called the optic axis, has the same refractive index for both rays. In crystals of these three systems there is only one optic axis and they are therefore termed uniaxial crystals.

The refractive indices in other directions are best discussed in terms of the indicatrix constructed as follows. From a point within the crystal lines are drawn in all directions, the length of each line being proportional to the refractive index for light vibrating along that line. The ends of these lines fall on the surface of an ellipsoid of revolution, called the indicatrix, which has the same shape and orientation as the wave surface of the extraordinary ray (Fig. 7). The optic axis is the axis of rotation of the indicatrix, and the two principal axes in the circular section perpendicular to it, *i.e.* two of the radii, are equal to ω, the refractive index of the ordinary ray. The third principal axis is ε, either the greatest (positive crystals) or the least (negative crystals) refractive index exhibited by the extraordinary ray. ω and ε are known as the principal refractive indices of a uniaxial crystal. The difference $\varepsilon - \omega$, which may be either positive or negative, is known as the birefringence of the crystal. It can be found by measuring the refractive indices ε and ω exhibited by a crystal section containing the optic axis. Sections normal to the optic axis, parallel to the circular section of the indicatrix, have both refractive indices equal to ω and are therefore isotropic.

The indicatrix for crystals of the remaining systems, orthorhombic, monoclinic, and triclinic, is a general type of ellipsoid with three unequal principal axes, corresponding to which there are three principal refractive indices, α (least), β and γ (greatest). Note that β is not necessarily the mean of α and γ. It is always possible to find two circular cross-sections of such an ellipsoid and so there are two sections in the crystal which are isotropic and two optic axes (Fig. 8). These crystals are therefore termed biaxial. The

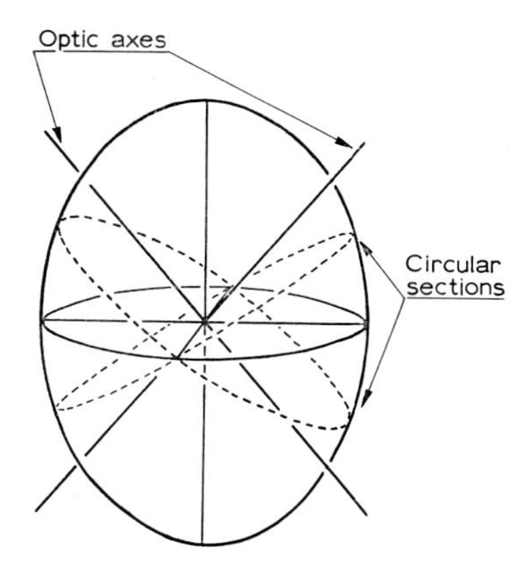

Fig. 8. Biaxial indicatrix.

orientation of the indicatrix is related to the symmetry axes (where present) in the crystal. Thus in an orthorhombic crystal, the three principal axes are parallel to the three crystallographic axes; in the monoclinic system one of the principal axes (either α, β or γ) is parallel to the two-fold axis, usually taken as b, but the other two may lie anywhere in the ac plane. For triclinic crystals there is no restriction whatever on the orientation of the indicatrix with respect to the crystallographic axes.

When an anisotropic crystal section is viewed under the polarising microscope using crossed polars (*i.e.* a polarizer and analyzer with their vibration directions mutually perpendicular) and the stage is rotated, the crystal will be observed to extinguish (*i.e.* to become dark) in four positions at intervals of 90°. At the position in which extinction occurs, if the eyepiece cross-wires, which indicate the vibration directions of the polarizer and

References p. 32

TABLE II

CORRELATION OF OPTICAL CHARACTER AND STRUCTURE

Shape of molecules and their arrangement	*Optical character*	*Deduced molecular orientation*	*Examples*
1. *Flat molecules placed*			
(*a*) all parallel	High negative birefringence	Molecules perpendicular to vibration direction of least refractive index	Uracil, diketopiperazine
(*b*) parallel to one direction but not to each other	High positive birefringence	Common molecular direction parallel to vibration direction of greatest index	Urea, ribonucleic acid in rod-shaped viruses
2. *Rod-shaped molecules placed*			
(*a*) all parallel	High positive birefringence	Length of molecule parallel to vibration direction of greatest index	*trans* β-ionylidene crotonic acid, cellulose, nylon
(*b*) in parallel planes but not parallel to each other	High negative birefringence	Planes of molecules perpendicular to vibration direction of least index	Octadecyl ammonium chloride
3. *Quasi-spherical molecules* in any arrangement *or flat or rod-shaped molecules* inclined to each other	Low birefringence or isotropic	Orientation cannot be deduced	Strychnine hydrobromide, hexamethylenetetramine

analyzer, are parallel to the length of the crystal or to a prominent edge, the extinction is said to be *straight* or *parallel*; if the cross-wires bisect the angle between two prominent edges, there is *symmetrical* extinction. If neither of these is observed the extinction is *oblique*. The type of extinction is of value in indicating the crystal system. Straight or symmetrical extinction can only occur when the axes of the indicatrix are parallel to crystallographic axes, *i.e.* for tetragonal, trigonal, hexagonal, and orthorhombic crystals and also for monoclinic crystals when b is parallel to a cross-wire. A section of a monoclinic crystal parallel to (010) will show oblique extinction.

Biaxial crystals are also classified as positive or negative. The criterion of classification will not be explained here but it is often (but not always) true to say that a biaxial positive crystal has β nearer in magnitude to α than to γ; *i.e.* there are two small and one large principal refractive indices (*cf.* uniaxial positive also with two small (ω) and one large (ε) indices). Conversely a negative crystal has two large and one small indices. The birefringence of a biaxial crystal is equal to $\gamma - \alpha$. For information on the measurement of refractive index the reader is advised to consult *Chemical Crystallography*[3], or *Crystals and the Polarising Microscope*[4].

A knowledge of the principal refractive indices or even of just the birefringence can be very useful in determining the molecular shape and orientation in a crystal. Where flat molecules, particularly those having molecular orbitals of large area, are arranged parallel to each other in the structure, light vibrating parallel to the molecular plane will have a much larger refractive index than light vibrating perpendicular to the plane. Such crystals will be optically negative with a high birefringence. Similar considerations applied to other arrangements of flat or rod-like molecules lead to the general correlation of optical character and structure given in Table II. Polymeric molecules such as cellulose fibres, provided they are extended, show high positive birefringence. Wool, on the other hand, is only weakly birefringent showing probably that the chains are not extended.

Measurements of diamagnetic anisotropy are also useful for suggesting the molecular orientation, particularly where the molecules are planar. If the flat molecules are packed parallel, the numerically largest diamagnetic susceptibility (*i.e.* the lowest since the susceptibility is negative) lies perpendicular to the molecular plane. When the molecules are inclined to each other, the resultant diamagnetic susceptibility is the algebraic sum of the contributions from all the molecules. The magnetic anisotropy for any proposed structure can be calculated and compared with the experimental value[5].

4. The use of preliminary crystallographic data

A study of the X-ray diffraction pattern of a crystal, taken to the extreme

References p. 32

of complete structure determination, is capable of producing a detailed description of the molecular geometry, both intra- and intermolecular, and of the electron density distribution around the atoms. This, however, can be a very lengthy process and it is therefore profitable to consider what information the chemist can obtain from only a brief crystallographic study. We may divide the process of crystal structure analysis into six stages according to the information gained at each stage, *viz.* (*i*) identification of the substance, (*ii*) molecular weight determination, (*iii*) suggestions as to molecular shape, size, and orientation, (*iv*) structural formula, (*v*) bond lengths and angles—the stereochemistry, (*vi*) detailed electron density distribution. For the first three stages, which will be discussed in this section, the simple measurements of unit cell dimensions, space group and crystal density suffice, possibly supplemented by optical or magnetic data. The results of these measurements are referred to as preliminary crystallographic data.

(i) Identification by the X-ray powder method (see Chapter II, p. 44)

The disposition of lines in the powder pattern and their relative intensities are specific for each crystalline substance (except for isomorphous substances containing elements of similar atomic number). The method is easier to apply than the single-crystal method because the larger, well-formed crystals set accurately on the X-ray camera which are needed for the latter method are not required. The material used is not destroyed as in chemical analysis. Identification from the powder pattern may be approached in two ways:

(a) In a limited research field, where the same substances are likely to recur, a library of standard powder photographs of known substances can be collected. Photographs of unknown products are compared directly with the standards.

(b) When it is impossible to predict what the unknown substance might be, the interplanar spacings and relative intensities of the powder lines must be measured and the results compared with tabulated data for known substances. This is done by using the A.S.T.M. powder data file, which consists of cards, one for each substance, on which are listed the known powder data. The file is used in conjunction with a book-index in which are listed, in Hanawalt groups according to interplanar spacing, the three strongest lines for each substance. There are thus three entries in the index for a substance each of which gives the same index number leading to the appropriate card in the file. To use the file, the three strongest lines in the pattern of the unknown material are chosen and their d and intensity I (relative to $I_1 = 100$ for the strongest line) are measured. A search is made in the index for the three entries referring to the same card which fit most nearly the observed d and I values. The rest of the powder pattern is then checked against the full data given on the card. The card includes also any other available

crystallographic data such as system, optical data, etc. For a fuller discussion of the powder method the reader is referred to *X-ray Diffraction by Polycrystalline Materials*[6].

(ii) Molecular weight determination

For this we require the dimensions of the unit cell in order to calculate its volume V_c which for the most general case, the triclinic system, is given by

$$V_c = abc\,(1 - \cos^2\alpha - \cos^2\beta - \cos^2\gamma + 2\cos\alpha\cos\beta\cos\gamma)^{\frac{1}{2}} \qquad (1)$$

In favourable cases, *viz.* cubic, hexagonal or tetragonal crystals with small unit cells, the unit-cell dimensions can be found from powder photographs but generally it will be necessary to use single crystal photographs, calculating the lattice constants from layer line separations, and so on. The molecular weight M is related to the density ρ of the crystal in g/ml by

$$M = \frac{\rho V_c}{1.660\,n} \qquad (2)$$

where n is the number of molecules in the unit cell and V_c is expressed in $Å^3$. When the density has been measured, usually by the flotation technique, the product nM can be calculated directly from experimental measurements. The course subsequently taken depends on whether either M or n or neither is already known.

When M is known, we can use eqn. (2) to calculate the number of molecules in the unit cell; this number must be an integer so that even if M is known only approximately we can usually choose the correct value for n. Having done this, eqn. (2) can be used to recalculate M. This means of obtaining an accurate molecular weight from an approximate one has been used in particular for proteins, *e.g.* lysozyme[7], ribonuclease[8], β-lactoglobulin[9].

It is possible in certain cases to use knowledge of the space-group symmetry to place a limit on the value of n and hence on the molecular weight. For example, in space groups which contain no symmetry elements other than screw axes or glide planes, molecules cannot occupy special positions and n must be a multiple of the number of general positions in the unit cell, *e.g.* in $P2_1$ n must be a multiple of 2 and in $P2_12_12_1$ a multiple of 4.

(iii) Molecular size, shape and symmetry

Knowledge of unit-cell dimensions and space group can be used to place restrictions on the *molecular size, shape and symmetry*. A classic

References p. 32

example was the discovery by Bernal[10] that the Windaus–Wieland skeletal formula for sterols is at variance with the probable molecular dimensions of calciferol, ergosterol and cholesterol, as deduced from their unit-cell dimensions. This discovery was one of the factors which led Rosenheim and King[11] to suggest a new formula, now proved to be correct.

Where the number of molecules in the unit cell, deduced from eqn. (2) is smaller than the number of general positions, the molecules must occupy special positions on symmetry elements (see p. 8). In those space groups where only one type of special position is possible, the minimum molecular symmetry is immediately apparent. Such deductions showed that the substance formerly thought to be dihydroxymaleic acid was actually dihydroxyfumaric acid[12]. It crystallises with only 2 molecules in the unit cell, space group $P2_1/c$. The only special positions in $P2_1/c$ are centres of symmetry. The molecules must occupy these positions and are therefore *trans*.

However, such deductions must be treated with some caution. Many cases are now being found where the crystal structure is disordered with asymmetric molecules arranged statistically in different orientations, so that the *average molecule* appears to contain symmetry. To ensure that this is not the case one should cool the crystal to as low a temperature as possible to see if there is a transition to an ordered structure exhibiting less symmetry.

Optical and magnetic properties (see p. 12) can be used in conjunction with cell dimension measurements to suggest the orientation of the molecules in the crystal and possibly assist in the choice of molecular structure. Deductions based on optical birefringence and unit-cell dimensions were, for example, used in the early stages of the crystal structure analysis of Na, K, and Rb benzyl penicillin[13]. Measurement of magnetic anisotropy is particularly useful in suggesting the orientation in the unit cell of flat aromatic molecules; it was used in early work on the structures of naphthalene and anthracene[14].

5. Methods of determining crystal structure

To obtain the information discussed in the previous section only the geometry of the X-ray reflexions, *i.e.* their positions on the film, has been used. To proceed further to a solution of the crystal structure we must use the intensities of the reflexions, which are dependent on the arrangement of the atoms in the unit cell (see Chapter II, p. 47). It is a big step from stage (*iii*) to stage (*iv*) because, whereas the time taken to make the preliminary measurements can be counted in days, the measurement of the intensities and the subsequent calculations may take many months. In addition the process is not direct because we can measure only the structure amplitude

$|F(hkl)|$ for each reflexion; the phase $\alpha(hkl)$ is lost (Chapter II, p. 50). This means that we cannot proceed direct from measurement of intensities to calculate a Fourier synthesis for the electron density distribution. It is necessary to propose, by some means, a likely arrangement of the atoms in the unit cell—a trial structure—and to calculate for this arrangement $|F(hkl)|$ and $\alpha(hkl)$ for all the reflexions. If there is at least fairly good agreement between the calculated and observed intensities we can be confident that the calculated values $\alpha(hkl)$ are somewhere near the truth and we can proceed to the Fourier synthesis using the *observed* $|F(hkl)|$ and *calculated* $\alpha(hkl)$. Provided the trial structure is substantially correct the calculated electron density distribution will contain peaks corresponding to the atoms in the unit cell. If the *calculated* $|F(hkl)|$ had been used for the Fourier synthesis, the electron density distribution would show peaks at exactly the positions postulated in the trial structure. Since we have used the *observed* $|F(hkl)|$ the positions of the peaks should be a little nearer to the correct answer than the trial structure co-ordinates. These improved positions are then used to calculate a second set of structure factors, giving new and better values of $\alpha(hkl)$, which are in turn used to obtain a second Fourier synthesis. The improvement of co-ordinates by this alternate calculation of structure factors and Fourier synthesis constitutes the process of *Fourier refinement*.

The calculation of the electron density throughout the whole unit cell in three dimensions requires the inclusion of all the observed X-ray reflexions, the so-called three-dimensional data, in the Fourier summation. Since the measurement of all these intensities is a long and tedious task and in order to reduce the size of the calculations, it is usual in the early stages of Fourier refinement, to calculate only projections of the electron density onto planes perpendicular to the crystallographic axes. For a projection only a small group of reflexions are needed, those from planes which are parallel to the axis of projection. For example, $(hk0)$ reflexions are used for the projection down the c axis (*i.e.* a projection onto (001) if the system is orthogonal) calculated from

$$\rho(XY) = \frac{1}{A_c} \sum_h \sum_k F(hk0) \exp\left[-2\pi i(hX + kY)\right]$$

where A_c is the area of the cross-section of the unit cell perpendicular to c. A group of reflexions such as $(hk0)$ are contained in one layer of the reciprocal lattice and can therefore all be collected on one Weissenberg or precession photograph.

The remainder of this chapter will be devoted to outlining some of the methods used to obtain the trial structure.

References p. 32

(a) Use of outstandingly strong reflexions

In a crystal structure where all the atoms in the molecule are of approximately the same weight (*i.e.* of similar atomic number) the occurrence of an X-ray reflexion outstandingly stronger than other reflexions of similar sin θ signifies that the atoms are arranged in or close to the plane giving rise to this reflexion. With some knowledge of molecular shape and information from optical properties a small number of strong reflexions can be used to select a trial structure. In the structure analysis of uracil[15], for instance, from the observations that 00*l* reflexions are very strong, (001) is a cleavage plane, and the crystal has a large negative birefringence, it was clear that the molecules are arranged in layers parallel to the (001) plane. In order to choose the positions of the molecules within a layer, *i.e.* to find the x and y atomic co-ordinates, use was made of the outstandingly strong reflexions 360 and 0.10.0. The interplanar spacing, 1.23Å, of (0.10.0) is approximately half the width of a pyrimidine ring. This suggested placing one side of the ring in this plane because then all six atoms in the ring would lie on (0.10.0) planes and make the maximum contribution to the structure factor (see Fig. 9). The molecules were placed in this orientation in the (001) plane so

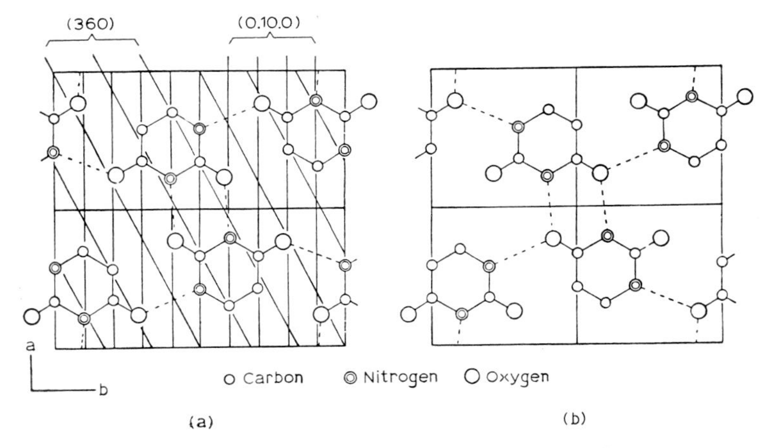

Fig. 9. Arrangement of molecules in the uracil crystal. (Courtesy of G. S. PARRY, *Acta Cryst.*, 7 (1954) 313.)

that the atoms also lie near to the strong (360) plane and so that there are no unusually close intermolecular distances. The structure initially chosen (Fig. 9a) was later modified to that shown in Fig. 9b when refinement indicated that one N and one C atom should be transposed. It is clear that in this analysis previous knowledge of the probable size of the pyrimidine ring and of intermolecular contacts has played a considerable part in the selection of a trial structure and that this could not have been so in the first structure analyses carried out many years ago. Reliance on this accumulated knowledge is reasonable, provided the final agreement between observed and calculated intensities for the fully refined structure is good enough to justify it.

(b) The Patterson synthesis

It was first suggested by Patterson[16] that the function

$$P(\mathrm{U, V, W}) = \frac{1}{V_c} \sum_h \sum_k \sum_l |F(hkl)|^2 \cos 2\pi(h\mathrm{U} + k\mathrm{V} + l\mathrm{W})$$

similar to the Fourier synthesis (see Chapter II, p. 50) but with $|F(hkl)|^2$ as coefficients in place of $F(hkl)$, could be of use in crystal structure analysis. The physical significance of the Patterson synthesis is that when there are two atoms in the structure at points (x_1, y_1, z_1) and (x_2, y_2, z_2), a peak occurs at point (U, V, W) in the Patterson such that $x_1 - x_2 = \mathrm{U}$, $y_1 - y_2 = \mathrm{V}$, $z_1 - z_2 = \mathrm{W}$, *i.e.*, the line joining the origin to point (U, V, W) is the vector between the two atoms. If the Patterson peaks can be assigned (*i*) to vectors between atoms within the molecule, the orientation and size of the molecule are immediately known, and (*ii*) to vectors between atoms in different molecules, the mutual placing of the molecules in the structure can be found. The great merit of the method is that the function can be calculated directly from the experimental data because $|F(hkl)|^2$ is known from the intensity, and no phase angles are involved. For this reason the Patterson synthesis, particularly when used in conjunction with the heavy-atom technique described on p. 24, is the most important and widely applied method for solving crystal structures so far known.

As an example of this method we shall take first the solution of the structure of N-acetylglycine[17]. This is another layer structure, all the molecules lying in the (100) plane of the monoclinic unit cell ($a = 4.86$, $b = 11.54$, $c = 14.63$ Å, $\beta = 138.2°$). The problem is then to find the y- and z-coordinates of the atoms. The Patterson projection down [100] was calculated using an expression analogous to that for Fourier projections. The part of the function lying within 3 Å of the origin is shown in Fig. 10a and a portion of the Fourier synthesis (calculated subsequently) which shows the molecule, in Fig. 10b. Since most intermolecular distances are expected to be greater than 3 Å, this region of the Patterson function will contain peaks corresponding only to vectors within the molecule. The innermost peaks, at ~ 1.4 Å, correspond to vectors between atoms directly bonded, such as

References p. 32

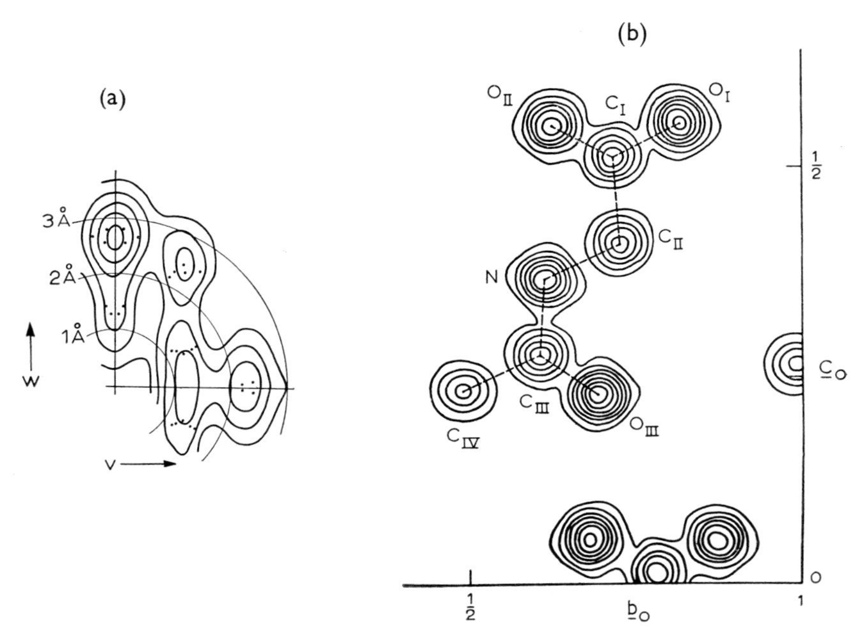

Fig. 10. (a) Part of the Patterson function for N-acetylglycine; (b) Fourier synthesis of N-acetylglycine. (Courtesy of G. B. CARPENTER AND J. DONOHUE, *J. Am. Chem. Soc.*, 72 (1950) 2315.)

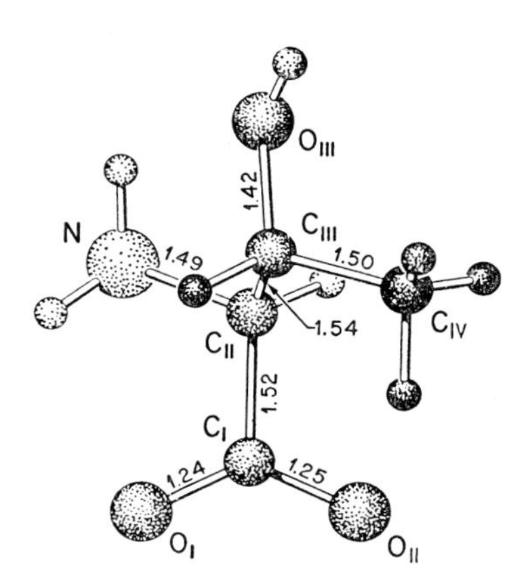

Fig. 11. The L_s-threonine molecule. (Courtesy of D. P. SHOEMAKER, J. DONOHUE, V. SCHOMAKER AND R. B. COREY, *J. Am. Chem. Soc.*, 72 (1950) 2328.)

C_IO_I, $C_{II}C_I$, NC_{II}, etc. The peaks lying between 2 and 3 Å from the origin are due to vectors between atoms more widely separated, *e.g.* NO_{II}, $O_{III}C_{II}$, NC_I, etc. Comparison of the Patterson map with vectors taken from a model of the molecule suggested three possibilities for the molecular orientation. One, which allowed the molecules to be placed in the unit cell so that they were separated by normal Van der Waals distances and which also gave intermolecular vectors which fitted Patterson peaks more distant from the origin, was chosen for the trial structure. The dots in Fig. 10a mark the positions of interatomic vectors taken from the final refined structure.

The use of a projection of the Patterson function was successful in determining the structure of N-acetylglycine because this is essentially a problem in two dimensions since there are planar molecules arranged in layers. Where, as is more generally the case, the molecules are not planar or they overlap in projection, one may have to use the full three-dimensional Patterson function. Such was the case, for instance, in the structure analysis of L_s-threonine (Fig. 11). Projected in any direction, the molecule will have some interatomic vectors (intramolecular) foreshortened, making their recognition in the Patterson projection difficult. In addition molecules over-

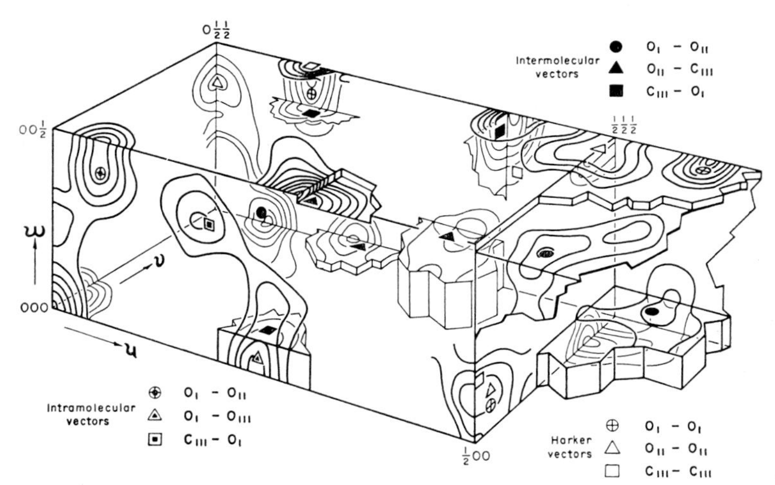

Fig. 12. Three-dimensional Patterson function for L_s-threonine. (Courtesy of D. P. Shoemaker, J. Donohue, V. Schomaker and R. B. Corey, *J. Am. Chem. Soc.*, 72 (1950) 2328.)

lapping in projection result in intermolecular vectors falling within the 3 Å limit. Clearly in three dimensions these difficulties do not arise because there is no foreshortening or overlap. The inter- and intramolecular vectors occupy each their own region of the Patterson, and can thus be distinguished.

References p. 32

Fig. 12 shows part of the three-dimensional Patterson function for L_s-threonine[18] which was used to deduce the orientation and arrangement of the molecules in the structure. The positions of the various interatomic vectors are marked in the figure. (Harker vectors are those between atoms (in different molecules) which are related to one another by a symmetry operation, in this case a 2_1 axis. Necessarily one of the co-ordinates U, V or W of each Harker vector has the special value of $\frac{1}{2}$ in this structure.)

(c) Direct methods of sign determination

The methods for obtaining a trial structure which have already been discussed and also those to be considered in sections 5d and 5e are based on the use of some previously known stereochemical information. However, even if no such information is available, there remains information of a general kind concerning the distribution of scattering matter. For example, we may say (*i*) the electron density is everywhere positive, (*ii*) the atoms are to a first approximation spherically symmetrical and have the same shape, or (*iii*) the structure consists of identical atoms (this is approximately true for organic crystals) fully resolved from each other. Such conditions, apart from any knowledge of the relative positions of the atoms, are sufficient to place some limitations on the phases of the reflexions. Attempts have therefore been made to use these conditions to set up relationships between the phases by means of which they can be deduced. These direct methods have had a considerable success in the solution of centrosymmetric crystal structures where we have only to discover whether each reflexion is positive or negative.

(i) Harker–Kasper inequalities

By taking account of the symmetry of the electron density distribution (*e.g.* $\rho(xyz) = \rho(\overline{xyz})$ for a centrosymmetric structure or $\rho(xyz) = \rho(\bar{x}y\bar{z})$ if there is a diad parallel to b, etc.) and using conditions (*i*) and (*ii*) above, it is possible to apply Schwarz's or Cauchy's inequality[19] to provide inequality relations between the structure factors. It is convenient to formulate the inequalities in terms of the unitary structure factor $U(hkl)$ instead of $F(hkl)$. By condition (*ii*) we assume that the general form of all atomic scattering factor curves is approximately the same so that we can use one unitary atomic scattering factor $\hat{f} = f_r/Z_r$ where Z_r is the number of electrons in an atom of scattering factor f_r. Then

$$U(hkl) = \frac{F(hkl)}{\hat{f}\,F(000)}$$

The merit of this representation of the structure factor is that all values of

$U(hkl)$ lie in the range $0 \leqslant |U(hkl)| \leqslant 1$ with $|U(000)| = 1$ as the maximum (no reflexion can be stronger than $F(000)$, equal to the total number of electrons in the unit cell). The effect of the atomic scattering factor in causing a general fall-off in $F(hkl)$ as $\sin\theta$ increases is removed by dividing by $\hat{f}$; it is then immediately clear from the U values which are the "strong" reflexions.

Harker and Kasper showed that for a centrosymmetric crystal

$$|U(hkl)|^2 \leqslant \tfrac{1}{2} + \tfrac{1}{2}U(2h, 2k, 2l) \tag{3}$$

Thus if a reflexion can be found which has $|U(hkl)|^2$ greater than $\frac{1}{2}$, then $U(2h, 2k, 2l) > 0$, *i.e.* the reflexion $(2h, 2k, 2l)$ must have positive sign. $U(2h, 2k, 2l)$ is also proved positive if at the same time $|U(2h, 2k, 2l)| \geqslant \frac{1}{2}$ and $|U(hkl)|^2 > \frac{1}{4}$, or in general whenever $U(2h, 2k, 2l) > 1 - 2|U(hkl)|^2$. The presence of other symmetry elements allows the formulation of further inequalities, *e.g.*:

$|U(hkl)|^2 \leqslant \frac{1}{2} + \frac{1}{2}U(2h, 0, 2l)$ if there is a diad axis parallel to b passing through the origin, or

$|U(hkl)|^2 \leqslant \frac{1}{2} + \frac{1}{2}U(0, 2k, 0)$ for a mirror plane perpendicular to b. For a fuller list of inequalities see refs. [20,21].

(ii) Sign relations

Closely allied to Harker–Kasper inequalities is the derivation by Cochran[22], Sayre[23], and Zachariasen[24] of the relation between the signs of strong reflexions

$$S(hkl) = S(h'k'l')\cdot S(h + h', k + k', l + l') \tag{4}$$

S being the sign of a reflexion, *i.e.* ± 1. This relation is considered to be probably, but not necessarily, true if the U values of the three reflexions involved are all large. Provided certain rules are satisfied[25] it is possible to fix the signs of 3 reflexions arbitrarily, the choice of sign corresponding to choice of origin in the structure. It may then be possible, using the above relation, to work out a scheme whereby the signs of all the strong reflexions can be determined from the signs of the three chosen reflexions, so that a Fourier synthesis can be calculated. Zachariasen further proposed using the statistical equality

$$S(hkl) = S\{\overline{S(h'k'l')\cdot S(h + h', k + k', l + l'}\} \tag{5}$$

an average being taken over as many pairs of reflexions $h'k'l'$ and $h + h'$, $k + k'$, $l + l'$ as possible for each sign derivation.

References p. 32

Harker–Kasper inequalities and sign relations have been successful in determining structures where there is only a small number of atoms in the molecule (say 10 or less) but unfortunately they become progressively less powerful as the size of the molecule increases. Qualitatively we may explain this by saying that as the molecular complexity increases it is less likely that a large proportion of the atoms will fall close to any one plane in the lattice, so that large U values will not occur. More specifically, Harker–Kasper inequalities are reckoned to be successful provided that at least 20% of the structure factors satisfy[24] the condition $|U| > 0.30$, or, what is equivalent, the root mean square average of the $|U|$ values, σ, must be greater than 0.22. For a structure containing N equal atoms in the unit cell, $\sigma = 1/\sqrt{N}$ so that inequalities are likely to succeed only if $N < 21$. Zachariasen's statistical sign relation (5) is somewhat more favourable in that it is expected to be true (*i.e.* eqn. (4) is true at least twice out of three times) provided $\sigma > 0.07$, *i.e.* provided $N < 205$. However, this still means that a great range of biochemically interesting structures are beyond the scope of these methods.

(d) Heavy-atom technique

An atom of high atomic number, a *heavy* atom, is a concentrated source of scattering compared with *light* atoms such as carbon, nitrogen and oxygen. Because of this, one heavy atom in a molecule composed largely of light atoms will dominate the diffraction pattern. The phases calculated for this atom alone, neglecting the other atoms, will be a good approximation to the true phases of the reflexions and can be used to calculate a Fourier synthesis.

The most favourable circumstance for the determination of phases by the heavy atom occurs when it is situated at a centre of symmetry. Choosing the heavy atom position as origin, the structure factor is given by

$$F(hkl) = f_M + \sum^{N-1} f_n \cos 2\pi(hx_n + ky_n + lz_n) \tag{6}$$

where f_M is the atomic scattering factor of the heavy atom and the second term is the total contribution to $F(hkl)$ of all the other atoms in the molecule. (It is assumed here that there is only one molecule in the unit cell; the presence of more than one molecule modifies the expression for $F(hkl)$ but does not invalidate the argument.) Since the structure is centrosymmetric all phase angles must be 0° or 180°, *i.e.* $F(hkl)$ is either positive or negative. The heavy atom contribution f_M to each $F(hkl)$ is positive. The total contribution of all the other atoms may be positive or negative but since they tend to cancel each other out it is likely that their contribution will always be smaller than that of the heavy atom. $F(hkl)$ will then be positive for all reflexions and a Fourier synthesis of the structure can be calculated directly.

The outstanding example where this condition is completely satisfied is platinum phthalocyanine, for which it was possible to calculate a Fourier synthesis without any previous knowledge of the molecular geometry. However, it is more usually the case that the heavy atom is large enough to force most but not all of the signs to be positive; occasionally the contribution of the other atoms to a reflexion will be negative and larger than f_M. Even so a Fourier synthesis calculated on the assumption that all the signs are positive will give an approximate picture of the structure from which the positions of the light atoms can be found.

When the heavy atom lies at a general position x_M, y_M, z_M its contribution $F_M = f_M \cos 2\pi(hx_M + ky_M + lz_M)$ to $F(hkl)$ may be positive or negative, large or small, for different reflexions, but it is still possible to use some at least of the heavy-atom signs for the Fourier synthesis. In those cases where F_M is large and almost equal in magnitude to the observed structure amplitude $|F_o|$, it is probable that the sign of F_o is the same as that of F_M. For example, suppose that $|F_o| = 20$ and $F_M = -15$. Then if F_o is equal to -20, the contribution of the light atoms must be -5, while for F_o to be $+20$, the contribution would have to be $+35$. Clearly it is more likely that the light atoms will make the smaller contribution and that the sign of F_o will be negative. A Fourier synthesis calculated including only those terms for which $|F_M|$ and $|F_o|$ are similar and using the F_M signs will give a reasonable approximation to the structure. In order to apply the method we must first know the position of the heavy atom and this is most easily found using the Patterson synthesis. Just as a heavy atom gives a high peak in the electron density diagram so a vector between two heavy atoms corresponds to a higher peak in the Patterson than a vector between light atoms. It is therefore a comparatively simple matter to identify the heavy atom–heavy atom vectors and to find the co-ordinates of these atoms.

The technique can also be used for non-centrosymmetric structures but here the process is less certain. The phase angles may take any value instead of being limited to only 0° or 180°. The phase angles calculated for the heavy atom alone, which must be used for the Fourier synthesis, will be an approximation to the true phase angles but will not be absolutely correct. Subsequent Fourier refinement will give improved approximations to the true phases.

The heavy-atom technique has had a very wide application in organic crystal structure analysis. An important example is the elucidation of the structure of vitamin B_{12} where the first step was the location of the Co atom from the three-dimensional Patterson function[26]. A section of this function containing four symmetry-related high peaks (p) due to Co–Co vectors is reproduced in Fig. 13. Of course it is often desired to know the structure of

References p. 32

Fig. 13. Section of the Patterson function for air-dried vitamin B_{12} crystals. (Courtesy of D. C. HODGKIN *et al.*, *Proc. Roy. Soc. (London)*, A242 (1957) 228.)

an organic molecule which comprises only light atoms such as carbon, nitrogen and oxygen. With the resources of preparative organic chemistry at our disposal it is usually possible to introduce a heavy atom into the molecule, by making a metal salt or an iodo or bromo derivative, without changing the stereochemistry so that we can still obtain the information we require from the derivative. This was done, for example, in order to determine the structure of penicillin, by making rubidium, potassium and sodium benzyl penicillin[27], and for sterols by the preparation of cholesteryl iodide[28], calciferyl 4-iodo-5-nitro-benzoate[29], and lanostenyl iodoacetate[30].

It is sometimes possible to use the Patterson map of a heavy-atom derivative to locate also some of the light atoms before a Fourier is calculated. In order of decreasing importance the peaks in the Patterson will be those from (*i*) heavy atom–heavy atom vectors, (*ii*) heavy atom–light atom vectors and (*iii*) light atom–light atom vectors. For a molecule of even moderate complexity we cannot hope to unscramble the many hundreds of type (*iii*) vectors but those of type (*ii*) may be recognisable. In particular a group of neighbouring atoms around the heavy atom will give a similar group of Patterson peaks around the heavy atom–heavy atom peak, *i.e.* an image of the group as seen from another heavy atom appears in the Patterson. Such an image was detected in the Patterson map of vitamin B_{12}. The cobalt atom is surrounded octahedrally by six nearest neighbours—4 nitrogen atoms of the porphyrin-like group, 1 nitrogen of the benziminazole group, and the carbon atom of the cyanide group. In the Patterson there appeared an octahedron of peaks at about 1.9 Å from the Co–Co peak; four of them, labelled *d, e, f, g,* are present in the section shown in Fig. 13. Their detection was valuable in suggesting the orientation of the porphyrin-like nucleus of the vitamin and the position of the cyanide group, which was identified with the slightly elongated peak *d*.

The optimum condition for the success of the heavy-atom technique is that the sum of the squares of the atomic numbers of the heavy atoms in the unit cell shall be equal to the sum of the squares of the atomic numbers of all the other atoms. If the atomic number of the heavy atom is too small, the atom is not phase-determining; if it is too large, the rest of the structure does not have a significant effect on the intensities of the reflexions and so the light atoms cannot be located accurately.

(e) Method of isomorphous replacement

In cases where the heavy atom is too small to be phase-determining as for example with protein structures, where the scattering from the large molecules will hopelessly outweigh that from even the heaviest heavy atom, it is possible to determine the phases by comparing the intensities from two (or more) derivatives which contain different heavy atoms. It is essential that these derivatives be isomorphous so that the shape and arrangement of molecules are the same in the two compounds. The differences in the intensities in the two diffraction patterns are then attributable solely to the difference in scattering power of the two heavy atoms.

The structure of the strychnine molecule was found using the isomorphous salts, strychnine sulphate and selenate pentahydrate[31]. The structure factor for any reflexion (*hkl*) in the selenate or sulphate is given by

$$F_{\text{selenate}} = F_{\text{Se}} + F_{\text{R}}$$

or $$F_{\text{sulphate}} = F_{\text{S}} + F_{\text{R}} \qquad (7)$$

where F_{Se}, F_{S} are the parts of the structure factor due to the heavy atom and

References p. 32

F_R the part due to the remainder of the structure. Since the structures are isomorphous, F_R is the same in both equations and therefore

$$F_{\text{selenate}} - F_{\text{sulphate}} = F_{Se} - F_S = \Delta F \qquad (8)$$

With the position of the selenium (or sulphur) known, F_{Se} and F_S, and hence ΔF, can be calculated for each pair of reflexions (*hkl*) in the two compounds. In these structures the selenium and sulphur atoms occupy special positions at 0, 0, 0 and $\frac{1}{2}, \frac{1}{2}, 0$ so that, for all reflexions, $\Delta F = 2(f_{Se} - f_S)$ which is always positive and of approximately the same magnitude. The projection down [010] is centrosymmetric so that the (*h0l*) structure factors are real with a sign to be determined but all other reflexions involve a phase angle. For the (*h0l*) reflexions, knowing $|F_{\text{selenate}}|$ and $|F_{\text{sulphate}}|$ from the intensities, the signs of the structure factors can be found using eqn. (8). For example, for (002) (see Table III) $|F_{\text{selenate}}| = 48$, $|F_{\text{sulphate}}| = 12$, $\Delta F = 32$, so that F_{selenate} and F_{sulphate} must be positive; for (202) $|F_{\text{selenate}}| = 16$, $|F_{\text{sulphate}}| = 44$, $\Delta F = 29$ and the signs must therefore be negative. In the case of (001) it is clear that F_{selenate} and F_{sulphate} must have opposite signs (+ and − respectively) in order that eqn. (8) be satisfied (note that due to experimental errors in the intensities, the data in Table III do not satisfy eqn. 8 exactly).

TABLE III

STRUCTURE FACTORS OF STRYCHNINE SELENATE AND SULPHATE

hkl	$\lvert F_{selenate} \rvert$	$\lvert F_{sulphate} \rvert$	ΔF	*Deduced signs*	
				selenate	*sulphate*
200	48	16	36	+	+
400	50	75	36	−	−
600	132	92	33	+	+
001	16	12	35	+	−
601	88	53	32	+	+
801	70	44	29	+	+
002	48	12	32	+	+
202	16	44	29	−	−
402	110	82	29	+	+

As is always the case, the non-centrosymmetric structure factors are more difficult to deal with. Eqn. (8) is still satisfied, provided each term is represented as a vector, the situation being as shown in Fig. 14. As before, ΔF has a phase angle of zero because the Se and S atoms occupy special positions. The method would nevertheless be applicable to structures where the heavy atom occupies a general position but then the vector ΔF would have to be inserted in Fig. 14

with its appropriate phase angle. The phase angles α_{selenate} and α_{sulphate} can be deduced from Fig. 14 by solving triangle OPQ but an ambiguity remains because eqn. (8) would be equally well satisfied by the vectors in triangle OP′Q′, *i.e.* the deduced phase angles may be either positive or negative. It is not possible, using only two isomorphous derivatives, to decide which is correct. For the strychnine salts this difficulty was overcome by calculating a Fourier synthesis in which every term was included twice, using the negative value of α as well as the positive. The result was an electron density map containing spurious symmetry in which every atom appeared twice but it was nevertheless possible to select the correct atomic positions from this Fourier.

For more complicated structures, as for example those of haemoglobin and myoglobin, to which the method of isomorphous replacement has been applied with success, we would not expect to be able to select the correct structure from a Fourier synthesis containing spurious symmetry as was done for strychnine. In order therefore to determine the phase angles, more than two isomorphous derivatives have been used. It had already been suggested that this could have been done for strychnine by using, say

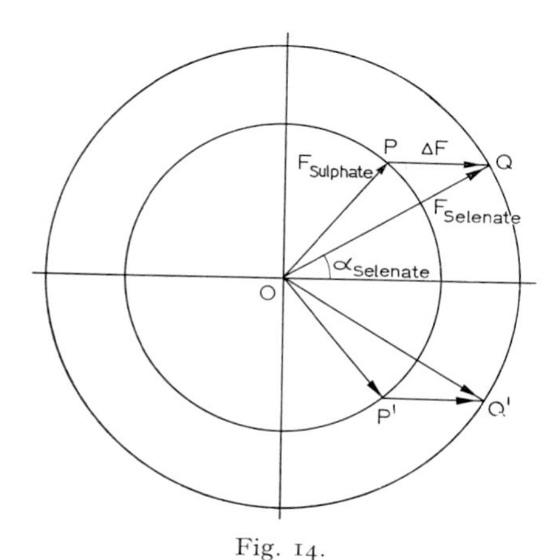

Fig. 14.

(I) α-chloro-strychnine sulphate, (II) α-chloro-strychnine selenate, and (III) α-bromo-strychnine sulphate. The comparison of (I) and (II) would lead to two possibilities for each phase angle from which the correct angle could be chosen by comparing (I) and (III). The isomorphous replacement would be made to take place at two different sites in the structure. This is essential for the use of three derivatives to be successful in resolving the ambiguity, *i.e.* the vector $\Delta F_{\text{I}-\text{II}}$ must have a different phase from $\Delta F_{\text{I}-\text{III}}$.

References p. 32

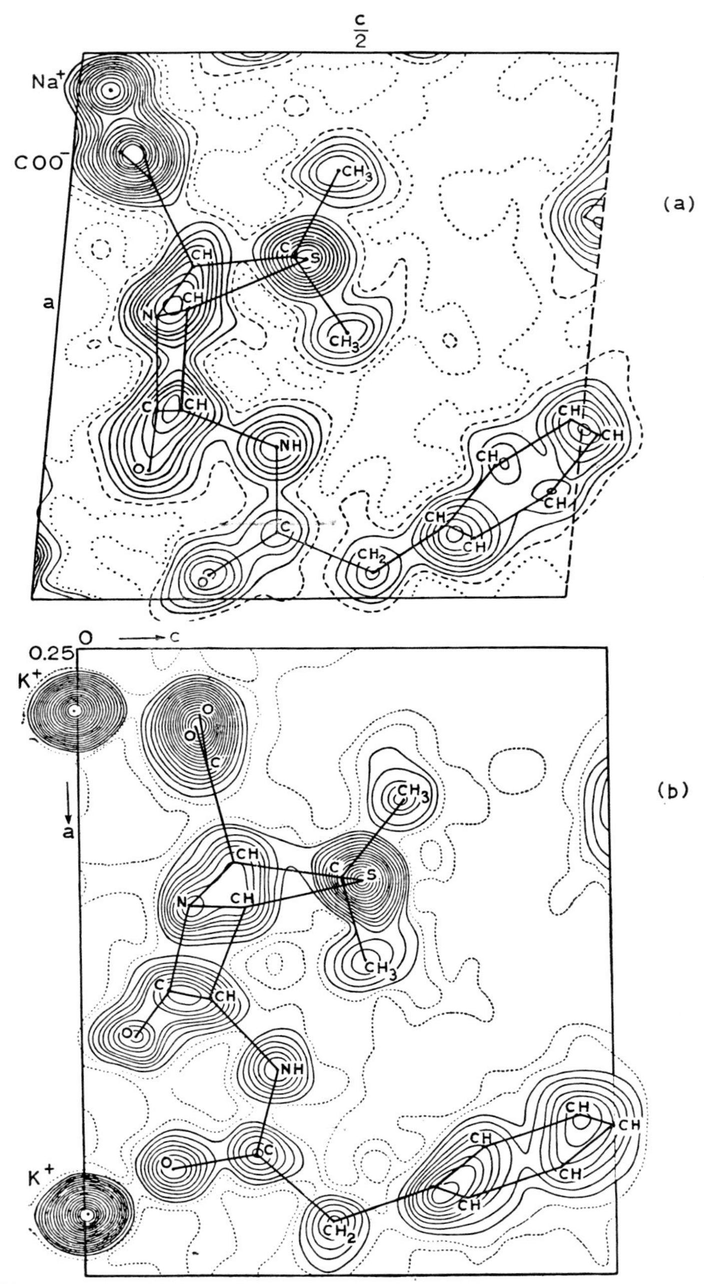

Fig. 15. Fourier projections of (a) sodium benzyl penicillin, (b) potassium benzyl penicillin. (Courtesy of D. CROWFOOT *et al.*, in *The Chemistry of Penicillin*, Princeton Univ. Press, New Jersey, 1949, p. 338.)

In applying the method to the structures of haemoglobin and myoglobin, several isomorphous replacements have been used (employing for instance Hg, I, Au, or Ag for myoglobin, Type A) in order to make the process of phase determination more certain. The metal-free proteins are themselves used as one of the isomorphous series since the insertion of the metal does not affect the structure. Due to the complexity of these structures the positions of the metal atoms cannot be deduced straightforwardly from the Patterson synthesis in the way described in section 5d. Crick and Kendrew[32] describe the subtler methods used and also discuss in more detail than is possible here the application of the isomorphous replacement method to protein structures.

Finally mention should be made of the comparison of structures which are similar but not strictly isomorphous. In work on the monoclinic form of ribonuclease the technique of isomorphous replacement is being used with the metal-free protein and the protein containing *p*-chloro-mercuribenzoate although the unit-cell dimensions of the two crystals differ slightly due to a small shift of the molecules from one structure to the other[33]. It is hoped that deduction of the phases will still be successful though it cannot be so certain as it would be if strictly isomorphous crystals were used.

The successful determination of the structure of penicillin was actually achieved by comparing trial Fourier projections of sodium benzyl penicillin, which is monoclinic, and rubidium benzyl penicillin, which is orthorhombic. Although the two crystal structures are sufficiently different for them to belong to different crystal systems, it happens that in projection they appear very similar (see Fig. 15, which shows the sodium and potassium salts. The latter is isomorphous with the rubidium derivative). Comparison of the projections of the two compounds enabled a trial structure to be found when other methods had failed.

References p. 32

REFERENCES

[1] N. F. M. Henry and K. Lonsdale (Eds.), *International Tables for X-ray Crystallography*, Vol. I, Kynoch Press, Birmingham, 1952, p. 22.
[2] *Ibid.*, pp. 53, 54.
[3] C. W. Bunn, *Chemical Crystallography*, Oxford University Press, 1946, Chapter 3.
[4] N. H. Hartshorne and A. Stuart, *Crystals and the Polarising Microscope*, Edward Arnold, London, 1950, pp. 224, 316 ff.
[5] K. Lonsdale, *Repts. Progr. in Phys.*, 4 (1937) 376.
[6] H. S. Peiser, H. P. Rooksby and A. J. C. Wilson, *X-ray Diffraction by Polycrystalline Materials*, The Institute of Physics, London, 1955, Chapter 3.
[7] K. T. Palmer, M. Ballantyne and J. A. Galvin, *J. Am. Chem. Soc.*, 70 (1948) 906.
[8] D. Harker, in J. H. Lawrence and C. A. Tobias (Eds.), *Biological and Medical Physics*, Academic Press, New York, 1956, Vol. IV.
[9] D. W. Green, A. C. T. North and R. Aschaffenburg, *Biochim. et Biophys. Acta*, 21 (1956) 583.
[10] J. D. Bernal, *Chem. & Ind. (London)*, 10 (1932) 466.
[11] O. Rosenheim and H. King, *Chem. & Ind. (London)*, 10 (1932) 464.
[12] M. P. Gupta, *J. Am. Chem. Soc.*, 75 (1953) 6312.
[13] D. Crowfoot *et al.*, in *The Chemistry of Penicillin*, Princeton Univ. Press, New Jersey, 1949, p. 325.
[14] S. Bhagavantam, *Proc. Roy. Soc. (London)*, A124 (1929) 545.
[15] G. S. Parry, *Acta Cryst.*, 7 (1954) 313.
[16] A. L. Patterson, *Z. Krist.*, 90 (1935) 517.
[17] G. B. Carpenter and J. Donohue, *J. Am. Chem. Soc.*, 72 (1950) 2315.
[18] D. P. Shoemaker, J. Donohue, V. Schomaker and R. B. Corey, *J. Am. Chem. Soc.*, 72 (1950) 2328.
[19] G. H. Hardy, J. E. Littlewood and G. Polya, *Inequalities*, 2nd ed., Cambridge Univ. Press, 1952, pp. 16, 132.
[20] N. F. M. Henry and K. Lonsdale (Eds.), *International Tables for X-ray Crystallography*, Vol. I, Kynoch Press, Birmingham, 1952, p. 541.
[21] H. Lipson and W. Cochran, *The Determination of Crystal Structures*, Bell, London, 1953, p. 250 ff.
[22] W. Cochran, *Acta Cryst.*, 5 (1952) 62.
[23] D. Sayre, *Acta Cryst.*, 5 (1952) 60.
[24] W. H. Zachariasen, *Acta Cryst.*, 5 (1952) 68.
[25] K. Lonsdale and H. J. Grenville-Wells, *Acta Cryst.*, 7 (1954) 490.
[26] D. C. Hodgkin *et al.*, *Proc. Roy. Soc. (London)*, A242 (1957) 228.
[27] D. Crowfoot *et al.*, in *The Chemistry of Penicillin*, Princeton Univ. Press, New Jersey, 1949, p. 321.
[28] C. H. Carlisle and D. Crowfoot, *Proc. Roy. Soc. (London)*, A184 (1945) 64.
[29] D. Crowfoot and J. D. Dunitz, *Nature*, 162 (1948) 608.
[30] J. Fridrichsons and A. McL. Mathieson, *J. Chem. Soc.*, (1953) 2159.
[31] C. Bokhoven, J. C. Schoone and J. M. Bijvoet, *Acta Cryst.*, 4 (1951) 275.
[32] F. H. C. Crick and J. C. Kendrew, *Advances in Protein Chem.*, 12 (1957) 180.
[33] J. D. Bernal, C. H. Carlisle and M. A. Rosemeyer, *Acta Cryst.*, 12 (1959) 227.

Chapter II

X-Ray Diffraction

G. J. BULLEN

Birkbeck College, Crystallography Laboratory, University of London (Great Britain)

1. Laue conditions and the Bragg equation

A crystal consists of a three-dimensional regular array of atoms and so can act as a three-dimensional diffraction grating to X-rays, which are particularly suitable for diffraction because their wavelength is of the same order of magnitude as the interatomic distances. The conditions for diffraction were first set out by Von Laue who considered the effect of a single row of lattice points. Suppose the incident beam makes an angle α_0 with a row of period a (Fig. 1). As with a ruled grating, reinforcement will occur if the path

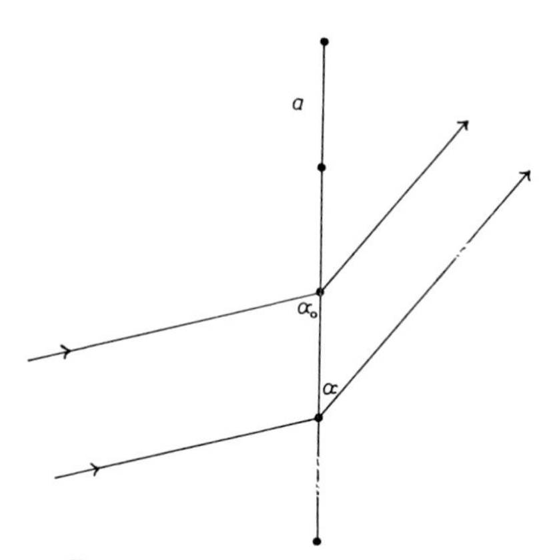

Fig. 1. Diffraction from a lattice row.

difference between waves scattered from successive points is an integral number of wavelengths. For a diffracted beam at an angle α to the row, the condition is

$$a\,(\cos\alpha - \cos\alpha_0) = n\lambda \tag{1}$$

References p. 51

n being an integer. The locus of the diffracted rays is a cone of semi-angle α whose axis coincides with the lattice row. However, there will not be a continuous cone of rays. Since the crystal lattice extends in three dimensions, diffracted rays will occur only when three conditions corresponding to (1) are simultaneously satisfied. If the incident beam makes angles α_0, β_0, γ_0 with three non-coplanar lattice rows of periods a, b, c, the three Laue conditions are

$$\begin{aligned} a\,(\cos\alpha - \cos\alpha_0) &= n_1\lambda \\ b\,(\cos\beta - \cos\beta_0) &= n_2\lambda \\ c\,(\cos\gamma - \cos\gamma_0) &= n_3\lambda \end{aligned} \qquad (2)$$

In addition, since specification of any two of the angles α, β, γ will fix the third, there exists a fourth equation (*e.g.* $\cos^2\alpha + \cos^2\beta + \cos^2\gamma = 1$, when the three lattice rows are orthonormal) to be satisfied. It is in general impossible to satisfy all four equations simultaneously with an arbitrary choice of α_0, β_0, γ_0, and λ. This means that, using a monochromatic incident beam, a diffracted ray will appear only when the lattice (and hence the crystal) is turned until α_0, β_0, γ_0 assume special values which allow the four conditions to be met. For a simple geometrical picture of this we may look upon the direction of a diffracted ray as specified by the line of simultaneous intersection of all three cones of semi-angles α, β, γ. Three cones will not in general intersect in the same line; α, β, γ and hence α_0, β_0, γ_0, must assume special values. The triple set of integers $n_1 n_2 n_3$ denotes the order of the spectrum.

Diffraction according to the Laue conditions is difficult to visualize and we are indebted to W. L. Bragg[1] for simplifying the interpretation by introducing the concept of reflexion of X-rays from a set of planes in the crystal lattice. An X-ray beam AB of wavelength λ incident on a crystal plane at an angle θ (Fig. 2) will be reflected in the direction BC. The path difference between this beam and that reflected from the next parallel plane

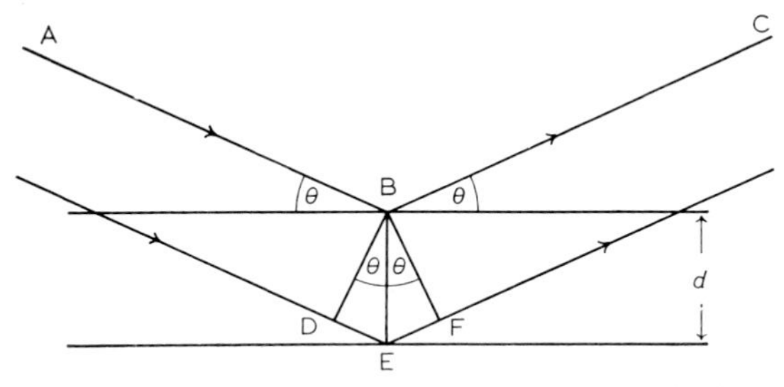

Fig. 2. Diffraction from lattice planes (Bragg reflexion).

is DE + EF = $2d \sin \theta$, where d is the interplanar spacing. For reinforcement we have the condition

$$n\lambda = 2d \sin \theta \tag{3}$$

n being integral. This equation is known as the Bragg equation. The X-ray beam will thus be reflected only at certain angles θ which depend on the interplanar spacing and the wavelength of the radiation. (Note that θ is the complement of the angle of incidence as usually used in optics.) It can be shown that the Laue conditions and the Bragg equation are equivalent; the limitation of diffraction to certain angles θ corresponds to the necessity of choosing special values α_0, β_0, γ_0. The integers $n_1 n_2 n_3$ are proportional to the Miller indices (hkl) (see Chapter I, p. 5) of the lattice plane which is parallel to the Bragg reflexion plane. Rearranging eqn. (3)

$$\lambda = 2 \frac{d}{n} \sin \theta = 2d' \sin \theta \tag{4}$$

and comparing (4) with (3), we see that the nth order reflexion from planes (hkl) with spacing d is the same as the first order from planes with spacing d/n, which will have Miller indices ($nh.nk.nl$). It is customary to regard every X-ray reflexion as a first-order reflexion and to modify the Miller indices accordingly. Thus the orders of reflexion from the (111) lattice plane will be labelled 111, 222, 333 etc.

The first X-ray photographs were taken with a stationary crystal and radiation consisting of a continuous range of wavelengths (white radiation). Although the angle of incidence of the radiation on each crystal plane was fixed, it was possible for reflexions to occur in accordance with the above conditions by the choice of a wavelength, different for each crystal plane, which would satisfy the Bragg equation. Such photographs, called Laue photographs, when recorded on a plane film placed perpendicular to the incident beam, show spots lying on a series of intersecting ellipses passing through the trace of the incident beam (the central spot). Each spot has been produced by a different wavelength.

2. Rotation and oscillation photographs

As we do not know which wavelength is responsible for any particular reflexion in the Laue photograph we cannot apply the Bragg equation to determine d. This is a great obstacle to further study of the crystal which can be overcome by causing all reflexions to be produced by X-rays of the same wavelength. To obtain reflexions from all lattice planes the orientation of the crystal must then be changed so that each plane, in turn, makes the

References p. 51

angle θ_{hkl} with the incident beam required by the Bragg equation. This is done by rotating the crystal about a prominent zone axis (most often one of the crystallographic axes) which is placed perpendicular to the X-ray beam.

The output of an X-ray tube (Fig. 3) consists of a continuous range of wavelengths extending from a minimum threshold wavelength together

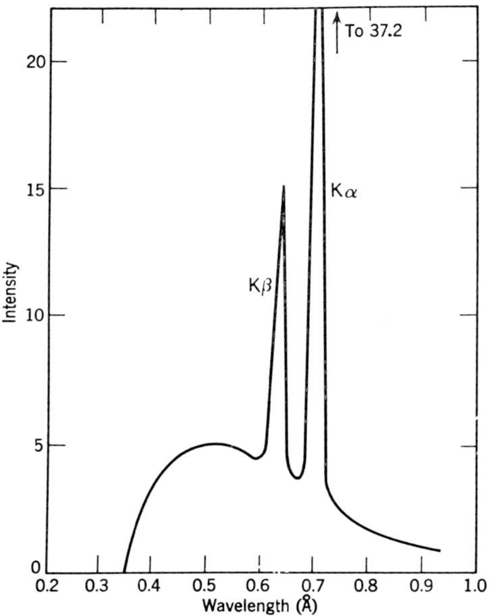

Fig. 3. Intensity distribution in X-ray beam from molybdenum target. (Courtesy of ULREY, *Phys. Rev.*, 11 (1918) 401.)

with the relatively very intense peaks of the characteristic radiation. The K characteristic radiation, most usually used, is made up of 3 peaks — $K\alpha_1$, $K\alpha_2$, and $K\beta$. The wavelengths of the two $K\alpha$ peaks are very close and the reflexions they produce are resolved only when θ is large. The weaker $K\beta$ reflexion is easily resolved. The intensity ratios[2] $\alpha_1:\alpha_2:\beta$ are approximately 4:2:1. The β radiation can be removed by passing the incident beam through a filter which absorbs it strongly but leaves the α radiation relatively[2] undiminished. Such a filter contains a high proportion of the element one or two places in the Periodic Table below the element of the X-ray-tube target generating the radiation, *e.g.* Ni used to filter Cu radiation.

Since a prominent zone axis and therefore a lattice row (of period a, say) is perpendicular to the incident beam, eqn. (1) reduces to

$$a \cos \alpha = n\lambda \tag{5}$$

All diffracted beams will lie on a set of cones coaxial with the rotation axis having semi-angles α given by eqn. (5), n taking the values 0, 1, 2 . . . . The photographic film is placed around the crystal in the form of a cylinder coaxial with the rotation axis so that the cones intersect the film in lines, called *layer lines*, which become straight when the film is opened out flat (Fig. 4). The layer lines are rows of spots; they are not continuous because diffracted rays are produced only at those angles which satisfy all three Laue conditions simultaneously. Measurement of the separations of the layer lines enables us to calculate the repeat distance along the lattice row parallel to the rotation axis, from the equation

$$a \sin \phi = n\lambda \tag{6}$$

derived from eqn. (5); ϕ is the angle of elevation of the nth layer line. Thus from three photographs taken with the crystal rotated about the three crystallographic axes, the lattice constants a, b, and c can be determined.

The indices (hkl) of reflexions on a particular layer line are governed by the relation $hu + kv + lw = n$ for the zone axis $[uvw]$ as rotation axis. If this axis is the crystallographic c axis, *i.e.* [001], the equatorial layer line contains $(hk0)$ reflexions, the first layer line $(hk1)$, and so on. The spots also lie on another set of lines which cross the layer lines. These lines, which are curved, are called *row lines*. For a rotation photograph taken about c, spots on a particular row line have constant h and k.

The assignment of indices to reflexions on a rotation photograph is difficult for all but the simplest crystals because there are many spots on each layer line and they overlap with one another. The method is therefore modified by restricting the movement of the crystal to a small oscillation, usually 15° or less. The resulting oscillation photograph still shows layer and row lines but they are populated by fewer spots than in a rotation photograph. The reflexions can be indexed easily provided the orientation of the crystal is known. For this purpose it is convenient to use the Bernal chart[3] by means of which the position of a spot on the photograph is specified by two coordinates ξ and ζ. To record reflexions from all crystal planes, a set of photographs with consecutive oscillation ranges must be taken.

3. Interpretation of photographs in terms of the reciprocal lattice

For the interpretation of X-ray photographs the concept of the reciprocal lattice is very important. This is a means of representing the assemblage of all the planes in the crystal (direct) lattice; its application to X-ray diffraction was developed by Ewald[4], Bernal[3] and Buerger[5]. The construction is as follows. From a point as origin the normal to each plane in the crystal lattice

References p. 51

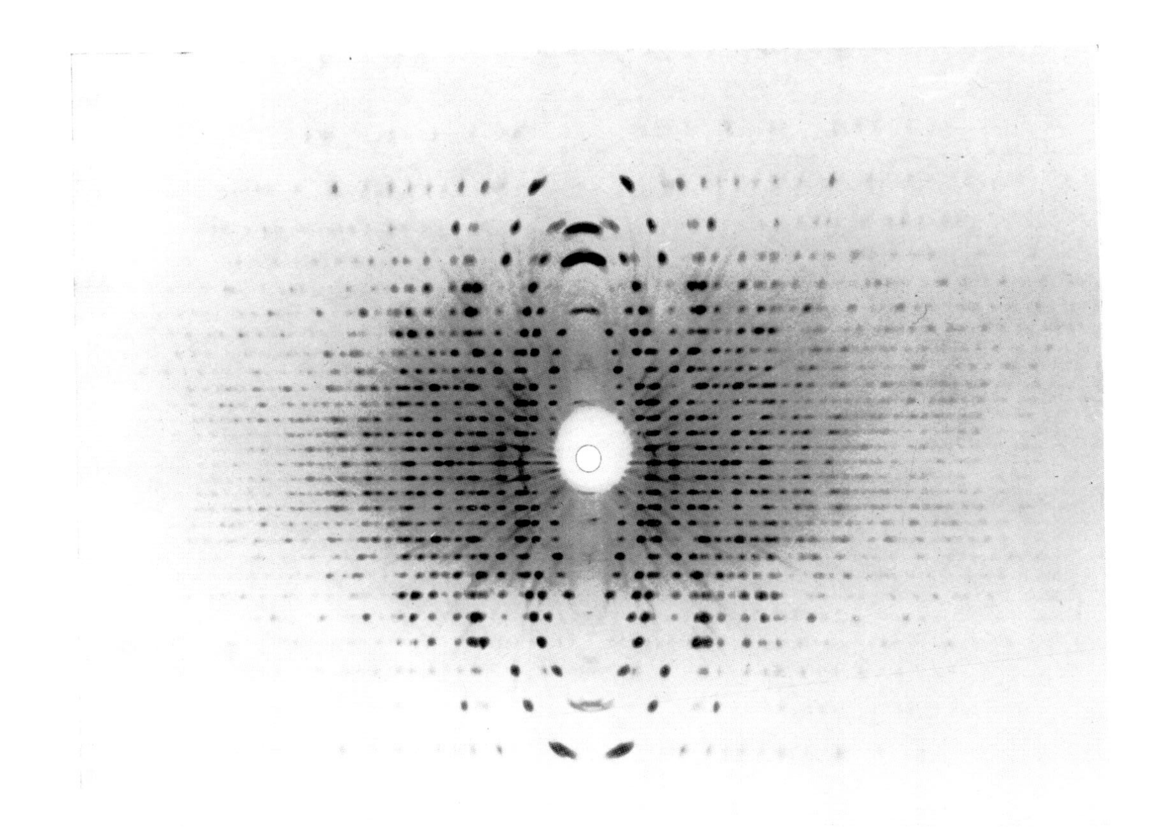

Fig. 4. Rotation photograph of crystal of cortisone acetate, form A, rotated about *b* axis. (Courtesy of Mrs. Olga Kennard.)

is drawn and the plane is represented by a point on the normal at a distance d^* from the origin, given by

$$d^* = k/d \tag{7}$$

where d is the interplanar spacing and k a constant, usually taken equal to λ, the wavelength. The array of points so placed form another lattice called the reciprocal lattice. The lengths of the axes of this lattice are given by expressions such as $a^* = \lambda/d_{100}$; the direction of a^* is the normal to the (100) plane, so that a^* is perpendicular to b and c in the direct lattice. Similar relations hold for b^* and c^*. For crystal systems described using orthogonal axes, a^* coincides with a, b^* with b, c^* with c, and the reciprocal axial lengths are λ/a, λ/b, λ/c respectively. In other systems the relations are more complex (see Buerger[6]). As an example, the layer of the reciprocal lattice representing (*hol*) planes of a monoclinic crystal is shown in Fig. 5. Since a^* is perpendicular to c, and c^* to a, the reciprocal interaxial angle β^* is equal to $180° - \beta$. Since, in the monoclinic system, b is perpendicular to a and c, b^* will coincide with the b axis. The rest of the lattice is therefore built up of layers like that shown in Fig. 5 placed one above the other. Note that orders of a reflexion such as 101, 202, 303 will be represented by points on a reciprocal lattice row passing through the origin. From the Bragg equation we see that

$$d^* = \lambda/d = 2 \sin \theta \tag{8}$$

so that no reflexion can occur which has a value of d^* greater than 2. A sphere,

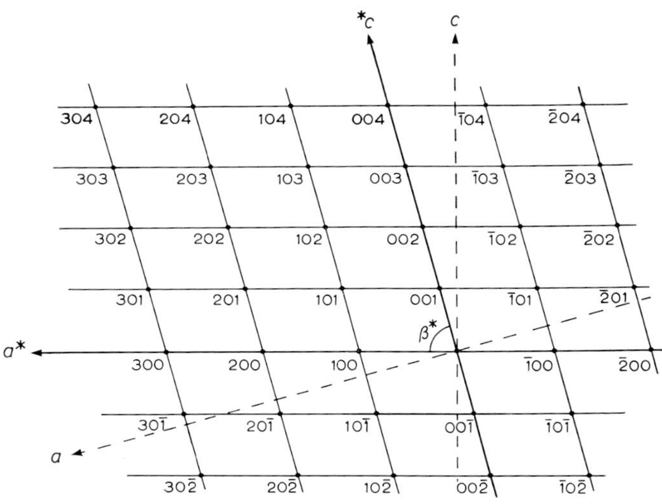

Fig. 5. The (*hol*) layer of a monoclinic reciprocal lattice. Directions of the direct lattice axes a and c are shown.

References p. 51

the limiting sphere, drawn with its centre at the reciprocal lattice origin and radius 2 units will contain all reciprocal lattice points corresponding to observable reflexions.

The reciprocal lattice is used in the following way to give a simple geometrical interpretation of diffraction by the crystal lattice. Suppose the incident ray AOB passes in the direction AB through the reciprocal lattice origin O (Fig. 6). A reciprocal lattice point P corresponding to plane (hkl) will give rise to a reflexion provided that the Bragg equation is satisfied, *i.e.* provided that, from eqn. (8),

$$2 \sin \theta = d^* = \mathrm{OP} \tag{9}$$

or since OA is the radius of the limiting sphere, equal to 2 units,

$$\mathrm{OA} \sin \theta = \mathrm{OP} \tag{10}$$

This condition is satisfied provided $\mathrm{O\hat{A}P} = \theta$ and $\mathrm{O\hat{P}A} = 90°$, *i.e.* for any point lying on the circle AOP of diameter AO (centre Q). The line AP,

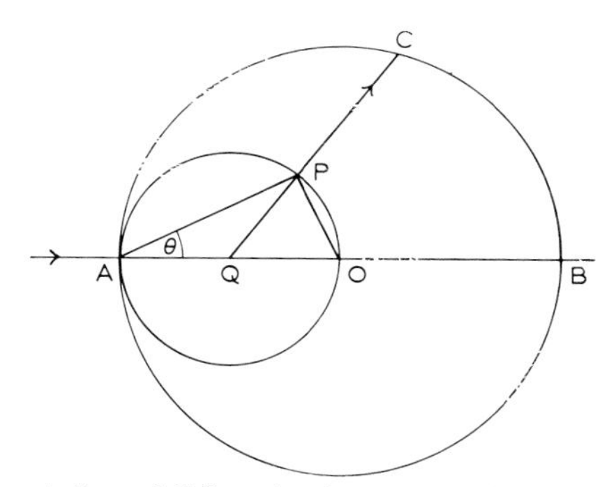

Fig. 6. Interpretation of diffraction by means of the reciprocal lattice.

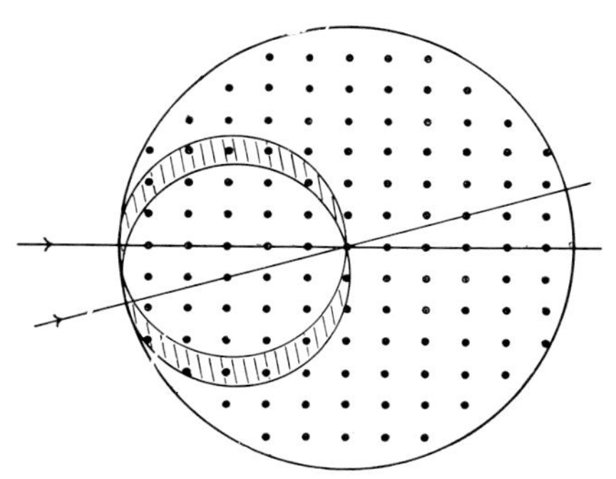

Fig. 7. Reciprocal lattice construction for an oscillation photograph.

being then perpendicular to OP, is the direction of the crystal plane (*hkl*) and makes an angle θ with the incident ray AOB. The reflected ray, at an angle 2θ to the incident ray will be in the direction QPC. The circle AOP becomes in three dimensions a sphere, the sphere of reflexion. Only those reciprocal lattice points, through which the sphere of reflexion passes, are capable of producing a reflexion. We can now appreciate more easily the point of rotating the crystal while taking an X-ray photograph. By so doing the reciprocal lattice is rotated relative to the incident beam and therefore relative to the sphere of reflexion. At the moment when each reciprocal lattice point passes through the sphere of reflexion a reflected ray flashes out and is recorded on the film.

It is actually simpler to regard the reciprocal lattice as stationary and the sphere of reflexion (and the incident ray) as rotating. Using an oscillation instead of a rotation only a part of the reciprocal lattice is swept by the sphere of reflexion. The shaded regions in Fig. 7, showing the area swept by the sphere of reflexion during a 15° oscillation, contain those lattice points which correspond to the spots on the photograph. Having thus decided which reflexions will occur on an oscillation photograph it is comparatively easy, by measuring their $\sin\theta$ values with a Bernal chart, to index them, *i.e.* to assign h, k, l.

Before the reciprocal lattice can be constructed and used to interpret photographs, the lattice dimensions must be determined either from layer-line spacings or from Weissenberg photographs (see below).

4. Weissenberg and precession photographs

In order to identify each reflected ray with a point in the reciprocal lattice we must specify (*i*) its $\sin\theta$ and (*ii*) its direction with respect to a chosen reference line in the crystal lattice. From an oscillation photograph we can measure $\sin\theta$ but cannot specify the direction exactly because we do not know the exact orientation of the crystal at the precise moment when the diffracted beam flashed out. The most we can say is that the direction lies between two extreme values which differ by the extent of the oscillation range (commonly 5, 10, or 15°). Often this is sufficient to identify each spot but sometimes ambiguities occur (if, for example, two reciprocal lattice points within the shaded regions of Fig. 7 have the same $\sin\theta$).

Such ambiguities are overcome by moving the film during the exposure. Of the various methods suggested the most widely used is that of Weissenberg[7] by which the film is translated in a direction parallel to the rotation axis while the crystal is oscillated through a large angular range (usually but not necessarily 180°). The translation of the film and the crystal oscillation are synchronised so that the distance of the reflexion along the film in the translation direction gives the angular setting of the crystal directly.

References p. 51

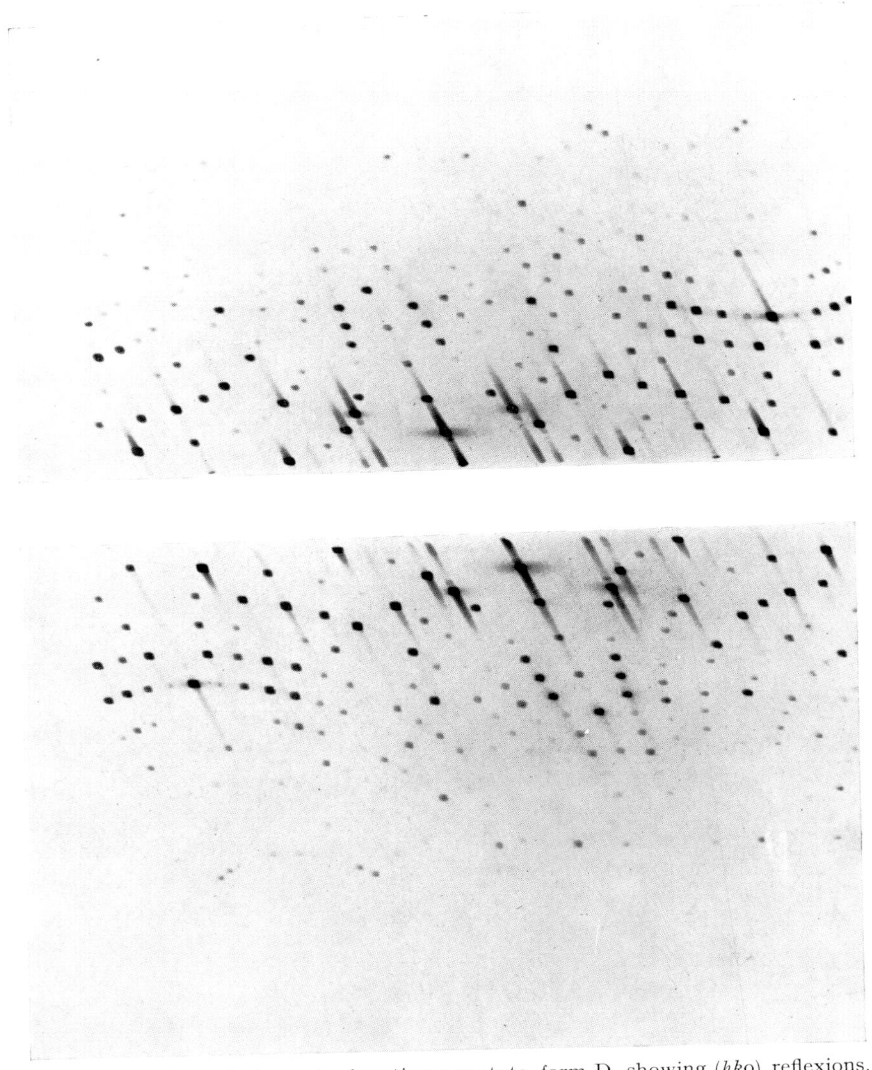

Fig. 8. Weissenberg photograph of cortisone acetate, form D, showing (*hk*o) reflexions. (Courtesy of Mrs. OLGA KENNARD.)

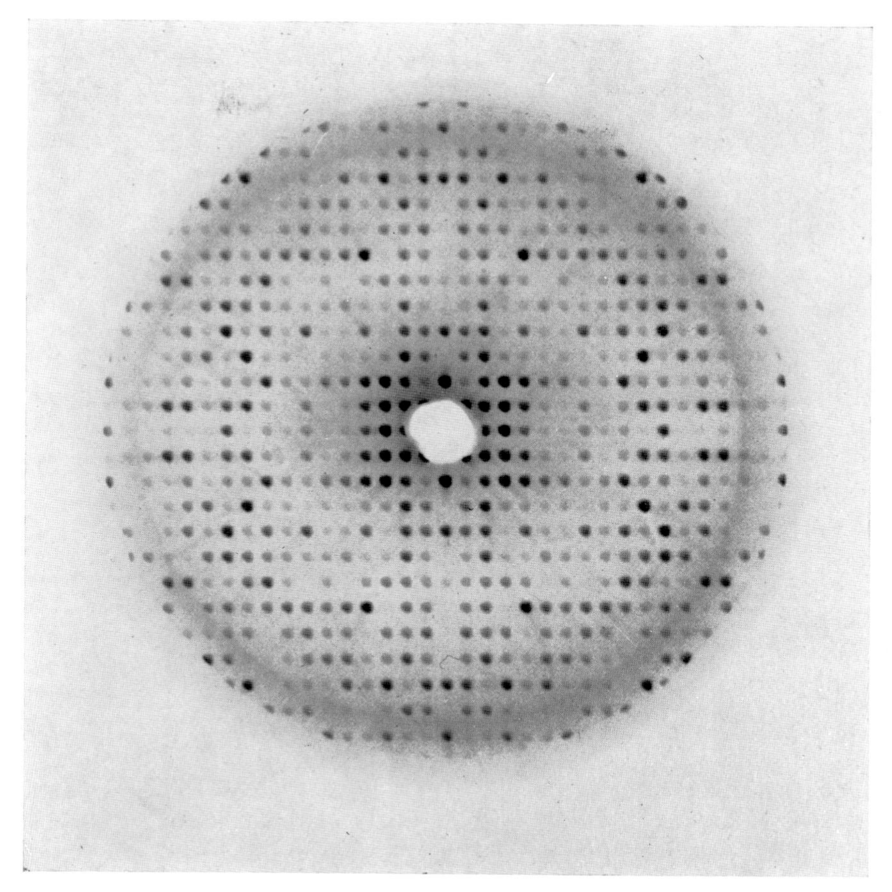

Fig. 9. Precession photograph of the (*okl*) reciprocal lattice layer of ribonuclease. (Courtesy of Mr. R. PALMER.)

Only one layer line is photographed at a time, the others being absorbed by a metal screen placed in front of the cylindrical film. A slit in the screen admits the reflexions of the layer being recorded. The spots on a Weissenberg photograph lie on a family of curves or festoons (Fig. 8). The orders of a reflexion lie on a straight line inclined to the translation direction (the length of the film) by an angle which depends on the rate of translation of the film relative to the crystal oscillation. With some practice a Weissenberg photograph can be indexed by inspection.

A more elaborate means of moving the film is used in the *precession camera*. Here the crystal is made to describe a precessing motion around the

References p. 51

incident X-ray beam and the flat film follows this motion remaining always parallel to the crystal. The resulting photograph (Fig. 9) is an undistorted picture of a reciprocal lattice layer and this is the great merit of the precession photograph. The spots lie on sets of straight lines (lattice rows) and it is consequently easy to measure their intensities using a microdensitometer. It is useful to think of a stack of precession photographs, one for each layer of the reciprocal lattice, as a model of the complete diffraction pattern showing both the spatial arrangement and intensities of the reflexions.

In order to collect all the available diffraction data one must record the reflexions corresponding to every reciprocal lattice point within the limiting sphere. One Weissenberg or precession photograph shows only one section through the reciprocal lattice. Therefore a set of photographs, one for each of a number of parallel layers, is needed to give full three-dimensional data. In practice, photographs showing sections through the reciprocal lattice in two or more directions are also usually used.

5. Powder photographs

When an X-ray beam falls on a finely ground crystalline powder, which will contain many thousands of crystal fragments orientated completely at random, some fragments at least will lie with any given set of lattice planes making exactly the correct angle θ with the incident beam for Bragg reflexion to occur. Since all orientations of the fragments are equally likely and the only necessary condition is that the planes shall make the angle θ with the incident beam, the diffracted rays will form a cone with semi-angle 2θ about the incident beam as axis. There will be a different cone for each set of planes (hkl). These cones would intersect a plane film set perpendicular to the incident beam in a series of concentric circles from the radii of which θ and hence d could be calculated for each reflexion. It is more usual, however, to record the pattern on a cylindrical film as for oscillation photographs. Since it is sufficient to record a short portion of each ring (powder line) a narrow strip of film is used (Fig. 10). The lines become straight at $2\theta = 90°$ and when 2θ is greater than $90°$ they curve in the opposite direction from

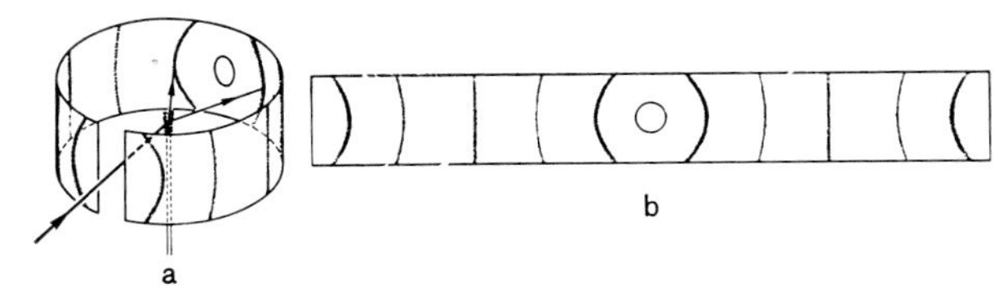

Fig. 10. (a) Arrangement of film around specimen for powder photography; (b) Appearance of powder photograph when opened out flat. (Courtesy of W. F. DE JONG, *General Crystallography*, W. H. Freeman & Co., San Francisco, Calif.)

those with low values of 2θ. Measurement of the distance x between the two arcs on opposite sides of the photograph belonging to the same powder line enables θ to be found from

$$x = 4\theta r \tag{11}$$

where r is the radius of the film. The interplanar spacing d can be calculated from θ using the Bragg equation.

The principal use of the powder method is in the identification of crystalline materials, which is discussed further in Chapter I (p. 14). It is a much simpler matter to obtain a powder photograph than a single-crystal photograph. A small amount of material is finely ground and placed in a thin-walled glass capillary or rolled with gum into a fine cylinder. The specimen is rotated, while the photograph is being taken, in order to make the orientation of the fragments even more random.

Powder photographs cannot generally be used to provide intensity measurements for the determination of crystal structure. In the randomization of orientation, too much information is lost. For all but the simplest crystals of the cubic, hexagonal, and tetragonal systems, the patterns consist of many lines whose interplanar spacings can be measured, but which it is very difficult to index.

6. Diffraction by macromolecular structures

Macromolecules (Vol. 1, Chapter III, p. 168) are of two types: (*a*) those which crystallize with a regular three-dimensional arrangement of molecules and (*b*) the fibres in which the long molecules lie parallel to a single direction, the fibre axis, but there is no order in other directions. Group (*a*) (for example globular proteins, spherical viruses) gives single-crystal X-ray photographs just like those of crystals of smaller molecules except that their unit cells are much larger and there are many more reflexions. The methods used to study them, *e.g.* precession and Weissenberg photographs, are substantially the same as for simpler crystals. Group (*b*) includes fibrous proteins and rod-shaped viruses as well as other fibres such as cellulose, the synthetics polyethylene and nylon. In these fibres there are regions called crystallites in which the molecular chains are arranged with a high degree of order. The crystallites are oriented so that the chains lie parallel to the fibre axis, but their orientation in other directions is more or less random.

A photograph taken with the fibre axis placed perpendicular to the X-ray beam is similar to a single-crystal rotation photograph except that the spots are drawn out into small arcs. The effect of rotation is obtained with a stationary fibre because of the randomness of orientation of the crystallites; the spots are blurred because the orientation of the chains along the axis

References p. 51

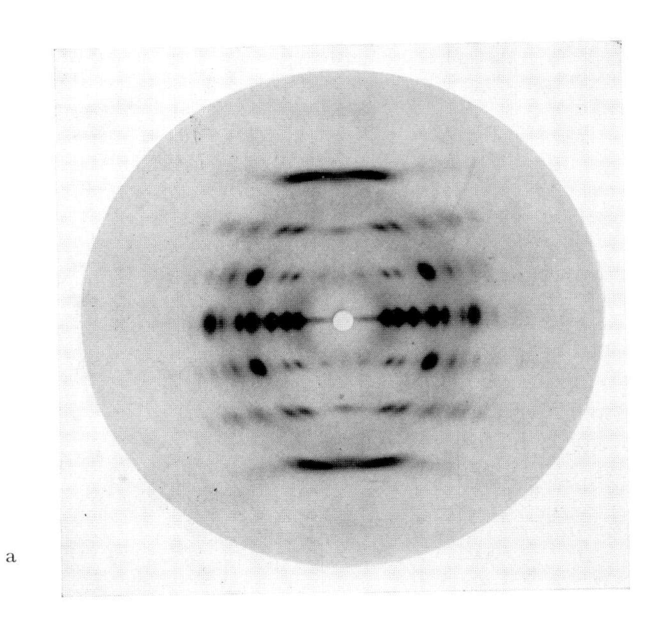

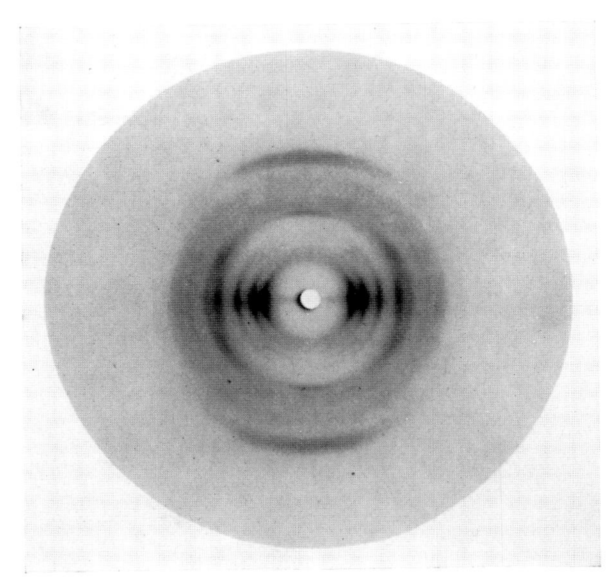

Fig. 11. X-ray fibre photographs: (a) cellulose triacetate yarn, hot stretched; (b) cellulose triacetate yarn, after heating at 220° C without tension. (Courtesy of Dr. C. H. Bamford.)

is not perfect and the crystallites are very small. The degree of order in different fibres varies tremendously, the X-ray photographs ranging from those such as Fig. 11a showing fairly sharp spots on layer lines to photographs showing almost continuous rings like a powder pattern (Fig. 11b).

The repeat distance along the fibre axis is deduced from the separation of the meridional reflexions, *i.e.* those reflexions lying on a line drawn through the centre of the photograph parallel to the direction of the fibre axis (usually vertical). This is analogous to the measurement of layer line separations for single crystals. The pattern of equatorial reflexions, *i.e.* those lying on a line through the centre of the photograph perpendicular to the meridional line, is a consequence of the molecular arrangement in the plane normal to the fibre axis. Sometimes the unit cell in the crystallite can be deduced from the equatorial reflexions but it is often not possible (*cf.* the difficulty of using a complex rotation photograph to find the unit cell of a single crystal). If the unit cell can be found and the reflexions indexed we can proceed to calculation of a Fourier synthesis as for a single crystal (see p. 50). Otherwise we must be content with a calculation of the radial distribution of electron density treating the molecular arrangement in the fibre as cylindrically symmetrical.

7. Relative intensities of X-ray reflexions; electron density distribution

The intensity of each recorded spot *hkl* depends on many factors, such as wavelength of radiation, temperature, types of atoms in the crystal, etc. These factors may be divided into two groups depending (*i*) on the nature of the atoms in the unit cell and their arrangement, and (*ii*) on the texture of the crystal and the experimental conditions. We shall discuss here only the effect of factors (*i*).

(a) Scattering by the atom

Diffraction of X-rays is due to scattering by the electrons in the atom. Hence to a first approximation the diffracting power of an atom is proportional to the number of electrons it contains, *i.e.* to its atomic number. Suppose that scattering by atoms A and B lying on Bragg reflexion planes is contributing to a reflected ray with Bragg angle θ (Fig. 12a). The rays scattered at A and B must have a path difference $n\lambda$. But in reality atoms are not scattering points. The diameter of the electron cloud is comparable with the interplanar spacing and with λ, so that there will be scattering also from electrons situated at C and D, near the outside of the atom (Fig. 12b). The path differences between these scattered rays and a ray from A will not necessarily be a whole number of wavelengths. There will not be complete reinforcement by all the rays scattered from all the electrons and hence the

References p. 51

diffracted ray will be weaker than if the atoms were infinitesimal points. The degree of weakening increases as the interplanar spacing decreases, *i.e.* as $\sin\theta/\lambda$ increases. As a measure of scattering power we use the atomic scattering factor f which is the scattering from the atom relative to the scattering from a single electron. It is equal to the number of electrons in

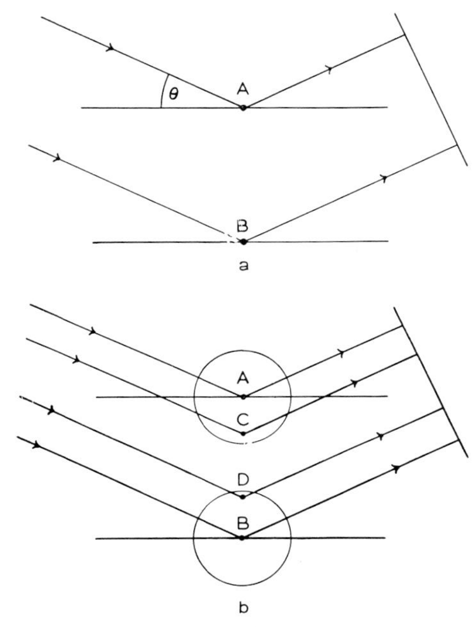

Fig. 12. Scattering of X-rays by atoms on Bragg reflection planes: (a) point atoms, (b) atoms of finite size.

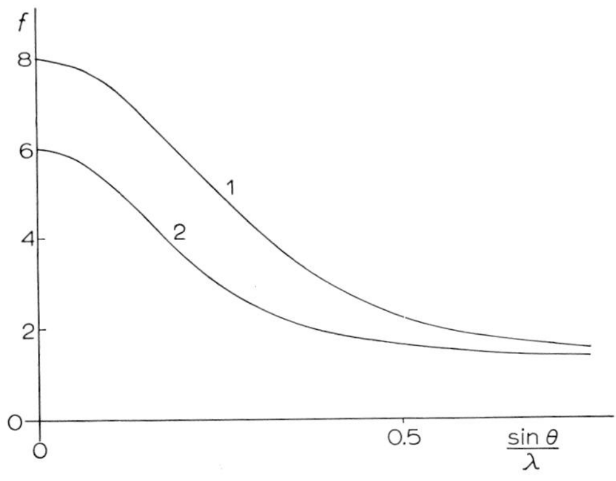

Fig. 13. Variation of atomic scattering factors with $\sin\theta/\lambda$: (1) oxygen, (2) carbon.

the atom, *i.e.* to the atomic number Z, when $\sin\theta/\lambda = 0$, and decreases steadily as $\sin\theta/\lambda$ increases (see Fig. 13).

(b) Scattering by the assembly of atoms in the unit cell

In general not all the atoms will lie exactly on any particular set of Bragg reflexion planes (*hkl*). Some, as atoms P and Q in Fig. 14, will lie between the

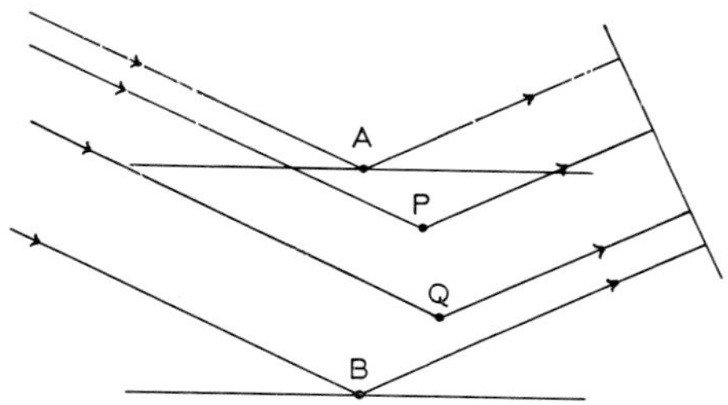

Fig. 14. Scattering of X-rays by the assembly of atoms in the unit cell.

planes, and rays scattered by them will have different path lengths from those scattered at A and B (for simplicity we draw the atoms again as points in Fig. 14). Let us choose atom B as the origin of the unit cell and suppose that atom P has co-ordinates x_1, y_1, z_1 referred to the crystallographic axes. The contribution of atom P to the total scattering is $f_p \exp[2\pi i(hx_1/a + ky_1/b + lz_1/c)]$ since the phase difference of the rays scattered from P and from B is $2\pi(hx_1/a + ky_1/b + lz_1/c)$. For any plane (*hkl*) the total scattering from all atoms is

$$F(hkl) = \sum_{n=1}^{N} f_n \exp[2\pi i(hx_n + ky_n + lz_n)] \tag{12}$$

(Here x/a is replaced by x, etc., co-ordinates being expressed as fractions of the unit-cell edges.) $F(hkl)$ is known as the *structure factor*, N is the number of atoms in the unit cell, f_n the atomic scattering factor of the nth atom for plane (*hkl*). $F(hkl)$ is a complex quantity having an amplitude $|F(hkl)|$ and a phase $\alpha(hkl)$ which are evaluated by putting F equal to $A' + iB'$:

$$A' = \sum_{n=1}^{N} f_n \cos 2\pi(hx_n + ky_n + lz_n) \tag{13}$$

$$B' = \sum_{n=1}^{N} f_n \sin 2\pi(hx_n + ky_n + lz_n) \tag{14}$$

Then $|F(hkl)|^2 = A'^2 + B'^2$, $\tan\alpha(hkl) = B'/A'$.

References p. 51

In calculating $F(hkl)$ account must also be taken of the thermal motion of the atoms. Even in a solid, the atoms are not at rest but are vibrating, the amplitude of the vibrations increasing with temperature. The electron cloud is effectively spread through a larger volume than the atom at rest would occupy, causing a further weakening of the diffracted ray. To take account of this, the contribution of each atom to $F(hkl)$ must be multiplied by a thermal factor $\exp(-B\sin^2\theta/\lambda^2)$ where B, the Debye factor, is related to the amplitude of vibration of the atom. The Debye factor is a constant for all values of $\sin\theta$ but is different for different atoms, in different crystals, and at different temperatures. We then have

$$A' = \sum_{n=1}^{N} f_n \cos 2\pi(hx_n + ky_n + lz_n)\exp(-B\sin^2\theta/\lambda^2)$$

and so on. The intensity I of the X-ray reflexion is proportional to $|F(hkl)|^2$ so that $|F(hkl)|$ is a measurable quantity. It is, however, impossible to measure the phase $\alpha(hkl)$ so that the structure factor cannot be completely determined experimentally. The test of whether a proposed crystal structure is correct lies in the agreement between the calculated amplitude $|F_c|$ and the observed $|F_o|$ (proportional to $I^{\frac{1}{2}}$) for each plane. The degree to which this agreement fails is usually expressed by the factor

$$R = \frac{\sum ||F_o| - |F_c||}{\sum |F_o|}$$

often given as a percentage, the sum being over all observed reflexions. It is not possible to say by a rigid rule how low R must be for a structure to be correct, but most structures published at the present time have R less than 20% and for the most accurate work on structures containing small molecules R is about 5%.

Since a crystal is periodic in three dimensions, it can be represented as an electron density distribution obtained by recombining the structure factors using a three-dimensional Fourier series. The electron density at *any* point (X, Y, Z) in the unit cell is given by

$$\rho(XYZ) = \frac{1}{V_c}\sum_h\sum_k\sum_{l=-\infty}^{\infty} F(hkl)\exp[-2\pi i(hX + kY + lZ)] \quad (15)$$

$$= \frac{1}{V_c}\{\sum_h\sum_k\sum_l |F(hkl)|\cos\alpha(hkl)\cos 2\pi(hX + kY + lZ)$$

$$+ \sum_h\sum_k\sum_l |F(hkl)|\sin\alpha(hkl)\sin 2\pi(hX + kY + lZ)\} \quad (16)$$

X, Y, Z being fractional co-ordinates and V_c the volume of the unit cell. The summation should be over all values of h, k, l from $-\infty$ to ∞, but in practice it can include only those planes (hkl) from which a reflexion is observed. In order to evaluate the electron density we must know for each plane, $|F(hkl)|$ and $\alpha(hkl)$. Since the phase cannot be measured, crystal structure determination cannot proceed directly from the experimental data. Methods used to overcome this limitation are discussed in Chapter I. In a centrosymmetric structure, for every atom at (x_n, y_n, z_n) there is another at $(\bar{x}_n, \bar{y}_n, \bar{z}_n)$ so that $B' = 0$. $\alpha(hkl)$ is then either 0° or 180° depending on whether A' is positive or negative. The problem of finding the phase angles thus reduces to the choice of one of only two alternatives for each reflexion. This is a tremendous simplification but as there are many hundreds or thousands of reflexions, the problem remains formidable.

REFERENCES

[1] W. L. BRAGG, *Nature*, 90 (1912) 410.
[2] A. GUINIER, *X-ray Crystallographic Technology*, Hilger and Watts, London, 1952, p. 4.
[3] J. D. BERNAL, *Proc. Roy. Soc. (London)*, A113 (1926) 117.
[4] P. P. EWALD, *Z. Krist.*, 56 (1921) 148.
[5] M. J. BUERGER, *Z. Krist.*, 91 (1935) 276.
[6] M. J. BUERGER, *X-ray Crystallography*, Wiley, New York, 1942, pp. 121, 157.
[7] K. WEISSENBERG, *Z. Physik*, 23 (1924) 229.

Chapter III

Analysis by Emission Spectroscopy

NORMAN H. NACHTRIEB

Department of Chemistry and Institute for the Study of Metals, The University of Chicago, Ill. (U.S.A.)

One of the most powerful methods of analysis at the disposal of the biochemist is provided by emission spectroscopy. Briefly, the method depends upon the identification of the wavelengths of characteristic radiations emitted by atoms which are electronically excited, and upon the measurement of the intensities of these radiations. Practically speaking, emission spectroscopy as an analytical tool is limited to the detection and determination of the metallic elements, which comprise about 80% of the elements of the periodic table. Although all the chemical elements possess emission spectra, it is generally not feasible to attempt the determination of the non-metallic elements, such as the halogens, noble gases, carbon, nitrogen, oxygen, and sulfur. Their most intense radiations lie either in generally inaccessible regions of the spectrum or else, as is the case with oxygen and nitrogen, they are elements of such common occurrence as to make their isolation from atmospheric contamination a practically insuperable task. Notwithstanding, the non-metallic elements phosphorus, boron, and silicon have strong radiations in the ultraviolet portion of the spectrum which permit ready identification and determination of these three elements.

1. Basic principles

The basis of qualitative spectrochemical analysis rests upon the fact that the valence electrons of atoms lie in discrete energy levels, and that when the electrons are excited to higher energy states they may return to the ground state with the emission of light quanta of definite energy. This is summed up in the simple Einstein equation:

$$\Delta E = E_2 - E_1 = h\nu = hc/\lambda \qquad (1)$$

where E_2 is the energy of the excited state, E_1 is the energy level of a lower state, h is Planck's constant, c is the velocity of light, and ν and λ are, respectively, the frequency and wavelength.

Not merely one, but many characteristic frequencies of electromagnetic radiation, are emitted by excited atoms; the number depends upon the complexity of the energy level system of each different kind of atom and upon the extent to which these energy levels are "populated" when an atom is electronically excited. Fig. 1 illustrates the energy level diagram for one

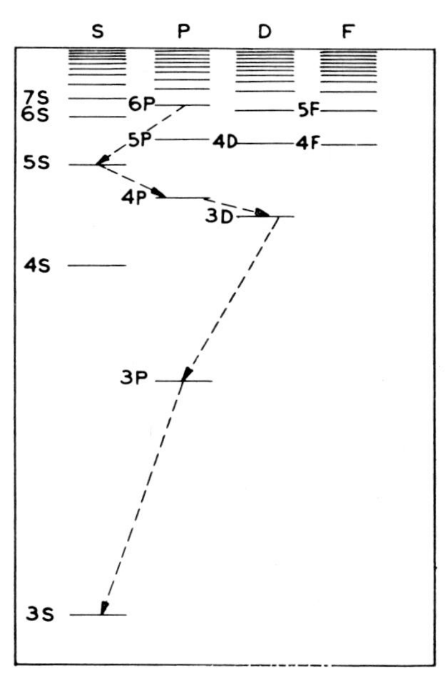

Fig. 1. Energy level diagram for sodium, showing a possible electron transition.

of the simpler atomic systems, the element sodium. The ordinate of the diagram represents an energy scale, and each of the horizontal lines corresponds to the energy of a state of the atom in which, classically, an electron is conceived to revolve about the nucleus in a fixed orbit. The four vertical columns of levels correspond to energy levels in which the electron orbit has a given orbital angular momentum, related to the ellipticity of the orbit. The orbital radius is related to the height of the energy level above the lowest possible value, which is termed the "ground state".

When an atom is excited, its valence electron may be promoted to one of the higher "excited" states, subject to certain selection rules which limit the kinds of transitions which are allowed. An electron which acquires sufficient energy to attain or exceed the uppermost energy level is no longer

References p. 65

bound to the nucleus by electrostatic forces, and the atom is said to be ionized. Only the energy states which correspond to the energy levels of the diagram may be occupied. Atoms remain in excited states for exceedingly short periods of time, following which they return to lower states with the concomitant emission of discrete quanta of radiant energy. When an electron in a sodium atom is excited to the 6P level, for example, it may return to the ground state by a number of permitted paths. One such route is illustrated in Fig. 1, the arrows representing energy transitions and the emission of light quanta of corresponding frequency. Other routes for the return of an excited atom to its ground state are possible; the number of transitions of a given type taking place for a very large number of excited atoms determines the intensity of that frequency of emitted radiation. When the number of atoms is very large, the relative intensities of the various radiations are fixed, and vary only when the temperature of the exciting discharge varies. Under given conditions of excitation, therefore, the intensity of any particular emitted frequency is proportional to the total number of atoms excited. This provides the basis for *quantitative* analysis by spectroscopy.

In practice, the measurement of the absolute intensity is a very difficult matter. Fortunately, it is sufficient to measure merely the ratio of the intensities of two radiations: one which has been properly selected from among the radiations emitted by the element in question, the other from the radiations emitted by another element which is present at known and unvarying concentration in the test sample. The latter, called an "internal standard" element, serves to normalize the unavoidable variations in excitation conditions, and eliminates the necessity for absolute intensity measurements. This procedure, which underlies all quantitative spectrochemical analysis, was devised in 1925 by Gerlach[1].

2. Spectrographs: their design and operation

The function of the spectrograph is to separate the characteristic radiations emitted from excited atoms into an ordered array and to provide for their photographic registration. Spectrometers which employ light-sensitive photocells in the place of photographic plates will not be considered in this discussion, since their principal use is not in the analysis of materials of biological interest but rather in the routine control of metallurgical products. Two different principles[2] are in use for the dispersion of light into its component frequencies: refraction and diffraction. Prism spectrographs make use of the phenomenon of refraction and sort out the components of mixed radiation by passing the light through a prism of glass or quartz. Parallel light, falling obliquely upon a face of such a prism, suffers a deviation in direction; the shorter wavelengths (higher frequencies) are deviated more than the longer wavelengths.

Fig. 2 shows schematically the dispersion of light into its components by a typical prism spectrograph. "A" is a slit whose height and width are both adjustable, "B" is a simple "collimator" lens whose function is to illuminate the prism face with parallel light, "C" is a 60°–60°–60° prism, and "D" is a simple "camera" lens, whose function is to focus the component rays upon the photographic emulsion in the camera cassette at "E". Since most of the

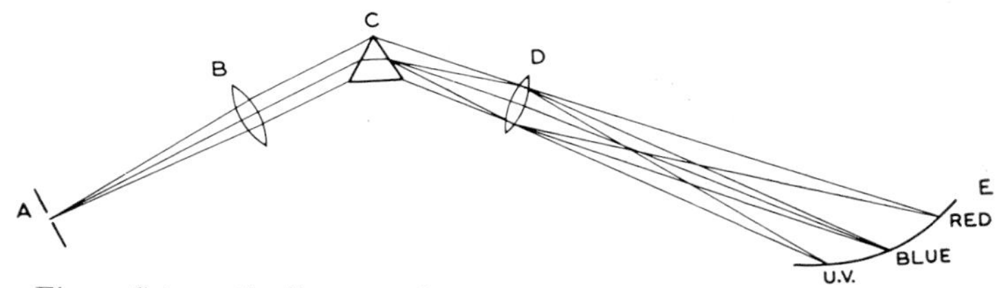

Fig. 2. Schematic diagram of medium dispersion quartz spectrograph.

wavelengths of interest for analysis lie in the wavelength range, 2400 Å–4000 Å (1 Å = 10^{-8} cm), the two lenses and the prism are generally made of clear quartz, which absorbs comparatively little ultraviolet light. It is seen that a spectrum "line" is merely an image of the narrow slit formed by light of a particular wavelength, and a "spectrum" is just the array of all such slit images formed independently by each of the characteristic radiations contained in the bundle of mixed radiation.

The arrangement of the optical elements shown in Fig. 2 is used in medium dispersion prism spectrographs, which are satisfactory for the analysis of biological materials and non-ferrous metals. Larger instruments, necessary for the analysis of substances having very complex spectra, are generally constructed according to the design shown in Fig. 3. Called a "Littrow"

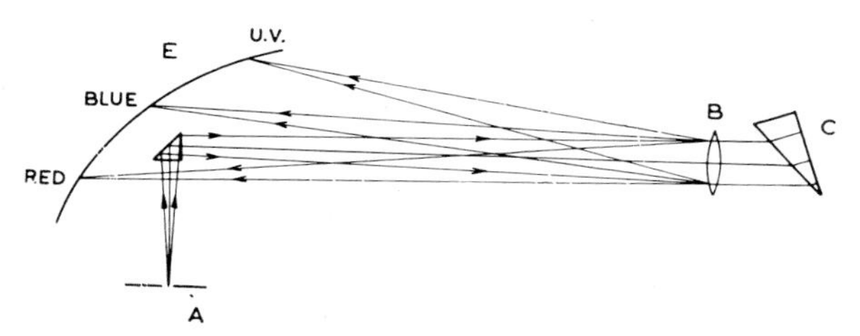

Fig. 3. Schematic diagram of Littrow prism spectrograph.

spectrograph, it uses a single large quartz lens which serves the dual function of collimating the light rays from the slit and of focussing the refracted rays upon the photographic plate. The large quartz prism is constructed with angles of 30°–60°–90°; light rays are reflected from the back face,

References p. 65

accomplishing thereby high dispersion with an economy of spectrograph length and quantity of quartz needed. All prism spectrographs have the characteristic that the dispersion decreases with increasing wavelength.

Grating spectrographs accomplish the dispersion of light by using the principle of interference or diffraction. Fig. 4 shows a schematic arrangement of the optical elements in such an instrument. "A" is the slit, "B" is a concave reflecting mirror upon whose surface many closely-spaced equidistant lines have been precisely ruled, and "C" is the camera cassette. No lenses are used within the instrument, the focussing being accomplished by the concavity of the grating. The principle of the operation of the diffraction grating is evident by examination of Fig. 5, which represents a small section

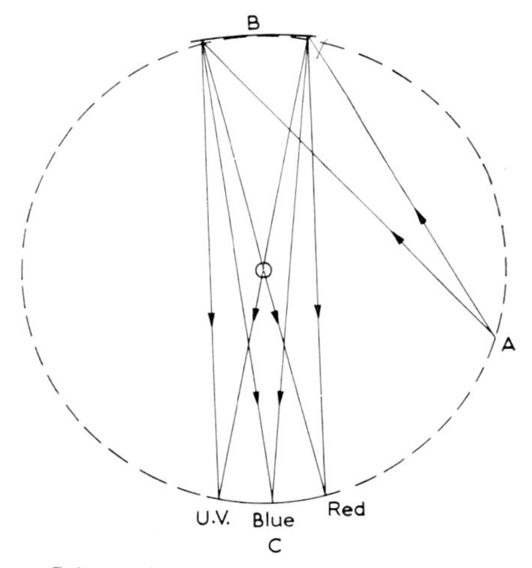

Fig. 4. Schematic diagram of grating spectrograph.

of the ruled surface, perpendicular to the rulings. The spacing of the rulings is designated by "*a*", and is commonly 1/15,000″. Let a bundle of parallel rays of light whose wavelength is λ make an angle θ_i with the grating normal. Such rays will reinforce one another after reflection from the grating only for a particular angle θ_r with the grating normal. Only for this particular angle θ_r will the path difference between successive rays, AOB and A′O′B′, equal one wavelength of light. For other arbitrary angles θ_r equivalent points on successive rays are partially out of phase with one another. The path differences are simply the differences in the projected lengths of the two adjacent rays, "*b*"—"*c*". These distances, in turn, are respectively equal to $a \cdot \sin\theta_i$ and $a \cdot \sin\theta_r$. Thus the condition that successive rays constructively reinforce one another is:

$$\lambda = a\,(\sin\theta_i - \sin\theta_r) \tag{2}$$

Successive rays which differ in path length from one another by two wavelengths (or n wavelengths, where n is an integer) will also be in phase. Moreover, when the diffracted rays lie on the same side of the grating normal as the incident rays, the path difference of successive rays is equal to "b" + "c". The general condition for constructive interference, known as the Grating Law, is therefore given by:

$$n\lambda = a\,(\sin\theta_i \pm \sin\theta_r) \tag{3}$$

where "n" is called the spectrum *order*.

Many modifications of the grating spectrograph have been designed, and several are produced commercially. They possess several advantages over prism instruments of comparable power, one of the most important being the possibility of photographing the spectrum in a higher order. Thus, two

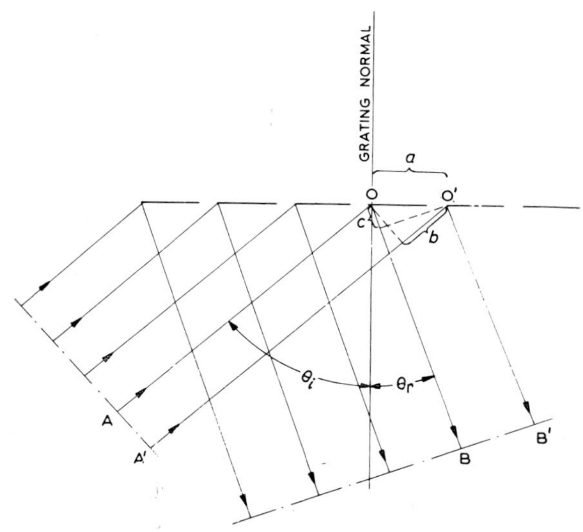

Fig. 5. Constructive interference of light rays by diffusion grating.

spectrum lines which are barely separated in the first order will have a two-fold greater separation in the second order. A further convenience of grating spectrographs, as compared with prism spectrographs, is that the dispersion of the former is "normal"; *i.e.*, essentially independent of wavelength. This

References p. 65

simplifies the problem of wavelength determination in an unknown spectrum. Good grating spectrographs are not inferior to prism spectrographs in the efficiency with which they utilize the light, moreover.

3. The excitation of spectra

The problem of exciting the emission spectrum of a sample is fundamentally one of imparting sufficiently large energies to the atoms by collision processes involving other high velocity atoms, molecules, or charged particles. It is, in effect, a thermal process in which the translational energies of atoms are converted into potential energies of electronic excitation by impact. Before the excitation process can be effective it is necessary to vaporize the sample from its (usually) solid condition. The two acts of vaporization and excitation are generally accomplished simultaneously (or nearly so) by the same energy source. Agencies for effecting the vaporization and excitation of samples fall into three main categories: (1) flames, (2) high-voltage spark discharges, and (3) electric arcs. Generally speaking, the energies available in flames are comparatively low. Only the spectra in the alkali and alkaline earth metals can be excited with reasonably high efficiency in flames, since the other elements have excitation potentials which are considerably higher. Nevertheless, the branch of optical spectroscopy called *Flame Photometry* has much importance in biological analysis in the quantitative determination of sodium and potassium in biological fluids and soft tissues. The sample, in the form of an aqueous solution, is sprayed into a mist and injected into an oxygen–acetylene flame. It is customary to use a photoelectric spectrophotometer instead of a spectrograph for isolating the characteristic radiations from the flame source. The reproducibility of excitation in flames is excellent, so that the relative intensities of the characteristic radiations may be read directly from the photocell output of the spectrophotometer without the need of employing the internal standard method. A previously established relation between line intensity and element concentration permits quantitative analysis.

Sample excitation by means of a high-voltage alternating current spark discharge finds little application in the analysis of biological materials. Well-suited for the analysis of metallic samples and prized for its flexibility and reproducibility, it lacks the high sensitivity generally needed for trace element analysis.

The most suitable method of sample excitation for materials of biological origin is provided by a stabilized direct current arc between graphite or carbon electrodes. Commonly, the arc current is between 5 and 10 amperes, and is provided by a motor–generator set or a high current full-wave vacuum tube rectifier operated at 220 volts. In operation the potential drop across the electrodes of the arc discharge is only 40 to 60 volts, and the remainder of the voltage drop is across a heavy-duty adjustable rheostat which tends to stabilize the current. The sample, usually in the form of an ashed product of the tissue or fluid or an aqueous solution evaporated to dryness, is contained within a crater bored in one of the graphite electrodes. Special spectroscopic grade graphite or carbon electrodes are required. They are available from several sources commercially and must at all times be protected from accidental contamination. Needless to say, they must never be touched with fingers nor left exposed, except for unavoidably short times, to the dust of the atmosphere. They may be purchased pre-formed to any one of a number of different shapes or in the form of long rods to be cut to length and fabricated to the desired shape on a lathe by the spectrographer. A simple and universally suitable form for electrodes is shown in Fig. 6. In this arrangement the upper and lower electrodes are held by friction fit to rods of less pure graphite, which may be used repeatedly and which permit the use of economical lengths of the more expensive pure graphite. The depth and

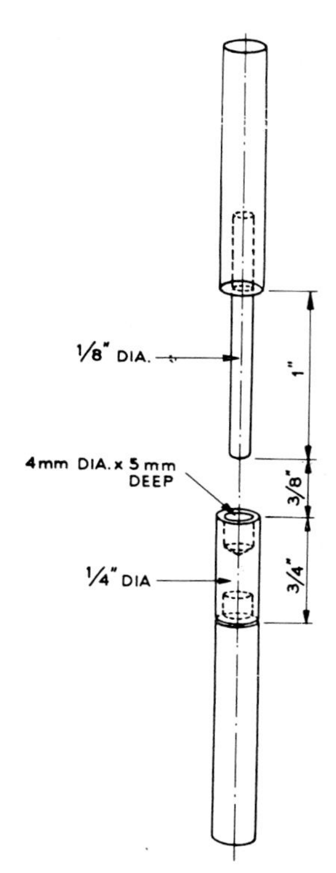

Fig. 6. Shape and arrangement of graphite electrodes for DC arc.

References p. 65

diameter of the sample crater in the lower electrode may be varied to suit the characteristics of the kind of material under analysis; once determined for a particular kind of sample, they should be held to reasonably close tolerances. During the course of the arc operation the electrodes are slowly consumed, and their separation should be maintained constant by manual adjustment with the aid of an enlarged image of the arc projected on a screen by an auxiliary lens.

4. Preparation of materials for analysis

Not only the absolute intensities, but the relative intensities of spectrum lines as well, depend upon the chemical composition of the sample matrix. This is because the effective temperature of the arc discharge is affected by the vapor pressures and ionization potentials of all the substances in the sample. It is therefore necessary to work out optimum analysis procedures for each basically different kind of substance under analysis. For example, the procedure adopted for the determination of trace metals in bone would be different from that devised for the determination of the same element in spinal fluid because of the effect of the calcium phosphate in the bone ash upon the impurity element line intensities. Sometimes it is convenient to admix the sample with a second substance which serves to dilute the sample and to serve as a spectroscopic "buffer"; small variations in the base composition of the sample are thereby minimized. Graphite or a non-hygroscopic inorganic salt is often used as the diluent. Samples must always be freed from organic material by dry or wet ashing in quartz or platinum vessels prior to analysis. An internal standard is added to each sample and to each standard to permit the evaluation of ratios of spectrum line intensities. Often the internal standard element is molybdenum or chromium in the form of a suitable salt, since these elements furnish many spectrum lines in all regions of the spectrum and are not likely to be found as trace impurities in the samples. The concentration is determined empirically, but is not critical as a rule. Once determined upon, however, it is maintained constant in samples and standards alike. For qualitative analysis, of course, internal standards are not used.

Exposure times should generally be of the order of one minute, and the depth of the sample crater, the sample weight, and the arc current are so chosen as to permit the complete vaporization of the sample in that period of time. Longer exposure times increase the spectrum background detrimentally, while shorter exposure times do not allow sufficient time for a suitable averaging of the unavoidable fluctuations in the discharge conditions.

5. Qualitative analysis

Ordinarily a preliminary qualitative analysis is performed on samples to assist in the preparation of suitable standards for subsequent quantitative work. The procedure is as described above, except that spectroscopic buffers, diluents, and internal standards are not incorporated. An iron spectrum is usually recorded on the photographic plate adjacent to the spectrum of the unknown, to facilitate the identification of lines of unknown wavelength. The search for the presence of unknown elements is most readily made by projecting the unknown spectrum and a master spectrum together upon a screen. The master spectrum, prepared with the same spectrograph, contains the most intense lines of all the chemical elements of interest, identified by element symbol. Such a master spectrum is often furnished with the instrument, but is easily made by the spectrographer from synthetic mixtures of salts. With the unknown and master spectra projected in juxtaposition it is a simple matter to search for line coincidences. The absence of the most intense line of an element from an unknown spectrum is sufficient to exclude the presence of the element. However, the presence of an element should be confirmed by line coincidences for at least three of the most prominent lines of the element in question, in order to insure against the possible accidental coincidences of the lines of different elements. The use of a master plate is urged as the most reliable and rapid method of qualitative analysis. The measurement of individual wavelengths of unknown lines and the search for them in tables of wavelengths is a laborious procedure which cannot often be justified.

6. Quantitative analysis

With a good knowledge of the base composition of the sample from prior chemical analysis or from previous experience with similar samples a series of standard samples must be prepared. Each standard (which may either be prepared synthetically or may be selected from a lot of natural material in which the sought elements are absent) must contain a fixed concentration of the internal standard substance. The series of standards is prepared with known and regularly varying concentrations of the elements to be sought; these may be added in the form of inorganic salts which are thoroughly mixed into the standards by grinding in an agate mortar, or may be added in the form of standard aqueous solutions. A standard photographic plate is then prepared, bearing the spectra of the standards.

For quantitative analysis it is next necessary to establish the relationship between the intensity of light and the corresponding photographic effect produced. For this purpose a microphotometer is required, whose function

References p. 65

is to measure the degree of transparency of the photographic image of spectrum lines. Let the transparency of a clear unexposed portion of the developed photographic emulsion be designated by the symbol, T_0, and given the arbitrary value 100. Let the transparency of a developed photographic image of a spectrum line be designated by the symbol, T. The photographic density of the image is then designated by the symbol, D, and is defined by the relations:

$$D = {}^{10}\log \frac{T_0}{T} \tag{4}$$

An image whose transmittance is 10% therefore has a density equal to 1.0, and one whose transmittance is 1% has a density of 2.0, etc. It is a property of the photographic emulsion that, over a wide range of light intensities to which it may be exposed, the optical density of the developed image is proportional to the logarithm of the light intensity[3]. This is illustrated in Fig. 7, in which deviations are seen to occur from linearity at both low and

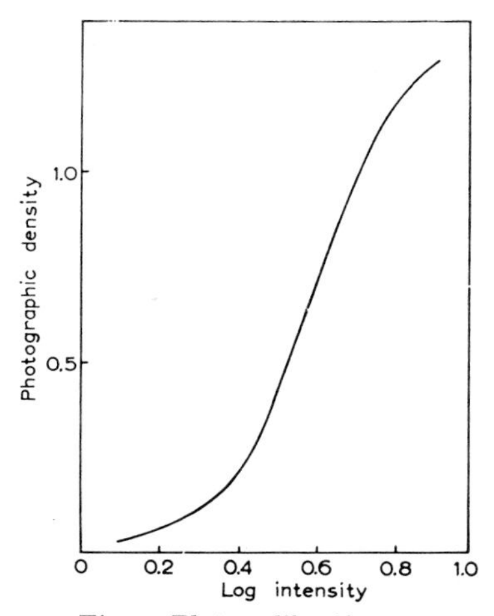

Fig. 7. Plate calibration curve.

high light intensities. Such a curve, nevertheless, provides a calibration of the photographic emulsion, and is called an H & D (Hurter–Driffield) plot, or simply a *Plate Calibration Curve*. In quantitative spectroscopic work it is desirable to calibrate each photographic plate; at very least, one calibration should be performed on each box of plates or emulsion lot. The calibration is conveniently carried out by photographing the spectrum of an iron arc (or an arc of some sample) with a graduated stepped optical wedge or a rotating logarithmic stepped sector placed in front of the slit of the spectrograph.

The function of the wedge or rotating sector is to provide five or six simultaneously photographed spectra, among which there is a known variation in light intensity. The design of the logarithmic sector or the relative transmittances of the graded optical wedge provides the known relative light intensities; *i.e.*, values of the abscissa of the plate calibration curve. Measurement of the photographic densities of the segments of the stepped spectrum lines permits the construction of the calibration curve. It should be mentioned in passing, that the slope of the calibration curve may depend upon the wavelength.

Given the calibration curve for the photographic emulsion, it is now possible to construct a *working curve* for each chemical element whose concentration has been made to vary in a known manner in the series of standard sample spectra. For example, suppose that the element vanadium is to be determined in bone ash, and that the series of standard samples of bone ash was prepared to contain vanadium at concentrations of 0.001%, 0.003%, 0.005%, 0.008%, and 0.010%. Suppose further, that the internal standard chosen was molybdenum, which was introduced into each standard at some constant concentration, *e.g.* 0.01%. The spectrographer selects the 3183.98 Å vanadium line and the 3193.97 Å molybdenum line and determines their photographic densities in each of the standard sample spectra. From the plate calibration curve he ascertains the logarithms of the intensity ratios of the two lines in each spectrum (Table I).

TABLE I

LOG INTENSITY RATIO DATA

% Vanadium	$^{10}log \frac{I_{V:3183.98}}{I_{Mo:3193.97}}$
0.001	0.204
0.003	0.681
0.005	0.903
0.008	1.108
0.010	1.204

He then constructs the working curve for the element vanadium by plotting the logarithm of the intensity ratio against the logarithm of the vanadium concentration (Fig. 8). A hypothetical and idealized example has been chosen, to illustrate the fact that the working curve should be linear in the coordinates chosen and with a slope of unity. These are reliable criteria for correct working curves. Factors which can lead to deviations from ideality are (1) the presence of an unsuspected residuum of vanadium in the standards, (2) the coincidence of another spectrum line which overlies

References p. 65

the analysis line, and (3) the presence of spectrum background which spuriously augments the density of the analysis line. With careful work[4] all of these factors can be discovered and corrections applied. Suppose now,

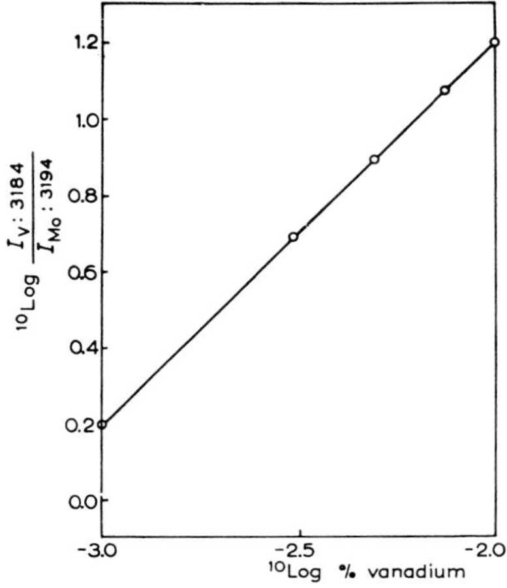

Fig. 8. Hypothetical working curve for vanadium in bone ash.

to conclude the example, that in a sample of bone ash the element vanadium is found, and the

$$^{10}\log \frac{I_{V:3184}}{I_{Mo:3194}}$$

ratio has the value 0.630. Reference to the working curve shows that the concentration of vanadium is 0.0027%.

Mention must be made of the importance of standardizing all aspects of the procedure in order to obtain the highest reproducibility and accuracy. The photographic process, in particular, must be well-controlled[5]. The photographic developer must be fresh and of unvarying composition. Its temperature should be controlled to within 1° for reproducible results from day to day. The overall average deviation of procedure is usually of the order of 5% when the direct current arc is used as the excitation source. It is both an advantage and a disadvantage of spectrographic procedures that the accuracy and precision do not depend significantly upon the concentration of the element sought. It is no easier to obtain results precise to 5% when the element concentration is 1% than it is to reach the same precision when the concentration[6] is only 0.01%. For this reason, spectrochemical procedures are generally superior to chemical methods for very low concentrations, but are inferior to the latter for high concentrations. Their great power, apart from high sensitivity lies in their ability to provide analytical information rapidly and simultaneously for a comparatively large number of elements in a single sample once the proper preliminary standardizations have been carried out. Much careful and time-consuming work is required in the preparation of reliable standards and working curves. The initial investment in time and effort is large, but can be justified when a large number of similar samples is to be analyzed.

REFERENCES

[1] W. Gerlach, *Z. anorg. Chem.*, 142 (1925) 383.
[2] R. Sawyer, *Experimental Spectroscopy*, Prentice Hall, 1944. (Recommended for principles of instrument design and operation).
[3] N. H. Nachtrieb, *Principles and Practice of Spectrochemical Analysis*, McGraw-Hill, New York, 1950. (A general reference on the principles of instrument operation and photographic photometry.)
[4] W. Brode, *Chemical Spectroscopy*, John Wiley & Sons, New York, 1943. (In the nature of a textbook, giving numerous laboratory exercises, as well as the general theory of spectrochemical methods.)
[5] G. R. Harrison, R. C. Lord and J. R. Loofbourow, *Practical Spectroscopy*, Prentice-Hall, 1948.
[6] W. Gerlach and W. Gerlach, *Die Chemische Emissions-Spektralanalyse*, Vol. II, L. Voss, Leipzig, 1933. (An excellent early monograph with numerous references to clinical analyses).

Chapter IV

Spectrophotometry in the Ultraviolet and Visible Regions

R. A. MORTON

Department of Biochemistry, The University of Liverpool (Great Britain)

"Les données numériques qui caractérisent l'absorption inégale des diverses lumières conduiront peut être prochainement à une méthode d'analyse chimique universelle."

(BERTHELOT, *Science et philosophie*)

1. Introduction

Spectrophotometry in the visible and ultraviolet regions of the spectrum is now widely accepted as an aid to research and testing in chemistry and biochemistry. Millikan once wrote that "no theoretical formula in the history of physics has had more spectacular successes than has Sommerfeld's relativity formula as applied to spectroscopic fine structure." By such a standard the spectrophotometry of relatively complicated organic substances is distinctly empirical, and the correlation of chemical structure with absorption spectra is superficial compared with the elegant analysis of atomic spectra or even of the band spectra of di- and tri-atomic molecules. Although from the standpoint of pure spectroscopy biochemical applications are empirical, this theoretical limitation has not prevented spectroscopic methods from playing an important part in some of the most fundamental biochemical studies made during the last thirty years.

Until the outbreak of the War of 1939–1945 ultraviolet spectrophotometry was used in relatively few laboratories. The technique rested on photographing the spectrum and it took a long time to obtain and read the negatives. Even then skill and experience were necessary.

During and after the War, photoelectric spectrophotometers became more readily available. These instruments were well-designed and gave results of considerable accuracy fairly speedily. The manually operated photoelectric spectrophotometers were followed by recording instruments, which for special purposes, have great merit. Some workers have adapted spectrophotometric methods to tracing the course of rapid processes in biochemistry. The special equipment so used is ingenious and valuable. For the greater part of the work described in this Chapter the manually operated photoelectric spectrophotometers (Beckman, Hilger, Unicam and other makes) are thoroughly satisfactory. Detailed descriptions of such instruments are given by the manufacturers, together with operating instructions and there is no need to repeat them here.

(a) Notation used in spectrophotometry

Monochromatic radiations are specified in terms of wavelength (λ), wavenumbers ($1/\lambda$) and frequency ν. Thus the sodium D_2 line is expressed as

5889.965 Å	588.9 mμ	0.589 μ	$5.889 \cdot 10^{-5}$
(Ångstrom units)	(millimicrons)	(microns)	(cm)

or $\nu = 509.2 \cdot 10^{12}$ where ν = true frequency, namely

$$\frac{\text{velocity of light (cm/sec)}}{\text{wavelength in cm}}$$

so that

$$\nu = \frac{3 \cdot 10^{10}}{5.889 \cdot 10^{-5}} = 509.2 \cdot 10^{12}$$

The term *fresnel,* abbreviated *f* is sometimes used as a unit of frequency, one fresnel being equal to 10^{12} oscillations per second.

The visible portion of the spectrum extends from about 410 to 760 mμ and the ultraviolet region (using quartz optics in air) from 185 to 400 mμ. The infrared spectrum is usually taken as extending from 0.76 μ to about 25 μ.

When light falls on any substance it may be reflected, absorbed or transmitted. In absorption spectrophotometry, reflexion losses are of little importance when a matched comparison cell, containing pure solvent only, is used. Both cells reflect the same proportion of the incident light.

Let I_λ be the intensity of incident light of wavelength λ. The weakening of light intensity will be proportional to I_λ and $\mathrm{d}l$ where $\mathrm{d}l$ is a small thickness of medium.

$$-\,\mathrm{d}I_\lambda = aI_\lambda\,\mathrm{d}l \quad \text{or} \quad -\frac{\mathrm{d}I_\lambda}{I_\lambda} = a\,\mathrm{d}l$$

References p. 131

Integrating, putting I_0 for $l = 0$, at wavelength λ

$$\ln I_0/I = al$$

Lambert's law restates this in the form

$$I = I_0 \, \mathrm{e}^{-al}$$

(where I_0 is the intensity of the incident light and I that of the emergent light, l is the thickness of the absorbing layer in cm and a is the absorption coefficient) so that each successive layer (of equal thickness) absorbs an equal fraction of the light.

By replacing e (natural base) by 10, $I = I_0 10^{-Kl}$ and K is the extinction coefficient of Bunsen and Roscoe. This may be defined as the reciprocal of the thickness (in cm) needed to weaken the light to one-tenth its incident intensity. Hence

$$\log I_0/I \text{ is } Kl = E \text{ (extinction)}$$

According to Beer's law, absorption is proportional to the number of molecules in the light path. [This refers to absorbing solute molecules in a solvent transparent to the radiation used.] Thus a 10-cm layer of 0.001 M solution or a 1-cm layer of 0.01 M solution exert the same absorption.

$I = I_0 \cdot 10^{-\varepsilon cl}$ where c is concentration in gram-molecules per liter and l is cell thickness in cm. This expression is conveniently rewritten

$$\log I_0/I = \varepsilon cl$$

ε being the molecular extinction coefficient. Photometric devices are frequently graduated to indicate extinctions

$$E = \log I_0/I = \varepsilon cl \text{ (0 to 2.0 or 0 to 3.0)}$$

and absorption curves are often plotted to display ε against λ. The expression E_{1}^{c} first used by Gillam and Morton[1] denotes an actual measurement, *i.e.* at a wavelength λ using a 1-cm layer of a solution of molar concentration c, $\log I_0/I = E$ as measured on the spectrophotometer. This notation may be modified to apply to natural products (*e.g.* fish liver oils) in which c is better expressed as percentage (wt./vol.) of solute in a transparent solvent.

If a 0.5-cm layer of 0.1% solution transmits 10% of the light at *e.g.* 275 mμ

$$E_{275\ \mathrm{m}\mu} = 1.0 \text{ and } E_{0.5\ \mathrm{cm}}^{0.1\ \%} = 1.0$$

From this

$$E^{1\%}_{1\,\text{cm}} \text{ at } 275\ \text{m}\mu = \frac{1.0 \times 1.0}{0.5 \times 0.1} = 20$$

This notation allows different samples of materials to be compared in terms of the relative concentrations of an absorbing constituent.

For certain theoretical calculations, absorption is expressed in terms of an *absorption index* k, such that

$$I = I_0\,\mathrm{e}^{-4\pi kl/\lambda}$$

To convert k to ε (molecular extinction coefficient)

$$k = 0.183\, c\lambda\varepsilon$$

It is sometimes necessary to describe concisely an absorption *band, i.e.* a more or less symmetrical absorption curve extending over a given range of wavelengths and rising to a peak at λ_{max} and ε_{max}. Two wavelengths λ_1 and λ_2 can be found such that their molecular extinction coefficient is half ε_{max}. The half width of the absorption band will then be $\lambda_1 - \lambda_2$ and the band strength will be $\int_{\nu_2}^{\nu_1} \varepsilon \mathrm{d}\nu$ where ν_1 and ν_2 are the frequencies corresponding to λ_1 and λ_2.

If now a solution of concentration c (gram-molecules per litre) is considered, the *number* of molecules in 1 cubic centimetre will be $cN/1000$ where N is the Avogadro number.

Let a be the (effective) cross-sectional area of an absorbing molecule and $\mathrm{d}l$ be a layer of solution so thin that there is no superposition of molecules in the path of the light

$$-\,\mathrm{d}I/I = Nacdl/1000$$

and

$$^{10}\log I_0/I = 0.43\, Nacl \cdot 10^{-3}, \text{ but } ^{10}\log \frac{I_0/I}{cl} = \varepsilon$$

$$\varepsilon = 0.00043\, Na = 2.6 \cdot 10^{20}\, a$$

Not all the solute molecules will be correctly oriented to exert maximum absorption and if a statistical factor of $\frac{1}{3}$ is introduced to allow for random orientation:

$$\varepsilon = \tfrac{1}{3}\,(2.6 \cdot 10^{20})\, a$$

For many organic molecules the cross-sectional area may be estimated from electron-diffraction or X-ray diffraction estimates of molecular dimensions.

References p. 131

Accepting as representative a figure of 10 Å^2 or 10^{-15} cm^2, a typical molecular extinction coefficient will be

$$\varepsilon = \tfrac{1}{3} \cdot 2.6 \cdot 10^{20} \cdot 10^{-15}$$

$$= 0.87 \cdot 10^5, \text{ or of the order } 10^5$$

This implies unit probability for the absorptive process (which in the ultra-violet region would be an *electronic* transition). In fact, molecular extinction coefficients of about 100,000 are seen in carotenoids and of 50,000 in vitamin A where the electronic transition owes its origin to a system of conjugated double bonds.

A great many compounds exhibit ε_{max} values between 5000 and 25,000 and the absorption bands concerned are described as *high intensity* bands in which the probability P of the electronic transition is at least 0.1. In contrast to these "allowed" transitions there are many examples of *low intensity* absorption bands such as those exhibited by saturated aliphatic ketones: λ_{max} *ca.* 270 mμ, ε_{max} about 20. The electronic transition is here "forbidden" and $P < 0.01$.

The theoretical aspect of the intensity and width of an absorption is discussed by Chako[2] and Förster[3]. They show that an approximate upper limit of 100,000 for ε_{max} is not inconsistent with quantum mechanics or general experience for a single electronic transition in a molecule.

(b) Checking and calibrating a spectrophotometer

The makers of most instruments give adequate instructions for checking the wavelength adjustment. This can be done quite easily by using a piece of "didymium" glass (*e.g.* Corning 5120) which has intense narrow bands at 441, 528.7, 585, 684.8, 743.5, 754, 808, 883 and 1067 mμ. Alternatively a simple solution of potassium permanganate will serve a similar purpose. The most satisfactory method of checking the performance on the intensity scale is to make determinations on solutions of pure substances which have been carefully studied. Haupt[4] found for potassium chromate in 0.05 N potassium hydroxide peaks very near to 275 and 375 mμ. She gave the following results:

K_2CrO_4 0.04 g/l in 0.05N KOH

λ(mμ)	230	275	313	375
E	0.171	0.757	0.043	0.991
$E^{1\%}_{1cm}$	42.75	189.25	10.75	247.8

Cama, Collins and Morton[5] also discuss this problem fully. For routine checking, a solution of potassium nitrate (1% in water) shows λ_{max} 301–303 mμ with a fairly flat peak, ε_{max} 7.0 ($E^{1\%}_{1cm}$ 0.71).

In order to test the performance of a spectrophotometer over its useful intensity range a number of solutions of pure K_2CrO_4 in 0.05 N KOH should be prepared with accurately known concentrations ranging from

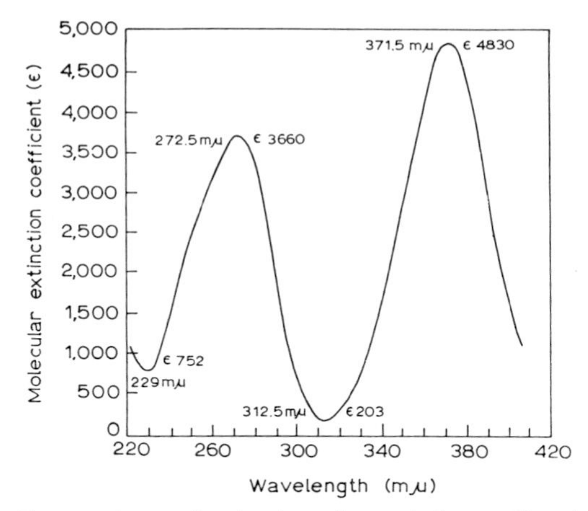

Fig. 1. Absorption spectrum of potassium chromate in 0.05N potassium hydroxide (see Bibliography[3]). For calibration purposes it is sufficient to work at the two maxima and the two minima. Compare the data from Haupt[4] for 0.004 % solution.

λ(mμ)	230	270	275	313.2	375
ε	832	3617	3676	211	4815
$E^{1\%}_{1cm}$	42.75	186.25	189.25	10.75	247.75

0.005–0.15 g/l, *i.e.* a range of 1 to 30. The wavelength should then be set at 273 mμ or 372 mμ and E values for a 1-cm layer of each solution should be measured. $E^{1\%}_{1cm}$ values are then calculated and plotted against observed E values. Ideally a horizontal line should be obtained but when E is $\langle$ 0.3 or $\rangle$ 1.8, observed values tend to err. The application of this test to each individual instrument will allow corrections to be introduced when quantitative analytical work is being done and it is inconvenient to avoid using the extremes of the density scale.

Minor defects in performance are often due to faulty placing of lamps in holders, or to tarnished mirrors which may need to be renewed. The more permanent settings are made very carefully when the instrument is assembled and it is rarely advisable for the user to tamper with them.

Fluorescent substances sometimes give rise to special difficulties (see Gibson[6], Braude, Fawcett and Timmons[7]), but the effect is not often serious

References p. 131

if the absorption spectra determinations are made with dilute solutions such that the E values fall with the limits 0.2 to 0.8.

(c) Presentation of results

There is no uniform system and the following notes (see Brode[8]) are intended to help in following the literature. When I_0 is the intensity of incident light (or of the transmitted comparison beam) and I is the transmitted intensity,

$T = I/I_0$ or transmittance
$T \times 100$ = percent transmittance
$t = T^{-cl}$, transmittivity, *i.e.* transmittance per unit concentration and unit thickness
A = Absorbance = ${}^{10}\log I_0/I$ (Extinction E)
$\varepsilon = A/cl$ = molar absorptivity (molecular extinction coefficient)

Most absorption curves for pure compounds published nowadays display molecular extinction coefficients, molar absorptivities, ε (epsilon) as ordinate. In some circumstances log ε is shown but this has the disadvantage of lacking the additive character of the former method. The abscissae may be wavelengths, wave-numbers or true frequencies, sometimes with shorter wavelengths to the left and sometimes with shorter frequencies to the left.

(d) Descriptive terms

If as a result of a change in the chemical constitution of the absorbing molecule, or of an environmental change, an absorption band is displaced in the direction of longer wavelengths the shift is said to be *bathochromic*. A displacement in the direction of shorter wavelengths is called a *hypsochromic* shift. An increase in intensity of absorption (absorbance) is a *hyperchromic* effect and a decrease is a *hypochromic* effect. A visible colour is *deepened* by a bathochromic shift and *lightened* by a hypsochromic displacement; the order of colour deepening is yellow-orange-red-purple-blue-green as the selective absorption is shifted across the spectrum from the violet to the red region. *Fading* or *bleaching* refers to changes which either reduce the concentration of selectively absorbing material, or convert the absorbing entity into a product which absorbs less strongly. *Dichroism* refers to changes in "colour" associated with changes in concentration; this means that the visual effects and the concentration changes do not keep pace with one another. *Halochromism* describes the change in absorption spectrum which occurs when a colourless substance is dissolved in a strong acid (such as sulphuric acid or perchloric acid) and which often gives rise to visible colour. Benzophenone exhibits this effect (see table below).

Partial chromophore refers to the fact that the absorption curves for some relatively complex molecules can best be interpreted on the assumption that two or more moieties are functioning independently of one another and additively. Absorption curves may be *symmetrical* or obviously *unsymmetrical*. They may show inflexions which under special conditions (*e.g.* use of inert solvents or low temperatures) become narrow absorption bands. Splitting of broad absorption curves is described as *resolution*; the position of the

ABSORPTION PEAKS FOR BENZOPHENONE

in ether		*in concentrated sulphuric acid*	
λ_{max} (mμ)	log ε	λ_{max} (mμ)	log ε
344	2.15	343	4.88
282	3.4	292	4.03
248	4.4		

absorption curve on the wavelength scale is determined by the magnitude of the electronic transition and the relatively narrow-banded *structure* reflects intramolecular vibrations. Polar solvents such as alcohols effect less resolution than non-polar hydrocarbon solvents such as hexane when, for example, the solute is phenol or pyridine. The position of λ_{max} may be displaced by changing one solvent for another; such displacements, which are normally small, are known as *solvent shifts*. When a solute can undergo a change such as keto–enol tautomerism, oxidation–reduction or "indicator" changes whereby two molecular species are in equilibrium, the absorption curves for the two "pure" or extreme states will intersect at *isosbestic points*. The intensity of absorption at these wavelengths will depend on the total amount of the solute and not on the proportions of the interchanging components.

2. Theoretical background

The absorption of visible and ultraviolet light by organic compounds nearly always arises from electronic transitions. The electrons which participate in single bonds are denoted σ-electrons, those which make up double or triple bonds are called π-electrons and unshared electron pairs are called p-electrons. Ions contain 'charge' electrons, and free radicals odd or unpaired electrons.

Saturated hydrocarbons have only one type (σ) of valency electrons. The paraffins exhibit selective absorption in the far ultraviolet region (< 185 mμ) which can only be explored by means of a vacuum spectrograph using a grating, or a fluorite prism. The act of absorption may be one of two kinds

References p. 131

(*a*) N–R or Rydberg transitions in which a σ-electron is removed by stages from both the atoms concerned until finally it is ejected (ionisation), thus C—C→ C^+—C. The absorption spectrum shows narrow bands and a continuous region. (*b*) N–V transitions which involve electron movements such that both atoms of a link C—C or C—H become temporarily charged *e.g.* C^-—H^+ to form a dipole.

In organic compounds containing oxygen, nitrogen or halogen the non-bonding *p*-electrons are more readily ejected by short-wave radiation than the σ-electrons, *i.e.* smaller quanta ($h\nu$) are needed and the Rydberg transitions are displaced towards longer wavelengths. Ionisation potentials, determined by electron bombardment, are in agreement with this. Alkyl substituents take the displacement further, thus C_2H_5SH shows λ_{max} 195 mμ and $C_2H_5S \cdot SC_2H_5$ has λ_{max} 255 mμ.

The electrons of unsaturated linkages (π-electrons) are more readily displaced than σ-electrons and in consequence the selective absorption to which they give rise occurs at longer wavelengths. Thus, ethylene $H_2C{=}CH_2$ and formaldehyde HCHO exhibit absorption of the Rydberg type (ionisation potentials near 10.5 electron volts [eV] or 118.5 mμ). Of wider importance perhaps is the fact that the ethylenic linkage and the carbonyl group strongly absorb radiations in the region 180–200 mμ, the processes being of the following nature:

$$C = C \rightarrow C^{+}—C^{-}$$
$$C = O \rightarrow C^{+}—O^{-}$$

the implication being that the transitions are of the N–V type.

Finally, there are weak bands in the near ultraviolet. Aldehydes and ketones show selective absorption near 275 mμ attributed to a "forbidden" transition (of low probability) in which a *p*-electron from the oxygen atom is involved. Other weak bands are attributed to biradical excited states (or triplet states)

$$C = C \rightarrow \dot{C} — \dot{C}$$

Any covalent unsaturated grouping (C=O, N=N, C=C, C_6H_5 etc.) which is the site of an electronic absorption process is called a *chromophore*. Many saturated groupings (OH, CH_3, NH_2, Cl, SH) when attached directly to a chromophore, shift the selective absorption in the direction of longer wavelengths and enhance the intensity of absorption; such groupings are described as *auxochromes*.

When two chromophores are separated by one or more CH_2 groups they are said to be isolated or insulated and their spectroscopic effects are additive. Constitutive effects are seen with *conjugated* double bonds; thus a system of two or three conjugated double bonds results in a new absorption spectrum.

If two chromophores are directly linked as in

$$>C{=}C{=}O \qquad \text{or} \qquad >C{=}C{=}C<$$

the result is a new absorbing pattern in which the bathochromic shift is rather larger than in the corresponding conjugated arrangement but the intensity of absorption is a good deal less.

The absorption curves for benzene, naphthalene and other aromatic compounds are characteristic and distinct, and there is good reason to think of the "phenyl" chromophore as an entity in itself.

Burawoy[9] has referred to the absorption bands of high intensity, due to (π–π) conjugation as arising from K-chromophores (German, *Konjugierte*) whilst the low intensity bands at longer wavelengths are ascribed to R-chromophores (*Radikal*). Mesityloxide $(CH_3)_2C{=}CH\cdot COCH_3$ and phorone $(CH_3)_2C{=}CH\cdot CO\cdot CH{=}C(CH_3)_2$ illustrate how the absorption curves exhibit considerable displacements (Table I).

TABLE I

BATHOCHROMIC EFFECTS IN R BANDS AND K BANDS

Hydrocarbon solvent

	R-band C=O		*K-band C=C*	
	λ_{max} (mμ)	ε_{max}	λ_{max} (mμ)	ε_{max}
$CH_3\cdot CO\cdot CH_3$	279	15		
$(CH_3)_3C\cdot CO\cdot C(CH_3)_3$	296	20		
$(CH_3)_2C{=}CH\cdot COCH_3$	327	40	229	12,600
$(CH_3)_2C{=}CH\cdot COCH{=}C(CH_3)_2$	375	80	295	23,500
$CH_3CH{=}CH\cdot CH{=}CH\cdot COCH_3$	masked		264	20,800
$CH_3CH{=}CH\cdot CH{=}CH\cdot CHO$	masked		270	26,500

In methanol (as solvent) the mesityl oxide peaks occur at 315 mμ (ε_{max} 55) and 238 mμ (ε_{max} 10,700). The chromophoric system could be written:

$>C^*{=}CH\cdot COCH_3$ to denote a transition occurring in the ethylenic linkage influenced by the conjugation with carbonyl. Similarly,

$>C{=}CH\cdot C^*OCH_3$ indicates a transition involving a carbonyl electron influenced by the conjugated ethylenic grouping. Woodward[10] and Evans and Gillam[11] have shown that the displacements suffered by the K bands are of considerable diagnostic value. The generalizations are empirical but none the less serviceable. Considering α–β unsaturated ketones

$$R{-}\underset{\underset{O}{\|}}{C}{-}\overset{\overset{\alpha}{|}}{C}{=}C{<}^{\beta}_{\beta}$$

TABLE II

Substitution	λ_{max} (mμ)
mono, α or β	225 ± 5
di, αβ or ββ	239 ± 5
tri, αββ	254 ± 5
ββ both H	218
di-, no exocyclic C=C bond	235 ± 5
tri, no exocyclic C=C bond	247 ± 5

the position of λ_{max} (ethanol solutions) varies as listed in Table II.

Solvents other than ethanol can be used but the wavelengths of peaks will differ (Woodward[10]).

The effects of conjugated double bonds in ring systems on one another will be discussed later.

3. Spectroscopic properties of various compounds

(a) Derivatives of carbonyl compounds

The spectroscopic properties of some of the well-known derivatives of aldehydes and ketones help to distinguish between simple carbonyl compounds and those exhibiting αβ unsaturation:

X>C=O (X, Y on C) X·CH=CH·CO(–Y)

The main band of acetone is at about 187 mμ and that of αβ-unsaturated aldehydes varies around 230 mμ. Table III summarises the position.

TABLE III

K BANDS OF CARBONYL COMPOUNDS AND DERIVATIVES IN ETHANOL

	Saturated		αβ-Unsaturated	
	λ_{max} (mμ)	ε_{max}	λ_{max} (mμ)	ε_{max}
Carbonyl compound	189–200		230	10,000–20,000
Oximes	*ca.* 200		235 (230–240)	12,000–23,000
Semicarbazones	229 (225–230)	11,500 (10,900–13,000)	265 259.5–271.5	*ca.* 20,000 (variable)
Thiosemicarbazones	271.5 (270–273)	22,400 (20,400–24,300)	301 (299.5–302.5)	32,500 (25,000–37,000)
2,4-Dinitrophenyl hydrazones	360	22,000 (17,500–25,000)	380	27,000 (25,500–31,500)

From the above results the confirmation of $\alpha\beta$-unsaturation is straightforward and an approximation to the molecular weight of a new carbonyl compound is possible, particularly if the "model" substances resemble the unknown substance fairly closely (see Gillam and Stern, Bibliography[5]).

(b) Effects of conjugated double or triple bonds on ultraviolet absorption curves

Butadiene shows λ_{max} 217 mμ, ε_{max} 21,000 whereas vinylacetylene shows a peak at 219 mμ, ε_{max} 6,500. Dimethylacetylene shows an R-band at 227 mμ, ε_{max} 360. The effect of conjugation is seen clearly again in diacetyl: $CH_3CO \cdot COCH_3$ where the carbonyl R-band is displaced to 435 mμ, but ε_{max} remains at 18 as in acetone. In crotonaldehyde the K band falls at 217 mμ (ε, 16,000) and the R-band at 321 mμ (ε, 20) whilst in propylethynylketone where the chromophore is $HC{\equiv}C \cdot COC_2H_5$, the peaks are at 214 m$\mu$ (ε_{max} 5,000) and 308 mμ (ε_{max} 20) (Braude[12]). The compound: 1,3,5-hexatriene, with three conjugated double bonds exhibits very intense absorption with resolution into three peaks at 247.5, 257.5 and 267.5 mμ. In 1,3,5,7-octatetraene the maxima are at 268, 278, 290 and 304 mμ. The bathochromic shift is obvious and the nearly constant spacing of the sub-maxima reflects an intramolecular vibration frequency. The alcohols $CH_3(CH{=}CH)_3CH_2OH$ and $CH_3(CH{=}CH)_4CH_2OH$ show peaks (in ethanol) at 268 and 310 mμ. Similarly the acids $CH_3(CH{=}CH)_nCOOH$ (in hexane) exhibit the following maxima:

$n =$	1	2	3	4
λ_{max} (mμ)	208	261	302	330
ε_{max}	12,200	25,200	36,500	48,200

The variation of λ_{max} with n when n is small is given roughly by $\lambda^2 = kn$ where k is a constant. It is probably more accurate to say that λ varies as the distance between the carbon atoms at the ends of the conjugated system; certainly this fits the effects of *cis–trans* isomerism as a first approximation. The relation between ε_{max} and n is roughly linear and the area covered by plotting ε against ν, *i.e.*

$$\int_{\nu_0}^{\nu_0+x} \varepsilon d\varepsilon$$

varies linearly with n (x being a measure of band-width). If the cross sectional area of a double bond (from X-ray diffraction) is taken to be about 2 Å^2

References p. 131

$$\varepsilon_{max} = 0.87 \cdot 10^{20} \cdot 2 \cdot 10^{-16} \cdot n$$
$$= 17{,}400\ n$$

a figure which is very approximately confirmed for some poly-enes and is of the right order for most.

(c) Benzene and its derivatives

Benzene exhibits weak resolved selective absorption ε_{max} 60–300 in the region 230–270 mμ. The principal peak near 255 mμ is part of a system which in hexane solution exhibits 8 narrow bands. Fine-structure is shown in great detail in the very well resolved absorption spectrum of benzene vapour. The low-intensity (B) absorption is attributed to a forbidden transition (electronic) to a non-ionised (homopolar) state. There are also regions of selective absorption at about 184 mμ (log ε_{max} 4.67) and 202 mμ (log ε_{max} 3.84). These bands are designated E bands (E_1 and E_2) and are due to transitions to dipolar excited states of the molecule, possibly of the types:

and

In naphthalene the E_1 band is displaced to 220 mμ (log ε_{max} 5.05) and the E_2 band to 275 mμ (log ε_{max} 3.75), while the B band reappears, again resolved, in the region of 310–330 mμ. The spectrum of anthracene shows two main areas of absorption, one near 252 mμ (log ε_{max} 5.3) and the other about 375 mμ (log ε_{max} 3.9).

The curve for phenanthrene exhibits bands at 252 mμ (log ε_{max} 4.7), 295 mμ (log ε_{max} 4.10) and 330 mμ (log ε_{max} 2.4). The positions of the E_2 bands depend on the distance within the molecule separating the charges in the excited state, accepting the very probable view that the charges are polarised along for example the long axis of anthracene.

Gillam and Hey[13] showed that the polyphenyls behave differently.

The main band of diphenyl (λ_{max} 252 mμ, log ε_{max} 4.26) remains unchanged in position in the m-polyphenyls, the ε values being simply additive. In the p-polyphenyls there is a K-chromophore

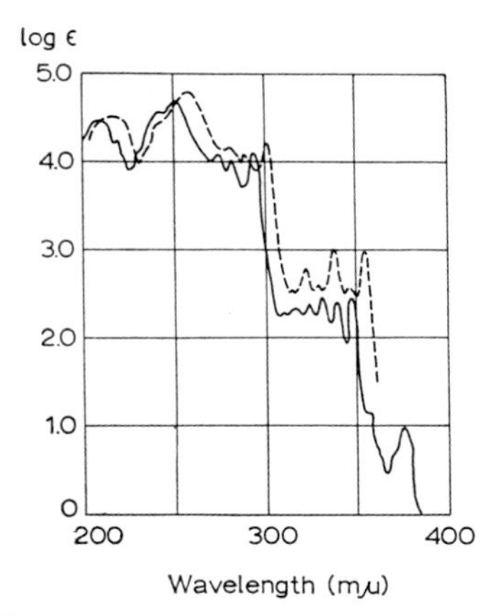

Fig. 2. Absorption spectra of phenanthrene (———) and cyclopentanophenanthrene in ethanol (– – – – –).

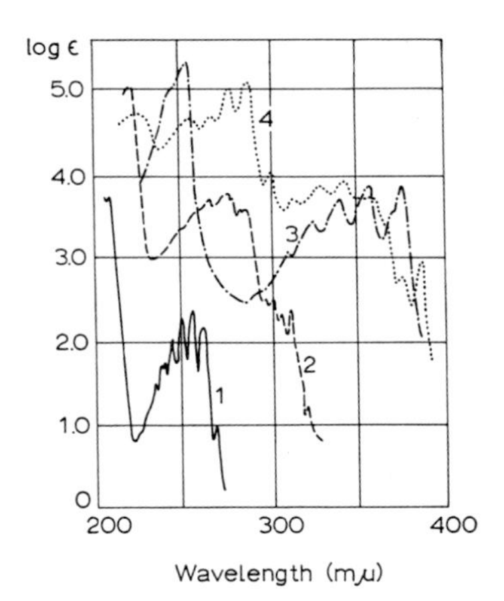

Fig. 3. Absorption spectra in ethanol of 1. benzene; 2. naphthalene; 3. anthracene; 4. 1,2-benzanthracene.

and the introduction of an additional group displaces the absorption peak to 280 mμ in *p*-terphenyl and 300 mμ in *p*-tetraphenyl.

(i) *Introduction of substituents*

Introduction of substituents into aromatic compounds tends to displace the absorption in the direction of longer wavelengths and to diminish the resolution shown in the absorption curve. Intensities of absorption usually increase. It is found that substituents such as CH_3, C_2H_5, $CH_3CH{=}CH_2$ and halogens, exert minor effects on the spectra. Other auxochromic substituents, *e.g.* OH, O-alkyl, COOH, COOR and NH_2, exert quite appreciable bathochromic effects, and in some instances the value of ε_{max} may be increased tenfold. (It will still be low in these B bands compared with that of a K-chromophore.) Thus phenol in hexane shows sharply resolved absorption in the region of 270–275 mμ, ε *ca.* 2,000 with a minimum near 238 mμ and a stronger peak near 210 mμ, ε_{max} *ca.* 10,000. Anisole has a very similar spectrum but unlike that of phenol it is not changed in an alkaline medium. Dihydroxybenzenes (catechol, resorcinol, quinol) exhibit bathochromic effects which are least marked in ortho compounds such as catechol, guaiacol, veratrole, eugenol and safrole. These compounds show selective absorption near 275–285 mμ usually with a double peak (*e.g.* 275, 283 mμ) with ε_{max} from about 2,500 to 4,500.

Aniline exhibits two regions of selective absorption with maxima at 234 mμ, log ε_{max} 4.06 and 285 mμ, log ε_{max} 3.24. In an acid medium the auxo-

References p. 131

chromic effect of the amino group is as would be expected largely abolished and the curve resembles that of benzene.

Conjugation of the "phenyl" group with ethylene as in styrene C_6H_5—$CH{=}CH_2$ gives rise to K bands which could be due to electronic excitation occurring in a transient entity:

$$^{+}C_6H_5{=}CH{-}CH_2^{-}$$

Whether this representation be valid or not it is a fact that the peak at 244 mμ is intermediate between that of a conjugated diene and that of a conjugated triene. This has led to the convenient suggestion that the bathochromic effect of a phenyl group is equal to that of 1.5 conjugated double bonds. As Braude has shown the charge separations of the dipolar structures

ethylene $-\overset{+}{C}-\overset{-}{C}-$

phenyl $^{+}C_6H_4{-}$

butadiene $\overset{+}{C}{-}C{=}C{-}\overset{-}{C}$

are in the expected order. Styrene also has a B band at 282 mμ, ε_{max} 450.

The spectrum of benzene is seen in its proper perspective by comparing:

octatriene $CH_3(CH{=}CH)_3CH_3$	λ_{max}	260 mμ	ε_{max}	8,000
cyclohexadiene		260 mμ		4,550
benzene		255 mμ		230

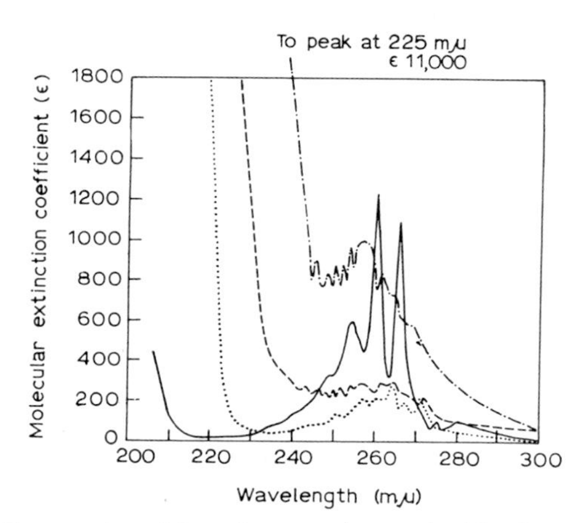

Fig. 4. Absorption spectra of fluorobenzene (———), chlorobenzene(·····), bromobenzene (– – – – –), and iodobenzene (—·—·—·) in ethanol[15].

The phenyl group must be regarded as a separate chromophore and a distinct *type* of chromophore. Substitution is illustrated in Table IV. It will be seen that there are bathochromic effects and increases in ε_{max}.

TABLE IV

BENZENE DERIVATIVES

	λ_{max} ($m\mu$)	log ε_{max}
Benzene	254.3	2.48
Toluene	262	2.48
Monochlorobenzene	264	2.51
Benzoic acid	267	3.25
	227	4.15
Phenol	273	3.25
	215	4.00
Phenyl mercaptan	279	2.9
	230	4.0
Anisole	272	3.35
Aniline	284.5	3.24
	234	4.06

Disubstitution shows clear-cut effects due to position isomerism.

Methyl groups and halogens (Table V). The effects of substitution are again small although wavelength displacements increase in the order *o*-, *m*-, *p*-.

TABLE V

METHYL GROUPS AND HALOGENS

	o-Compounds		*m-Compounds*		*p-Compounds*	
	λ_{max} ($m\mu$)	log ε_{max}	λ_{max} ($m\mu$)	log ε_{max}	λ_{max} ($m\mu$)	log ε_{max}
$C_6H_4Me_2$	263	2.52	265	2.49	268	2.68
$C_6H_4Cl_2$	270	2.56	271	2.62	272	2.59
$CH_3 \cdot C_6H_4Cl$	265	2.52	267	2.52	277	2.71

Substituents which produce considerable effects in mono-derivatives (Table VI). The second group has thus less effect than the first. In all cases the wavelength displacement is comparatively small, and is again greatest for the *p*-isomerides.

References p. 131

TABLE VI

SUBSTITUENTS WHICH PRODUCE CONSIDERABLE EFFECTS IN MONO-DERIVATIVES

	o-Compounds		*m-Compounds*		*p-Compounds*	
	λ_{max} $(m\mu)$	$\log \varepsilon_{max}$	λ_{max} $(m\mu)$	$\log \varepsilon_{max}$	λ_{max} $(m\mu)$	$\log \varepsilon_{max}$
$C_6H_4(OH)_2$	278	3.42	276	3.30	294	3.49
$C_6H_4(CO_2H)_2$	281	3.09	288	3.05	295	3.18
	274	3.01	280	3.11	284	3.24
			227	4.16	238	4.15
$C_6H_4(NH_2)_2$	293	3.58	293	3.43	290	3.51
	237	3.88			244	4.12

Substituents different, and when taken separately exerting considerable effects (Table VII).

TABLE VII

SUBSTITUENTS DIFFERENT, AND WHEN TAKEN SEPARATELY EXERTING CONSIDERABLE EFFECTS

	o-Compounds		*m-Compounds*		*p-Compounds*	
	λ_{max} $(m\mu)$	$\log \varepsilon_{max}$	λ_{max} $(m\mu)$	$\log \varepsilon_{max}$	λ_{max} $(m\mu)$	$\log \varepsilon_{max}$
$C_6H_4(OH) \cdot CO_2H$	305	3.68	299	3.48	255	4.20
	236	3.95	233	3.96		
	206	4.32	207	4.33	210	4.06
$C_6H_4(NH_2) \cdot CO_2H$	337	3.67	320	3.63	289	4.30
	247	3.83	~ 245	3.80	218	3.90
	218	4.40	220	4.30		
$C_6H_4(NH_2) \cdot OH$	286	3.60	286	3.52	301	3.43
	233	3.86			234	3.90

~ denotes an inflexion in the absorption curve.

When the phenyl and carbonyl chromophores are combined as in *benzaldehyde* or *acetophenone*, the resulting spectrum shows the superposition of chromophoric effects, each modified by the conjugation:

	a	*b*	*c*	*d*
λ_{max} $(m\mu)$	320	278	240	199
$\log \varepsilon_{max}$	1.7	3.02	4.12	4.3

a is (roughly) C=O influenced by C_6H_5, *b* is probably C_6H_5 influenced by CO, etc.

The hydroxy- and methoxy-derivatives are shown in Table VIII; the 325-mμ peak of salicylaldehyde is probably due to an electronic transition located in the benzene ring.

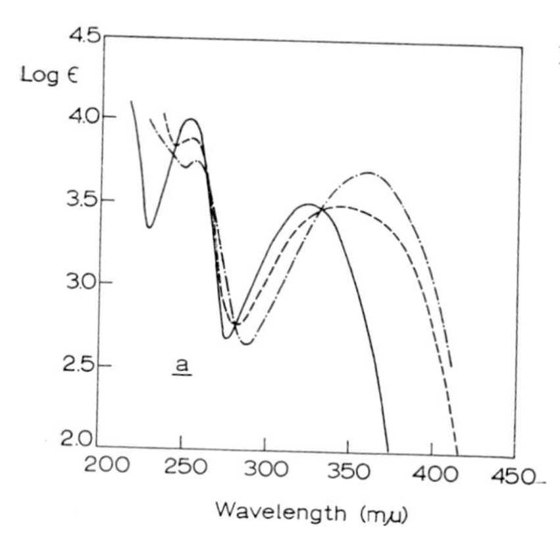

Fig. 5(a) *o*-Hydroxyacetophenone, ——— in water, – – – – – in 1 equiv. NaOH, –·–·–·– in $N/50$ NaOH.

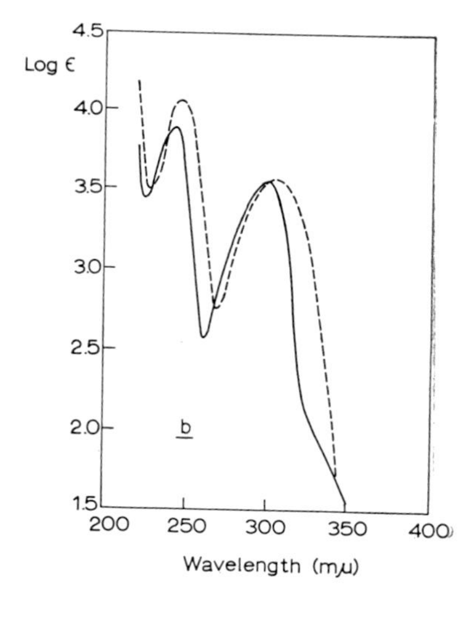

Fig. 5(b) *o*-Methoxyacetophenone, – – – – – in alcohol, ——— in hexane.

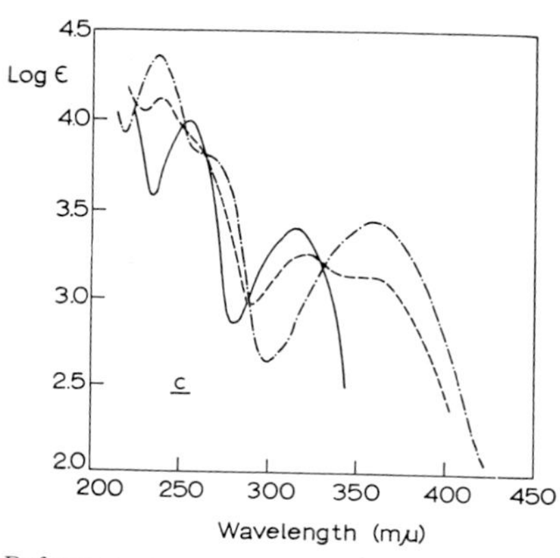

Fig. 5(c) *m*-Hydroxybenzaldehyde, ——— in water, – – – – – in 1 equiv. NaOH, –·–·–·– in $N/50$ NaOH.

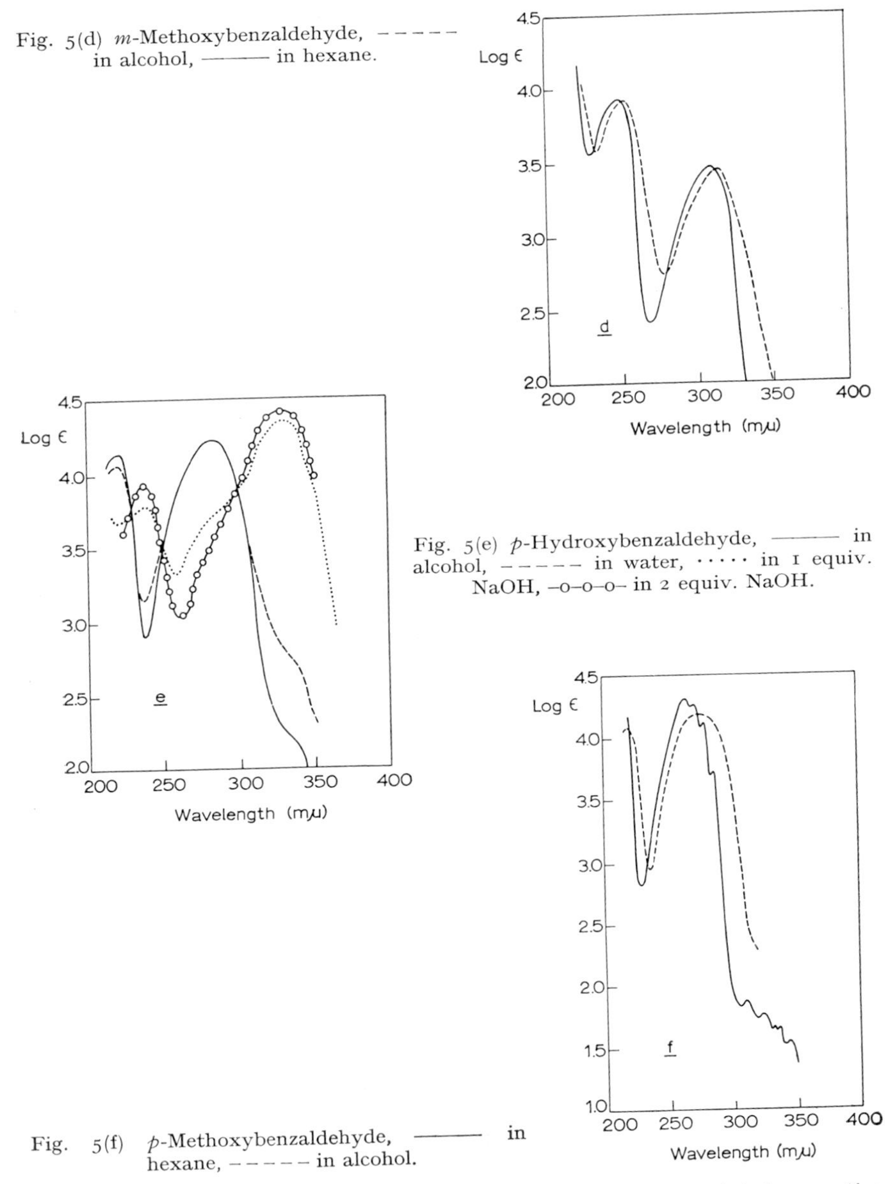

Fig. 5(d) *m*-Methoxybenzaldehyde, – – – – – in alcohol, ——— in hexane.

Fig. 5(e) *p*-Hydroxybenzaldehyde, ——— in alcohol, – – – – – in water, · · · · · in 1 equiv. NaOH, –o–o–o– in 2 equiv. NaOH.

Fig. 5(f) *p*-Methoxybenzaldehyde, ——— in hexane, – – – – – in alcohol.

Fig. 5. Absorption spectra of *o*-, *m*- and *p*-hydroxy-keto compounds and their respective methoxy derivatives[14].

In the main, the data in Table VIII reflect the effects of disubstitution and the differences between chelated and non-chelated substances are less important.

TABLE VIII

SPECTRA OF HYDROXY- AND METHOXY-DERIVATIVES

C_6H_4 a . . . b . . .	OMe CHO(*o*)	OH CHO(*m*)	OMe CHO(*m*)	OH CO_2H(*o*)	NH_3 CO_2H(*o*)
λ max (mμ)	319.5	316	314.5	305.5	337.5
log ε max	3.63	3.46	3.45	3.68	3.67

TABLE IX

SPECTRA OF SOME HYDROXYALDEHYDES AND HYDROXYKETONES

$\lambda = \lambda_{max}$ in mμ

Substance	*Hexane*		*Alcohol*		*1 equiv. NaOH*		*Excess NaOH*	
	λ	*log* ε	λ	*log* ε	λ	*log* ε	λ	*log* ε
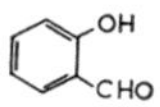 OH, CHO	~ 343	3.28	—	—	379	3.60	378	3.74
	328.5	3.51	325	3.48	327	3.10	—	—
	255	4.00	255	4.00	261	3.85	265	3.81
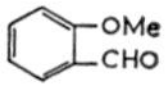 OMe, CHO	310	3.75	319.5	3.63	—	—	—	—
	246.5	4.08	253	4.07	—	—	—	—
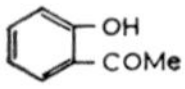 OH, COMe	329	3.63	327	3.50	341	3.50	359	3.71
	255.5	4.02	251.5	3.97	254	3.88	256.5	3.755
	249.5	4.025	—	—	—	—	—	—
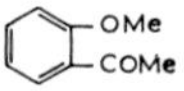 OMe, COMe	~ 330	2.00	—	—	—	—	—	—
	300	3.58	305	3.58	—	—	—	—
	242.5	3.90	246	4.06	—	—	—	—
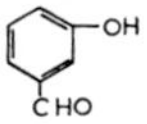 OH, CHO	333	2.78	—	—	~ 352	3.15	359	3.47
	~ 308	3.69	316	3.46	321	3.27	~ 312	2.78
	282	3.17	~ 293	3.04	~ 257	3.90	~ 264	3.81
	247	4.20	254	3.93	239	4.13	237	4.37
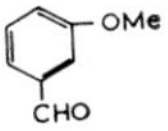 OMe, CHO	309	3.46	314.5	3.45	—	—	—	—
	249	3.93	252.5	3.92	—	—	—	—
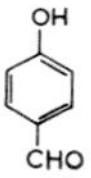 OH, CHO	—	—	~ 332	2.25	329	4.36	330	4.42
	—	—	284	4.24	~ 288	3.75	~ 275	3.35
	—	—	221	4.14	240	3.81	239	3.93
	—	—	—	—	—	—	—	—

(*Continued on p. 86*)

TABLE IX (*continuation*)

Substance	*Hexane*		*Alcohol*		*1 equiv. NaOH*		*Excess NaOH*	
	λ	*log* ε	λ	*log* ε	λ	*log* ε	λ	*log* ε
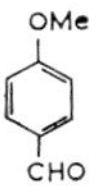 OMe / CHO	265.5 (f.s.)	4.29	277	4.17	—	—	—	—
	300	2.0	219	4.07	—	—	—	—
	350 (f.s.)	1.6						
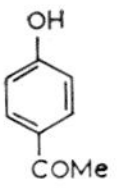 OH / COMe	—	—	276	4.13	325	4.18	325	4.39
	—	—	220.5	4.03	~278	3.79	—	—
	—	—	—	—	236	3.70	235	3.81
	—	—	—	—	225	3.71	—	—

~ Denotes an inflexion f.s. Denotes fine structure

TABLE X

UNSATURATED KETONES (IN ETHANOL)

	λ_{max} ($m\mu$)	$\varepsilon_{max} \times 10^4$
$C_6H_5CO \cdot CH{=}CH \cdot OC_6H_5$	267	15
	282	18
	291	18
$C_6H_5CO \cdot CH{=}CH \cdot SC_6H_5$	256	14
	335	19
$C_6H_5CO \cdot CH{=}CH \cdot NH \cdot C_6H_5$	242	18
	245	18
	374	31
$C_6H_5CO \cdot CH{=}CH \cdot SO_2C_6H_5$	245	16
	280	4

(ii) Tautomerism

Fig. 6 shows a very clear example of tautomerism[16]. Morton and Stubbs[14] studied the structure of 2-mercaptobenzthiazole (Ia, Ib). Two methyl derivatives of fixed structure are known (II and III). Compound I is shown unambiguously to have the thione structure Ia (Fig. 7a). A similar problem arises with the quinoline derivative IVa or IVb (Fig. 7b).

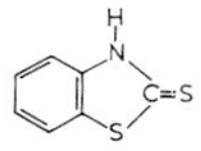

Ia — thione form; Ib — thiol form; II — N-methyl; III — S-methyl

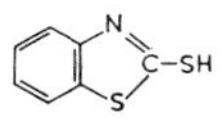

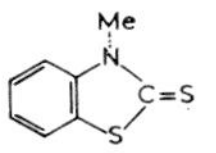

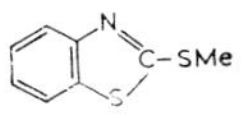

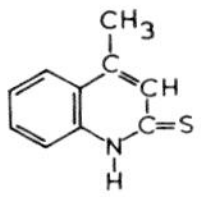

IVa; IVb; V

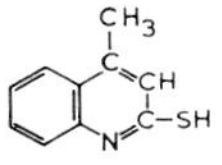

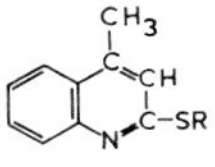

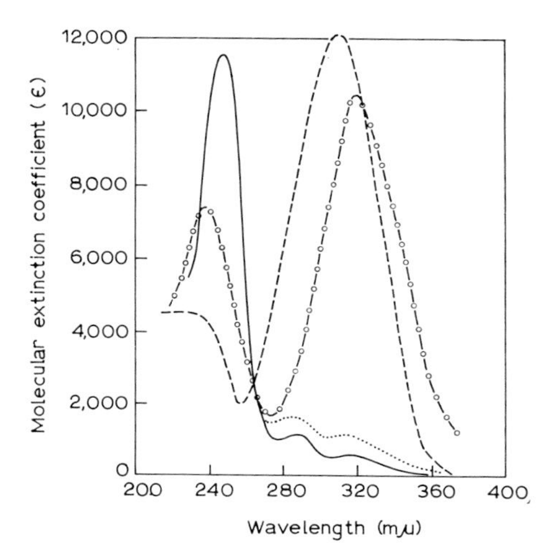

Fig. 6. Keto–enol tautomerism. Absorption curves for C-methylbenzoylacetone $C_6H_5COCHMeCOCH_3$. ——— ketonic form in ethanol; ····· some enol present; ----- enolic form in hexane; –o–o–o– enolic form in 5 equivalents of NaOEt (ref.[16]). [enol is $C_6H_5C(OH)=CMeCOCH_3$ or $C_6H_5COCMe=C(OH)CH_3$]

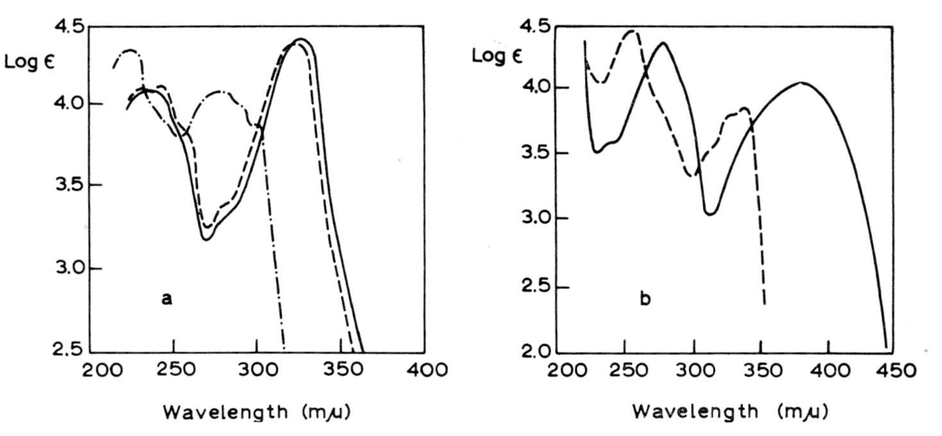

Fig. 7. Absorption spectra illustrating thiol–thione tautomerism[14] (a) ——— 1-thiol-benzthiazole; ----- 1-thio-2-methyl-1:2-dihydrobenzthiazole; –.–.– 1-methylthio-benzthiazole. (b) ——— 2-thiol-4-methylquinoline; ----- 2-isopropylthio-4-methyl-quinoline.

In V, R may be methyl, ethyl or isopropyl without significant change of spectrum. The parent substance shows a very different spectrum and must therefore have the thione rather than the thiol structure.

References p. 131

TABLE XI

Substance	λ_{max} ($m\mu$)	$\log \varepsilon_{max}$
OH, NH_2	286	3.6
	232.7	3.86
O, C=O, N, H	273.6	3.71
CH_3, S, C=O, N, H	292.5	3.63
	245	3.95
S, C=S, N, H	325	4.43
	235	4.1
CH, CH, C–OCH_3, N	322	3.57
	308.5	3.75
CH, CH, C=O, N, CH_3	328	3.78
	270.5	3.82
CH_3, C, CH, C–SR, N	339	3.81
	327	3.75
S, C–OCH_3, N	296	3.0
	291	3.0
	282	3.05
	260	3.9
S, C–SCH_3, N	300	3.9
	290	4.0
	280	4.1
	244	3.9
	224	4.36
CH, CH, C=O, N, H	327	3.83
	296	3.845

Now these compounds should be considered in the light of related simpler substances (Table XI). The effects of pH changes are nicely shown in the curves for pyridoxine[17] (Figs. 8 and 9).

(d) Ultraviolet absorption spectra of steroids

This field is of importance to biochemistry and affords a good illustration of the principles of interpretation (see Dorfman[18]). The absorption curves of steroids with one isolated double bond show a maximum near 200–210 mμ. Experimental work in this region of the spectrum has hitherto been difficult, partly because of instrumental defects and scattering. Many of the newer photoelectric spectrophotometers, however, give trustworthy results at 210 mμ. The intensity of absorption exerted by an isolated double bond increases with the degree of substitution, see Table XII (Bladon, Henbest and Wood[19]).

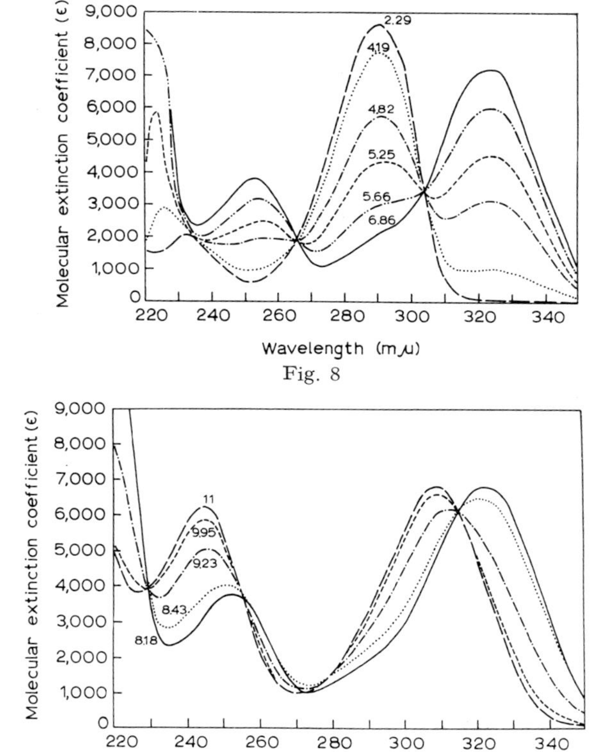

Fig. 8. and Fig. 9. Absorption spectra of aqueous solution of pyridoxine at known pH values[17]. Note the good isosbestic points in both diagrams. These indicate two-component systems in each set of curves.

The "weighting" effect of substituents also moves λ_{max} in the direction of longer wavelengths.

References p. 131

TABLE XII

Substitution in chromophore	*ε Values*	*Examples*
X—CH=CH—Y	1,000 at 210 mμ	Δ^{2} Δ^{6} Δ^{11} steroids
X—CH=C<	1,950–4,500 at 210 mμ	Δ^{4}, Δ^{5}, Δ^{7}, $\Delta^{9(11)}$ Δ^{14}
>C=C<	4,500 at 210 mμ	$\Delta^{8,(9)}$ $\Delta^{8,(14)}$ $\Delta^{9,(10)}$

(i) Conjugated dienes

Conjugated dienes are common among the steroids. 3-Methylene-4-cholestene (I) shows peaks at 233 and 239 mμ (ε, 16,230 and 17,260 in *cyclo*-hexane) and the absorption shown by 7-methylene cholesterol (II) is similar with λ_{max} 236 mμ, ε_{max} 20,000.

C_8H_{17} H_2C I — 3-Methylene-4-cholestene

C_8H_{17} HO CH_2 II — 7-Methylene cholesterol

Some resolution appears in cholest-3,5-diene (III) with λ_{max} 235 mμ, ε_{max} 19,700 and inflexions at 229 and 244 mμ (solvent isopropanol). The same type of chromophore occurs in pregna-3,5,20-triene and androst-3,5-diene-17-

III — Cholest-3,5-diene

IV — Cholest-4,6-diene

HO (or AcO) V

one. Cholest-4,6-diene (IV) has λ_{max} 238 mμ but if there is a substituent at position 3, two or three peaks are shown *e.g.* androst-4,6-diene-3β,17β-diol exhibits λ_{max} 232, 240 and 248 mμ, ε_{max} 21,000, 23,400, 19,300. Cholest-4,6-diene-3-β-ol-3-acetate is similar. Again the chromophores shown (VI to IX) give consistent results.

A significant bathochromic effect occurs when the two conjugated double bonds are in the same ring.

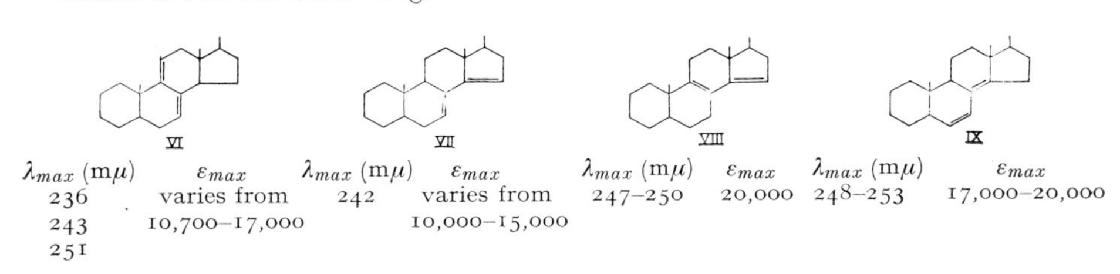

Examples of X are cholest-2,4-diene (λ_{max} 275 mμ, ε_{max} 6,300 with inflexions at 266 and 287 mμ) and isodehydrocholesterol (λ_{max} 275 mμ, ε_{max} 5,000). The chromophoric grouping in XI is outstandingly important. It occurs in the provitamins D such as ergosterol and 7-dehydro-cholesterol and the ab-

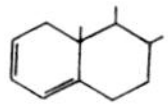

X 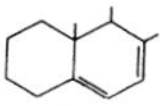 XI 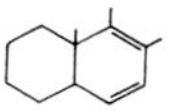 XII

sorption curve is well resolved with peaks at 271, 282 and 293 mμ and an inflexion near 262 mμ (ε_{max} 11,400, 11,900, 6,900 and 7,700). The same absorption spectrum occurs in 7-dehydrostigmasterol and 7-dehydrosito-sterol. Compounds of this nature are photolabile and yield a mixture of compounds on irradiation (see p. 96).

(ii) Conjugated trienes

Decatrienoic acid $CH_3 \cdot CH_2(CH{=}CH)_3 \cdot CH_2 \cdot COH$ in which the triene is isolated, shows λ_{max} 265 mμ, ε_{max} 43,000. The high molecular extinction coefficient is noteworthy.

In the calciferols (XIII) the same chromophore can be seen but ε_{max} is much

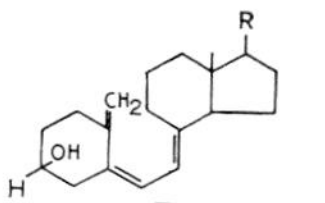

XIII

Calciferol

λ_{max} (mμ)	ε_{max}
265	18,200

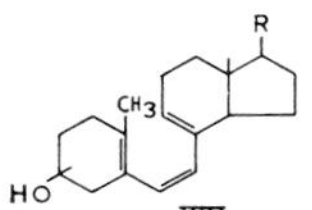

XIV

Tachysterol

λ_{max} (mμ)
280
~ 265

lower and in tachysterols (XIV) there is a sharp peak at 280 mμ as well as an inflexion near 265 mμ. Here two out of the three conjugated double bonds form part of ring systems. The bathochromic effects are more fully exhibited when two of three conjugated double bonds are in the same ring:

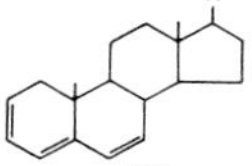

XV 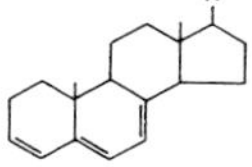 XVI 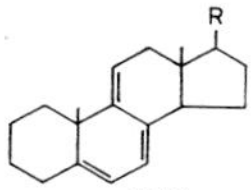 XVII 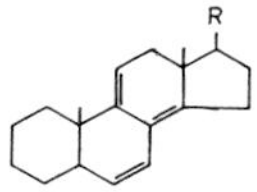 XVIII

In XV the main absorption is near 307 mμ (ε_{max} 15,500–22,000); sometimes there is resolution λ_{max} 296, 306, 320 mμ. In XVI resolution is good (see Table XIII).

Chromophore XVII shows λ_{max} 319 mμ, ε_{max} 17,500 with little evidence of resolution into narrow bands whilst XVIII shows a not surprising reversion to λ_{max} 285 mμ, ε_{max} 9,100.

TABLE XIII

	λ_{max} (mμ)	ε_{max}
cholest-3,5,7-triene	303	12,540
	315	15,700
	330	11,500
ergost-3,5,7,22-tetraene	302	16,000
	316	19,000
	332	14,000

(iii) Conjugated tetraenes

Conjugated tetraenes are not very numerous in the steroids but further bathochromic effects occur in conformity with experience on simpler compounds.

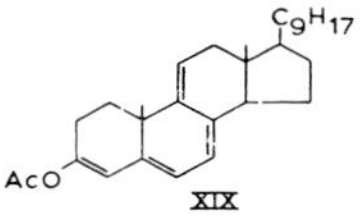

XIX

Ergost-4,7,9,22-tetra-en-3-one-3-enol acetate
λ_{max} (mμ) 339, 356, 375
ε_{max} 15,000, 17,400, 13,000

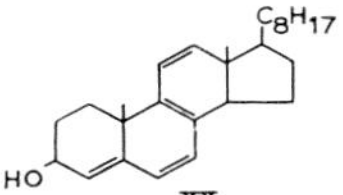

XX

Cholest-4,6,8,11-tetra-en-3β-ol
λ_{max} (mμ) 355
ε_{max} 13,500 no narrow bands (in ether)

(iv) Aromatic chromophores

A convenient point of departure is XXI (22-dehydro-neo-ergostatriene) which absorbs moderately intensely (ε_{max} 10,000) at 224 mμ and feebly at

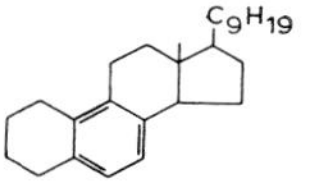

XXI

22-Dehydro-neo-ergostatriene

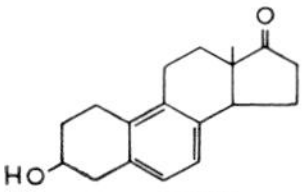

XXII

Oestra-5,7,9-triene-3-ol-17-one

269 and 277 mμ (ε, 400 and 250). Similarly, the compound XXII (oestra-5,7,9-triene-3-ol-17-one) shows weak bands at 270 and 278 mμ, ε_{max} 345 and 240. The resemblance here is clearly to tetra-substituted benzene derivatives.

An extra double bond in ring A or C increases the intensity of absorption considerably and the resemblance here is to styrene.

XXIII

λ_{max} (mμ)	ε_{max}
224	26,000
231	
268	6,300
308	
314	very low
323	

XXIV

λ_{max} (mμ)	ε_{max}
270	11,500

The naphthalenic spectrum appears clearly in XXV (β-*dl*-equilane) and XXVI (15-dehydroequilen-17-one) where the $\alpha\beta$-unsaturated ketone is isolated from the ring.

XXV

XXVI

β-*dl*-Equilane

λ_{max} (mμ)	ε_{max}
231	93,300
282	5,700
322	910

(ethanol)

15-Dehydroequilen-17-one

λ_{max} (mμ)	ε_{max}	λ_{max} (mμ)	ε_{max}
230	77,600	255	45,700
270	6,800	285	12,600
321	660	293	15,500
		305	12,900

By contrast, the 14-dehydroequilenane shows very clearly the enhanced absorption above 270 mμ caused by an additional double bond conjugated to the naphthalene ring system.

Oestrone (XXVII), oestradiol and oestriol show a single absorption peak

XXVII

Oestrone

XXVIII

6-Dehydro-oestrone

at 280 mμ, ε_{max} 2,300 which is clearly related to the absorption of the simple substituted phenols while 6-dehydro-oestrone (XXVIII) has three re-

References p. 131

TABLE XIV

$\alpha\beta$-UNSATURATED KETONES

	λ_{max} $(m\mu)$	ε_{max}
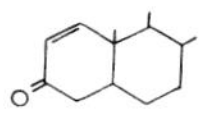	231	9,770
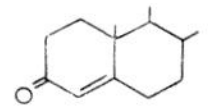	241 312	18,000 100
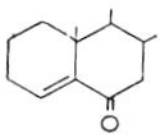	244 300	6,300 120
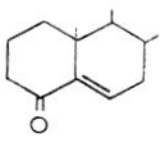	241	7,200
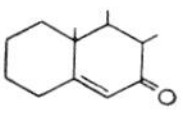	234	10,000
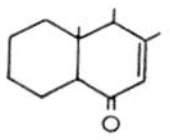	252 333	14,500
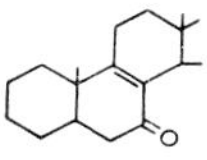	254	9,680
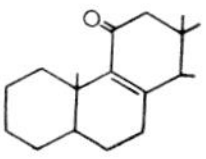	253	12,600
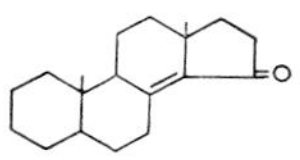	259	12,750
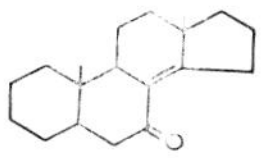	263	9,500

gions of selective absorption, 220 mμ (ε 31,000), 262 mμ (ε 8,910), 304 mμ (ε 2,750).

Equilin (XXIX) with λ_{max} 280, ε_{max} 2,000 resembles oestrone because the double bond is unconjugated.

The effects of conjugated double bonds are further illustrated in XXX and XXXI.

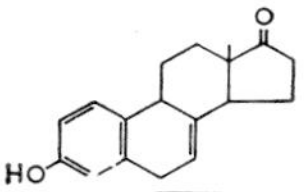

	XXIX Equilin	XXX	XXXI
λ_{max} (mμ)	280	275	263
ε_{max}	2,000	20,900	18,500

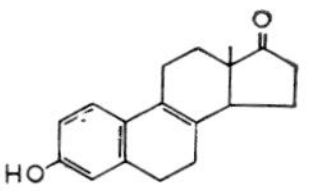

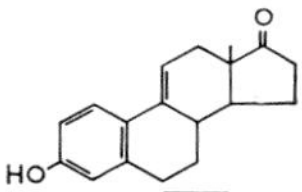

(v) Steroid ketones

The absorption shown by saturated ketones at 270–300 mμ is of very low intensity (ε_{max} 15–100) The position of λ_{max} is displaced when the carbonyl group occurs in a ring: thus λ_{max} for acetone is near 270 mμ, for cyclohexanone, 292 mμ, for cyclopentanone 299 mμ. Saturated steroid ketones (if highly purified) show λ_{max} 282–297 mμ, ε_{max} 16–100. In steroid diketones with isolated carbonyl groups the position of λ_{max} is not changed but ε_{max} will be about doubled compared with mono-ketones.

The $\alpha\beta$-unsaturated ketones are here of great interest and importance and the position of λ_{max} is of diagnostic significance[10,11] (Table XIV).

(vi) Dienones

Among the best-known steroid dienones is cholest-3,5-diene-7-one (XXXII). This has an intense peak at 277 mμ displaced in the direction of

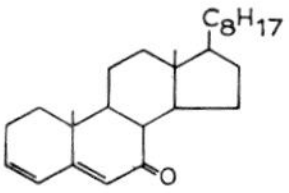

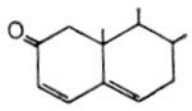

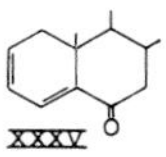

	XXXII Cholest-3, 5-diene-7-one	XXXIII	XXXIV	XXXV
λ_{max} (mμ)	277	284	290	314
ε_{max}	24,400	26,300	12,600	7,620

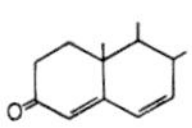

longer wavelengths in the isomers XXXIII–XXXV with concurrent changes in ε_{max}.

The two chromophores XXXVI and XXXVII illustrate extreme situations:

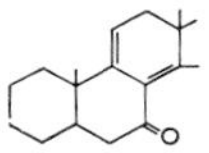

	XXXVI	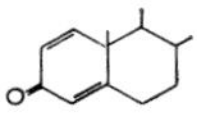	XXXVII
λ_{max} (mμ)	223	298	245
ε_{max}	15,600	5,000	14,500

References p. 131

(vii) Enediones

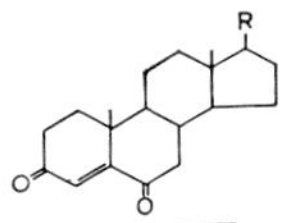

	XXXVIII	XXXIX	XL
λ_{max} (mμ)	252	270	255
ε_{max}	11,400	8,700	5,000

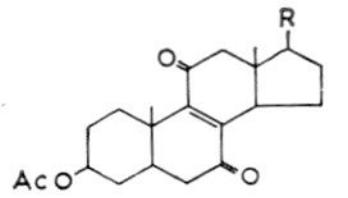

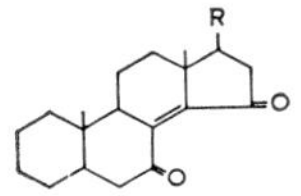

The 8(9)-en-7,11-dione (XXXIX) also shows weak selective absorption at *ca.* 320 mμ and 405 mμ. An interesting situation arises when enolisation occurs:

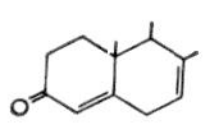

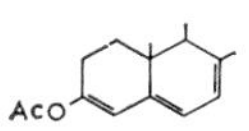

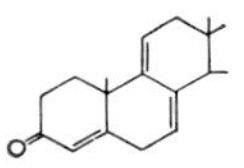

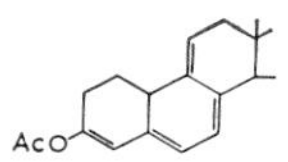

λ_{max} (mμ)	239	301, 315, 331	242	338, 355, 374
ε_{max}	15,100	19,300, 21,300, 17,700	32,000	14,600, 19,700, 14,600

These examples show how enolisation brings two isolated chromophores into conjugation.

The foregoing account is no more than a selection from a very large field reviewed by Dorfman[18] and to which additions are constantly being made.

(e) Pro-vitamins and vitamins D

The study of rickets from the standpoint both of geographical distribution and seasonal incidence suggested that sunlight, and particularly radiations near 300 mμ had broadly favourable effects. It was found that exposure of the body to ultraviolet radiation might prevent rickets. It emerged that the skin contains a minute quantity of a precursor (now known to be 7-dehydrocholesterol) which can undergo photochemical transformation to yield a vitamin D which can be absorbed into the blood stream. The specific antirachitic activity of cod liver oil was due to the presence in it of preformed vitamin D.

This is a classical problem in photochemistry and biochemical spectroscopy. The present picture has emerged by stages and reasonable but mistaken views have had to be corrected in the light of new information. Space permits only a brief account, mainly from the spectroscopic angle.

Cholesterol from animal sources is usually contaminated with very small amounts of 7-dehydrocholesterol which shows absorption peaks at 261, 271, 281.5 and 293.5 mμ (Figs. 10 and 11). This same spectrum is shown also by

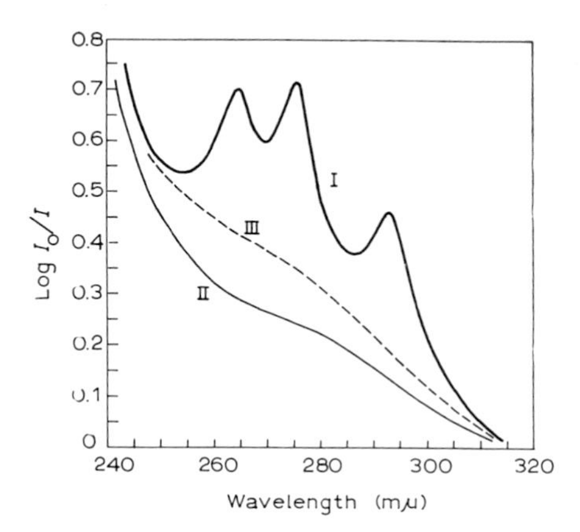

Fig. 10. Absorption curves illustrating the fractional crystallization of cholesterol[20a]. I. Least soluble fraction from cholesterol; II. Cholesterol after removal of active compound; III. Irradiated fraction. Early graphs; photographic technique.

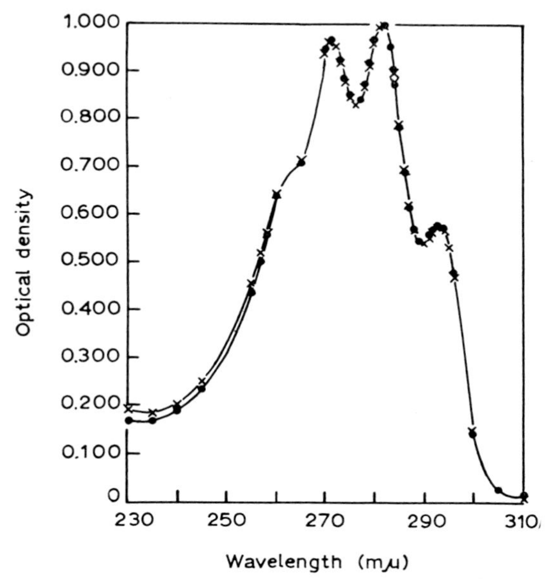

Fig. 11. Absorption spectrum characteristic of 7-dehydrosteroid[20b] (graph obtained by modern photoelectric technique). Comparison of the spectra of 7-dehydrocholesterol (–•–•–) and mouse preputial gland sterols (–x–x–).

References p. 131

ergosterol, 7-dehydrostigmasterol and a number of other steroid derivatives containing the same chromophore:

R = C_8H_{17}, 7-dehydrocholesterol

R = C_9H_{17}, ergosterol

The researches carried out by various schools and in particular that of Windaus led to the idea that ergosterol and 7-dehydrocholesterol were converted to vitamins D by a sequence of photochemical changes:

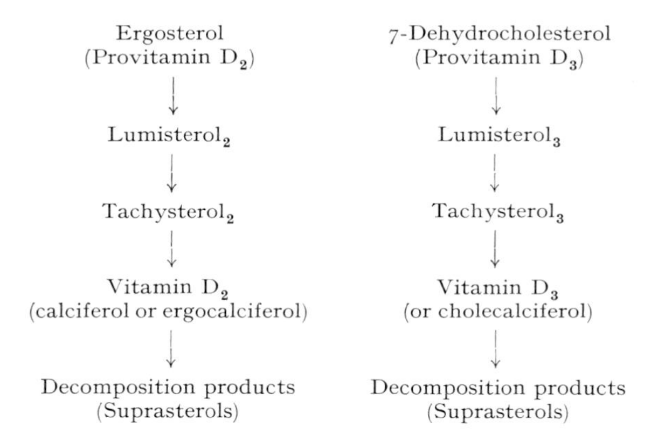

Certainly the irradiation product consists of a complex mixture of substances each with its own ultraviolet absorption and photochemical lability. The nature of the mixture will depend on the spectral distribution of the radiation used, on the temperature and on the procedure of irradiation (time of exposure, initial concentration of provitamin and solvent used).

The sequence just noted was accepted until the subject was re-opened by Velluz[21] who drew attention to the existence of non-photochemical steps. By keeping the temperature at 20° during and after irradiation, a new isomeride of ergosterol was isolated:

λ_{max} 271, 282, 293.5 mμ
ε_{max} 11,900

unstable intermediate

Previtamin D
λ_{max} 262 mμ
ε_{max} 9,000

heat (65°)

Vitamin D
λ_{max} 265 mμ
ε_{max} 18,300

It will be noted that the position of λ_{max} for previtamin D is very close to that of vitamin D but ε_{max} is only 9,000.

Previtamin D_2 undergoes change in the presence of a small amount of iodine. This gives tachysterol in very good yield and suggests that previtamin D is a 6,7-*cis*-isomeride of tachysterol. The low ε_{max} of 9,000 is in agreement.

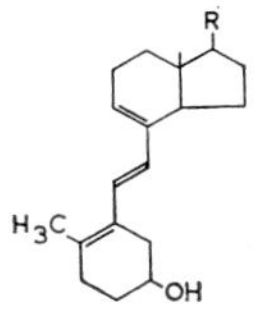

tachysterol
λ_{max} 284 mμ
ε_{max} 24,600

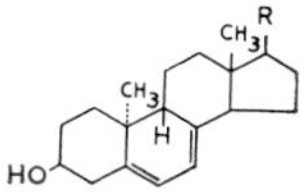

lumisterol
λ_{max} 280 mμ
ε_{max} 8,500

Ultraviolet irradiation of previtamin D_3 gave a mixture containing ergosterol, lumisterol and tachysterol.

It seems likely from the work of Havinga *et al.*[22] using ^{14}C-labelled ergosterol (from yeast) that lumisterol cannot be an intermediate and that most of the tachysterol is also off the sequence leading to vitamin D. The first effect of light on provitamins D is at the 9:10 bond, the point of weakness in the molecule. The unstable product, under the further action of light, may give ergosterol, lumisterol, tachysterol and previtamin D. When calciferols are heated (190°) they yield pyrocalciferols:

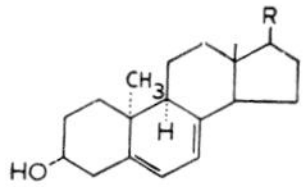

pyrocalciferol
λ_{max} 274, 294 mμ

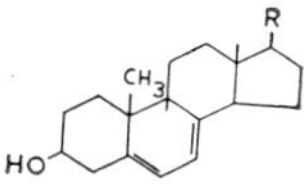

isopyrocalciferol
λ_{max} 262, 280 mμ

Both these substances yield non-selectively absorbing irradiation products. Iodine catalysis converts vitamin D_2 into 5,6-*trans* vitamin D_2, λ_{max} 272 mμ, ε_{max} 23,600. On irradiation this reverts to calciferol. The present account is simplified for brevity, but it illustrates the diagnostic relevance of the position of λ_{max}, of *resolved* absorption and of *intensity* of absorption, in describing closely related compounds.

(f) Absorption spectra of fatty acids[23]

The carboxyl group itself gives rise to a broad absorption band with λ_{max} 205 mμ, ε_{max} about 50, but there is stronger absorption below 185 mμ. Some

References p. 131

TABLE XV

ULTRAVIOLET ABSORPTION OF CERTAIN UNSATURATED ACIDS

Acid	*Configuration*	λ_{max} ($m\mu$)	ε_{max}	*Solvent*
Octadeca-9,11-dienoic (9,11-linoleic)	*trans–trans*	231 231.5	35,000 33,300	P
	cis–trans	234	24,600	E
Octadeca-10,12-dienoic (10,12-linoleic)	*trans–trans* *trans–cis*	231 232–235	33,000 28,700	EP M
Octadeca-9,11,13-trinoic (α-elaeostearic)	*cis–trans–trans*	262 271.5 283	36,200 48,100 37,000	CH
		261 271 281	36,000 47,000 38,000	E
(β-elaeostearic)	*trans–trans–trans*	259 268 279	47,000 61,000 49,000	E
(punicic)	*cis–cis–trans*	265.5 275 287	47,800	CH
18-Hydroxyoctadeca-9,11,13-trienoic (α-kamlolenic)	*cis–trans–trans*	262 270 282	39,400 52,900 41,500	E
(β-kamlolenic)	*trans–trans–trans*	258 268 279	45,000 60,000 47,000	E
Octadeca-9,11,13,15-tetraenoic acid (α-parinaric)	uncertain	292.5 306.5 321.5	52,700 77,900 66,300	H
		292 305 319	50,500 76,700 69,200	E
(β-parinaric)	all–*trans*	288 301.5 315.5	56,400 87,100 77,900	H
		301	81,700	E
Mono-enoic conjugated to carboxyl				
2,4,6-trimethyltetracos-2-enoic (mycolipenic)	?	214	13,200	M
Decadienoic conjugated to carboxyl				
Deca-2,4-dienoic (stillingic)	*trans–cis*	260 260	25,800 24,000	CH E
Dodeca-2,4-dienoic	?	260	33,400	M

M = methanol E = ethanol P = light petroleum CH = cyclohexane
H = heptane

TABLE XV (*continued*)

Acid	Configuration	λ_{max} (mμ)	ε_{max}	Solvent
Conjugated enynoic				
Octadeca-11-en-9-ynoic (ximenynic)	*trans*	229	16,200	CH
(santalbio)		228	16,600	E
Conjugated diynoic				
Octadeca-17-en-9,11-diynoic (erythrogenic or isanic)		227 238 253	370 344 120	E
Conjugated enediynic				
Octadeca-? ene ?? diynoic (bolekic)		227 240 253.5 267 282.5	3,060 6,300 11,700 17,400 13,600	E
8-Hydroxy octadec-14-en-10,12-diynoic (isanolic)		230 240 252.5 265 279	6,120 6,250 6,380 8,240 6,520	

branched chain fatty acids show higher values of ε_{max} at 205 mμ but saturated fatty acids are almost transparent to light of wavelength > 220 mμ. Oleic acid, with its ethenoid linkage distant from the carboxyl group, absorbs more strongly below 200 mμ as also do the poly-unsaturated acids linoleic, linolenic and arachidonic, in which there are no conjugated double bonds. The intensity of absorption at 210 mμ increases with increasing unconjugated unsaturation, but it is doubtful whether the quantitative results afford trustworthy estimates of the number of double bonds.

The conjugated poly-ene acids are of greater spectroscopic interest. It will be seen from Table XV that the conjugated diene chromophore shows λ_{max} 231 mμ approx., ε_{max} about 30,000 (varying with the configuration). The conjugated triene chromophore shows λ_{max} moved to about 270 mμ with ε_{max} 48,000 and two other peaks, one on each side of the most intense maximum. In the conjugated tetraene chromophore the absorption is again resolved and the principal peak has been displaced to 306 mμ and ε_{max} raised to 77,000–87,000 depending on the configuration. If the diene is conjugated to carboxyl to give the CH=CH—CH=CH—COOH chromophore, λ_{max} occurs at 260 mμ, a bathochromic effect (230–260 mμ) being characteristic of introducing the conjugated carboxyl, but no rise in ε_{max} occurs. The chromophore CH=CH—CH≡C is not very different from the conjugated diene but ε_{max} is approximately halved in the en-yne compound. The chromophore

References p. 131

C≡C—C≡C shows resolved absorption with very much lower intensity of absorption than in the conjugated diene. The chromophore C=C—C≡C—C≡C which occurs in bolekic acid shows very well resolved absorption of considerable intensity.

Alkali isomerisation of unconjugated fatty acids

The most widespread unsaturated fatty acids (linoleic, linolenic, arachidonic and the penta- and hexa-enoic acids of fish oils) are almost transparent in the ultraviolet region but the double bonds can be re-arranged to form conjugated systems. This process can be effected in a controlled manner by heating in the presence of alkali and the resulting intensity of selective absorption is used as a measure of the concentration of the original poly-enoic acid. This topic has been reviewed by Pitt and Morton[23] and the labours of many contributors to the subject are recorded. Only the broad principle can be described here.

Thus in determining linoleic and linolenic acids a 6.5% (w/w) solution of potassium hydroxide in glycol is placed in a boiling tube immersed to $4\frac{1}{2}$ inches in a bath at 180 ± 0.5°C and a current of nitrogen is bubbled through the liquid. The fat (100 mg) is dropped into the glycol (at 180°) with swirling and the heating at 180° is continued for exactly 25 min from the time the

TABLE XVI

PURIFIED POLY-UNSATURATED ACIDS SUBJECTED TO ALKALI-ISOMERISATION UNDER STANDARD CONDITIONS

Acid	*λ (mμ)*	$A^{1\%}_{1cm}$ *values*	
		"Weak" alkali procedure 6.5% KOH in glycol, 25 min	*Strong alkali procedure 21% KOH; 15 min*
Linoleic	233	921	916
Linolenic	233	616	475
	268	507	905
Arachidonic	233	569	397
	268	528	482
	315	215	606
Penta-enoic	233		415
	268		436
	315		697
	346		690
Hexa-enoic	233		417
	268		522
	315		296
	346		277
	375		293

fat was introduced. The tube is then cooled and the contents diluted and E values are determined at 233, 262, 268 and 274 mμ. Correction procedures may be applied and from the corrected figures the amounts of linoleic and linolenic acids are calculated, using factors based on trials with pure all–*cis* acids. An alternative method of isomerisation in which 21% KOH in glycol is used gives more effective isomerisation of the penta- and hexa-ene acids. It is obvious that with *e.g.* arachidonic acid, alkali isomerisation may give different "yields" of conjugated diene, triene and tetra-ene acids depending on the alkali concentration, the time and temperature of heating. Table XVI illustrates this in the relative efficacies of the "weak" and "strong" alkali. The paramount importance of carrying out the isomerisation under conditions which reproduce exactly those used in standardising the procedure is obvious. Nevertheless the method has been found to be very useful.

TABLE XVII

SPECTROSCOPIC EFFECTS OF *cis–trans* ISOMERISM IN STILBENE AND CINNAMIC ACID

	cis: H–C–C_6H_5 ‖ H–C–C_6H_5		*trans*: H–C–C_6H_5 ‖ C_6H_5–C–H	
Solvent	λ_{max} (mμ)	$\varepsilon_{max} \times 10^{-3}$	λ_{max} (mμ)	$\varepsilon_{max} \times 10^{-3}$
Hexane	200	24.8	200	21.5
	222	17.8	226	14.0
	280	10.4	295	27.0
Methanol	200	32	200	19.5
	222	23.5	226	11.7
	270			
	280	10.2	295	24
			310	
	cis: H–C–COOH ‖ H–C–C_6H_5		*trans*: H–C–COOH ‖ C_6H_5–C–H	
Hexane	195	14	204	14.3
	217	8.25	215	14.8
	278	10.4	279	25.2
Methanol	200	15.2	204	14.3
	214	9.55	215	14.8
	262	9.1	274	21.0
Water	258	8.7	275	19.5

References p. 131

TABLE XVIII

SPECTROSCOPIC EFFECTS OF *cis–trans* ISOMERISM IN HEXANE SOLUTIONS OF SUBSTITUTED ACETOPHENONES AND BENZALDEHYDE

	H–C=O; Me (ring)	Me–C=O; Me (ring)	H–C=O; Me, Me (ring)	Me–C=O; Me, Me (ring)	H–C=O; Me, Me, Me (ring)	Me–C=O; Me, Me, Me (ring)
λ_{max} (mμ)	251	242	251	251	264	242
$\varepsilon_{max} \times 10^{-3}$	15	8.5	12.5	5.5	15.5	3.5

TABLE XIX

SPECTRA OF DIENONES

	(cyclohexenyl)CH=CH COMe		Me, Me (cyclohexenyl)CH=CH COMe		Me, Me, Me (cyclohexenyl)CH=CH COMe		Me, Me, Me (cyclohexenyl)CH=C(Me)–COMe
λ_{max} (mμ)	281*	228**	281*	223**	296*	228**	278*
$\varepsilon_{max} \times 10^{-3}$	20.8	4.1	13	6.5	10.7	11.6	4.5

* = dienone chromophore ** = enone chromophore

4. Spectroscopic effects of steric configuration

Steric configuration is so important in biochemistry that an outline of the spectroscopic effects is necessary[24a,b].

As a first approximation λ_{max} and ε_{max} for the more intense (K) bands depend on the *actual length* of the chromophore, so that *cis–trans* isomerism may be expected to have notable consequences. Full interaction between conjugated unsaturated linkages requires a near approach to a uniplanar structure. Steric hindrance, in this context, offers resistance to the molecule attaining uniplanarity. When the hindrance is large, λ_{max} is displaced to shorter wavelengths. Attention must also be drawn to the point that if two moieties in a conjugated system are planar within themselves but not coplanar, the two portions will function as distinct chromophores. Thus some spectra can only be explained if "partial" chromophores are postulated. When steric hindrance is small, however, ε_{max} will tend to decrease, but λ_{max} will be relatively unchanged. The long-wave band shows greater solvent shifts for the *cis* than the *trans* isomer. In the stilbenes both λ_{max} and ε_{max} change considerably in the case of the long-wave band.

Substitution in benzaldehyde and acetophenone affords very interesting examples. In hexane both substances show λ_{max} 242 mμ. The effect of introducing methyl groups in the *o*-position is much greater for acetophenone than for benzaldehyde (Tables XVII–XIX).

Braude[24a] gave a convincing set of compounds from another field (Table XIX). With increasing substitution, the intensity of the dienone partial chromophore diminishes and that of the enone chromophore increases. The drop in ε values for the substituted acetophenones is paralleled by an increase in the interplanar angle between the phenyl and carbonyl groups. In the dienones (Tables XVII–XIX) the 6,6-gem-dimethyl group is more effective than the 2-methyl group. It can be seen that in a molecule such as vitamin A the actual position of λ_{max} reflects competing effects of conjugated double bonds and the steric effects of methyl groups.

The effects of *cis–trans* isomerism are seen in an interesting way in the carotenoids (Zechmeister[24b]). When a *trans* isomer is converted to a *cis* form the maxima are shifted in the direction of lower wavelengths and the value of ε_{max} falls. The resolution of bands is diminished and a new band appears at a wavelength shorter than the main peak by about 140 mμ. This new band is called a *cis* peak and is seen in the carotenes at 330–340 mμ.

5. Carotenoids[25]

Many carotenoids occur naturally, *e.g.* in plant tissues, in amounts which are of the order 100 μg/g and it is often very difficult to obtain them in pure crystalline form. Identifications can often be made unambiguously on quite small amounts of material by combining chromatographic and spectroscopic tests.

Reference has already been made to the displacements of absorption

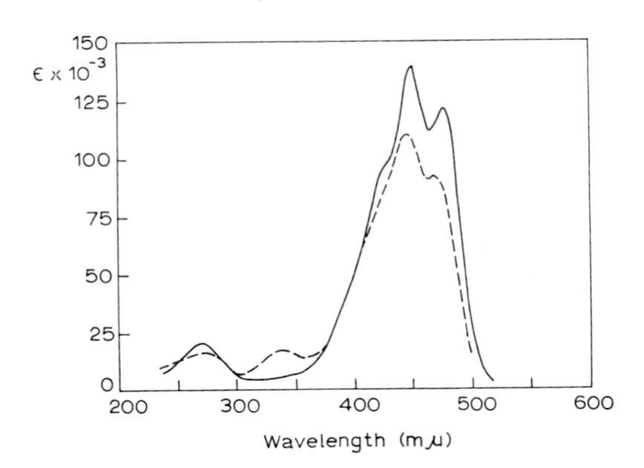

Fig. 12. Absorption curves of β-carotene in hexane showing *cis*-peak near 325 mμ. ——— all-*trans* β-carotene; – – – – – a mixture of *cis-trans* isomerides formed by iodine catalysis in light at room temperature (after Zechmeister[24b]).

References p. 131

TABLE XX

STRUCTURES OF SELECTED CAROTENOIDS

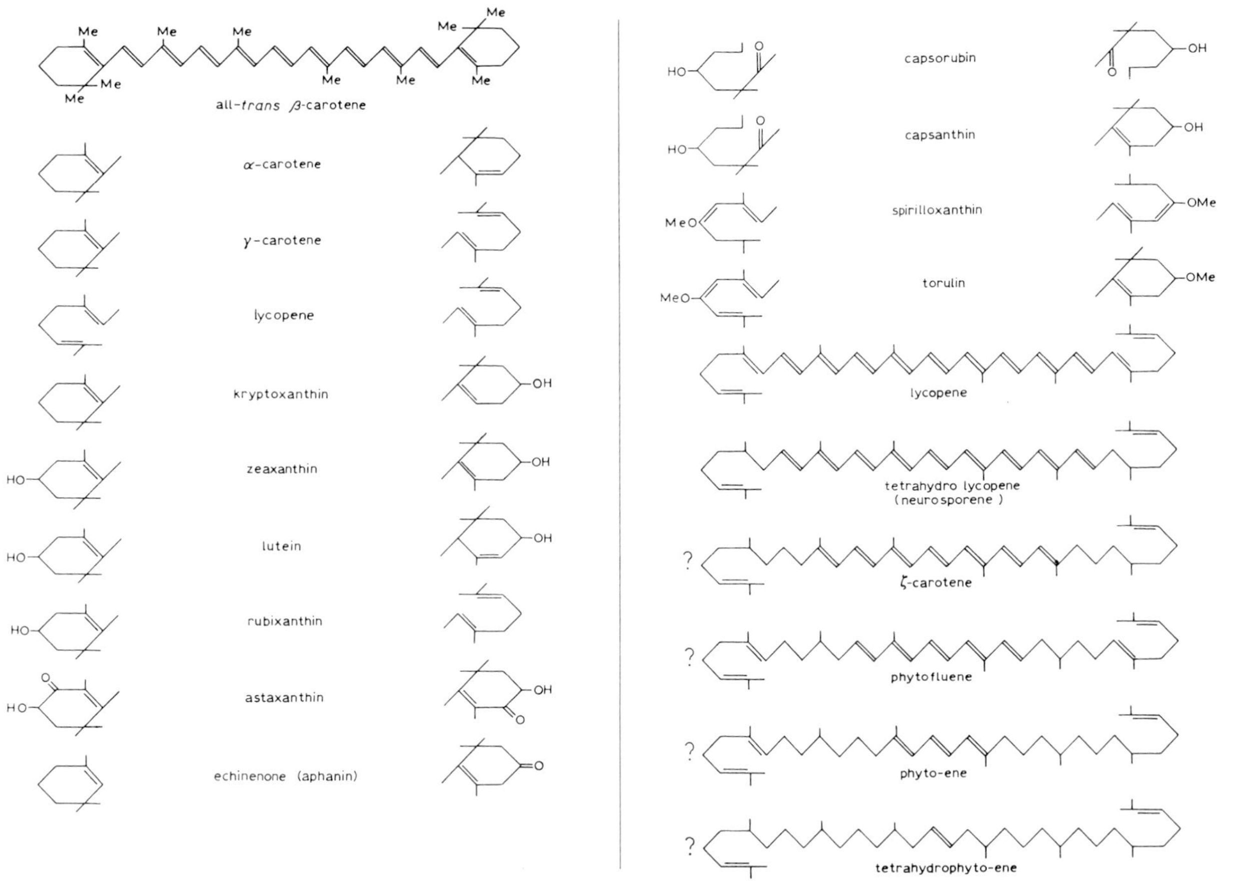

Left end group	Compound	Right end group
Me, Me, Me	all-*trans* β-carotene (chain Me, Me, Me, Me)	Me, Me, Me
	α-carotene	
	γ-carotene	
	lycopene	
	kryptoxanthin	OH
HO	zeaxanthin	OH
HO	lutein	OH
HO	rubixanthin	
HO, O	astaxanthin	OH, O
	echinenone (aphanin)	O
HO, O	capsorubin	OH, O
HO, O	capsanthin	OH
MeO	spirilloxanthin	OMe
MeO	torulin	OMe
	lycopene	
	tetrahydro lycopene (neurosporene)	
?	ζ-carotene	
?	phytofluene	
?	phyto-ene	
?	tetrahydrophyto-ene	

maxima which occur with increasing numbers of conjugated double bonds. In β-carotene there are 11 conjugated double bonds, two in β-ionone rings. Lycopene is an open chain isomeride with two additional unconjugated double bonds. Table XX illustrates the structures of selected carotenoids and Table XXI gives the positions of maxima and in many cases their intensities. (To convert $E^{1\%}_{1\,\mathrm{cm}}$ to molecular extinction coefficients the procedure is as follows: Carotene, $C_{40}H_{56}$ mol. wt. 536, 1% solution = $M/53.6$,

TABLE XXI

ABSORPTION PEAKS OF CAROTENOIDS IN DIFFERENT SOLVENTS

	λ_{max} (mμ)									$E^{1\%}_{1\,cm}$ at λ_{max}
	CS_2			$CHCl_3$			C_6H_{14}			
β-Carotene	450	485	520	466	497		425	451	482	2,580 Hexane
α-Carotene	477	509		454	485		420	445	475	2,720 Hexane
γ-Carotene	463	496	533	447	475	508	431	462	495	2,720 Hexane
Lycopene	477	507	547	456	485	520	446	464	506	3,470 Hexane
Kryptoxanthin	453	483	518	433	463	497	425	451	483	2,460 Hexane
Zeaxanthin	450	483	518	429	462	494	423	451	483	2,480 Ethanol
Lutein	445	475	508	428	456	487	420	447	477	2,540 Ethanol
Rubixanthin	461	494	533	439	474	509	432	462	494	
Astaxanthin		502								
Echinenone (aphanin)	488	494			473			453		2,000 Ethanol
Capsorubin	470	504	542				444	474	506	
Capsanthin		503	542				475	504		1,760 Ethanol
Spirilloxanthin	496	534	574	476	507	544				2,600 Hexane
Torulin	488	522	563	469	501	539				

$\varepsilon_{max} = 258 \times 53.6 = 13{,}828.8$.) It will be seen that the most intense peak is consistently displaced in the direction of longer wavelengths for the three solvents, hexane, chloroform and carbon disulphide. If reliance is placed on the positions of peaks in identifying carotenoids it is important that the

TABLE XXII

	λ_{max} (mμ)	$\varepsilon_{max} \times 10^{-3}$
α-elaeostearic acid	260, 270, 282	*ca.* 50
β-elaeostearic acid (—CH=CH—CH=CH—CH=CH—chromophore)	259, 269, 279	*ca.* 60
phyto-ene (—C(CH₃)=CH—CH=CH—CH=C(CH₃)—chromophore)	275, 285, 296	*ca.* 67.35

References p. 131

solvents should be pure (*e.g.* hexane and "light petroleum" are not interchangeable). Much work has been done on naturally occurring hydrogenated lycopenes. The structures shown in Table XX are not beyond dispute but it is clear that phyto-ene can be compared with the conjugated unsaturated acids (see Table XXII).

Conjugated tetra-enoic acids show peaks at 293, 306 and 320 mμ (approx.) with ε_{max} near 77,000, and conjugated penta-enoic acids probably at 315, 328 and 346 mμ with 333, 353 and 374 for conjugated hexa-enoic acids. Phytofluene with peaks at 332, 348 and 367.5 mμ appears at first to be nearer the hexa-enoic than the penta-enoic acid. This does not however take into account the weighting effect of the methyl groups:

$$\text{—CH=CH—}\underset{}{\overset{\displaystyle CH_3}{\overset{|}{C}}}\text{=CH—CH=CH—CH=}\overset{\displaystyle CH_3}{\overset{|}{C}}\text{—CH=CH—}$$

and it seems likely that phyto-ene has five conjugated double bonds.

(a) *Colour tests with carotenoids*

The Carr–Price reagent (anhydrous antimony trichloride in chloroform) is best known in connexion with vitamin A. The reagent produces a blue colour with β-carotene (λ_{max} 585 mμ, ε_{max} 22,000) at about $\frac{1}{8}$ the intensity produced with an equimolecular amount of vitamin A. Zeaxanthin and lutein both give a blue solution (λ_{max} 620, 586 mμ) even more closely resembling that produced by vitamin (λ_{max} 618 mμ, ε_{max} 180,000). Collins[26] found that with the $SbCl_3$ reagent carotenoids gave an intense band near 1020 mμ, ε_{max} 100,000. With concentrated sulphuric acid carotenoids give blue-green colours but the test has little specificity.

(b) *Analytical determinations*

The determination of β-carotene in dried grass and in feeding stuffs is relevant in assessing the nutritional value of a product in respect of its provitamin A content. Two procedures have gained wide acceptance (*i*) the A.O.A.C. method (1952)[27] and (*ii*) the S.P.A. method (1950)[28]. They illustrate very clearly that the spectrophotometric readings which finally assess the β-carotene content can only be meaningful if the extraction of carotenoids has been efficient and the chromatographic separations have been clean and the manipulative losses very small[29]. These considerations indeed apply to most applications of spectroscopy to analysis.

The reagents N-bromosuccinimide or N-bromoacetamide act upon carotenoids to form new dehydro compounds

$C_{40}H_{56}$	$\longrightarrow$	$C_{40}H_{54}$	$\longrightarrow$	$C_{40}H_{52}$
carotene		dehydrocarotene		bis-dehydrocarotene

The products are separated by chromatography (Karmakar and Zechmeister[30]). Using α-carotene the product dehydro α-carotene I shows a 3,4-dehydro structure and λ_{max} is displaced from 445 mμ (hexane) to 455 mμ. Dehydrogenation of β-carotene (λ_{max} 452 mμ) gives dehydro β-carotene II (λ_{max} 462 mμ)

etc.

and a small amount of dehydrocarotene III is formed. This appears to be the symmetrical bis-3,4-dehydro derivative (λ_{max} 471 mμ). All these dehydro derivatives show diminished resolution of the intense absorption in the visible region.

(c) Cis–trans isomerism

This phenomenon has been important in recent work on the spectroscopy of carotenoids (see Zechmeister[24b] for an introductory review). Isomerisations can be catalysed by acid, or by exposure to light, or by the use of traces of iodine. The all-*trans* isomeride generally shows the most intense absorption in the visible. The *cis* isomers exhibit much more intense absorption in the region 320–330 mμ (*cis*-peak). The original literature should be consulted.

(d) Vitamins A

Vitamin A_1, $C_{20}H_{29}OH$, is formed by the animal from provitamins A of the carotene type $C_{40}H_{56}$. Any carotenoid which contains one intact half of the symmetrical β-carotene molecule is a precursor of vitamin A. The predominant form of vitamin A stored in animal livers is the all-*trans* isomer (see Table XXIII). It shows a broad intense unresolved absorption band with a peak at 325 mμ, ε_{max} *ca.* 50,000. The spectrum varies a little with the solvent. As the formula indicates, vitamin A has five conjugated double bonds, one of them forming part of the β-ionone ring. In liver oils vitamin A exists mainly esterified (with higher fatty acids) and λ_{max} is slightly displaced to 328 mμ.

Vitamin A_2 has an additional conjugated double bond in the ring with a resultant change in absorption spectrum. The peak moves from 325 mμ in vitamin A_1 to 351 mμ in vitamin A_2 and there is a fall in intensity of ab-

References p. 131

sorption. At the same time a new and quite intense absorption band appears with λ_{max} 287 mμ. It has already been seen that every increase in the number of conjugate double bonds in an aliphatic chain has a bathochromic effect and causes a rise in ε_{max}. The additional double bond seen in vitamin A_2 results in a normal bathochromic effect but the spectrum as a whole suggests that the molecules are so distributed that some are effectively conjugated hexa-enes and some are effectively conjugated tetra-enes, as if the 287 band comes from a partial chromophore.

The molecular extinction coefficients at 287 and 351 mμ are respectively 19,680 and 41,460. As a first approximation the full effect of an extra double bond in vitamin A might well have raised ε_{max} at 351 mμ to over 60,000. Instead, the probability of the transition is reduced and two "partials" are seen.

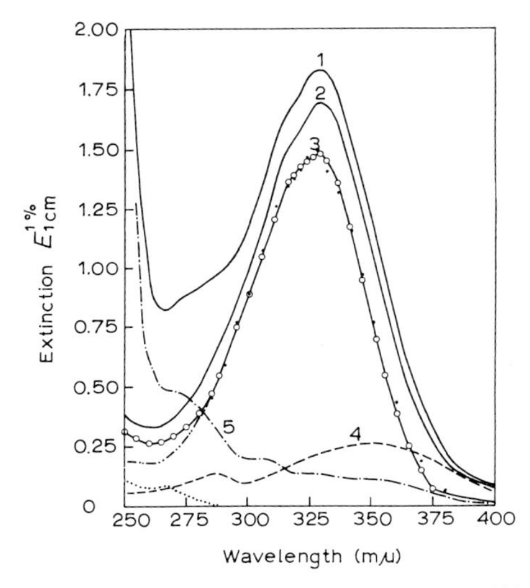

Fig. 13. An experimental analysis of the gross absorption exhibited by a typical cod liver oil containing both vitamin A_1 and A_2. Vitamin A_2 is determined from the colour test and curve 4 is calculated from the properties of pure vitamin A_2. 1, curve for oil; 2, unsaponifiable fraction; 3, vitamin A_1, *i.e.* curve 2 minus curve 4, –o–o–o– observed for pure vitamin A_1 using the peak as fixed point; 5, saponifiable fraction, curve 1 minus curve 2. $SbCl_3$ colour test $E^{1\%}_{1cm}$: 643 mμ 0.7 (vitamin A_2); 618, 4.4 (vitamin A_1); 582, 2.45.

In retinene$_1$ the carbonyl group of vitamin A_1 aldehyde is conjugated to the first double bond, and a considerable bathochromic effect is seen 325–385 mμ (Table XXIII).

In vitamin A_2 aldehyde (retinene$_2$) the displacement is from 351 mμ (vitamin A_2) to 386 mμ in cyclohexane or 405 mμ in chloroform. It will be seen that the aldehydes exhibit greater solvent shifts than the corresponding primary alcohols.

Vitamin A_1 acid shows λ_{max} 353 mμ in ethanol, ε_{max} 45,300. The displacement from 325 mμ to 353 mμ agrees with expectations.

The Carr–Price reagent gives with unsaponifiable extracts of liver oils (*i.e.* with vitamin A alcohol) a blue solution exhibiting a sharp absorption band at 617–620 mμ and a marked inflexion near 580–585 mμ. This colour test can be used for the determination of vitamin A in spite of its transient nature. If the blue solution is poured into excess of water, antimony oxychloride is formed from the trichloride but extraction with chloroform

TABLE XXIII

STRUCTURES AND SPECTROSCOPIC PROPERTIES OF VITAMINS A AND RELATED SUBSTANCES

	λ_{max} (mμ)	$E^{1\%}_{1cm}$	solvent	$SbCl_3$ test λ_{max} (mμ)	$E^{1\%}_{1cm}$
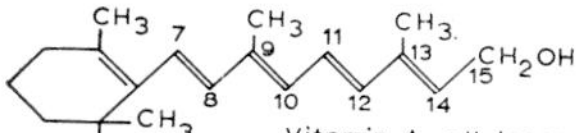 CH_3 7 CH_3 11 CH_3 9 13 CH_2OH 15 8 10 12 14 CH_3 CH_3 Vitamin A_1 all-*trans*	325	1830	E	618 (583)	4.400
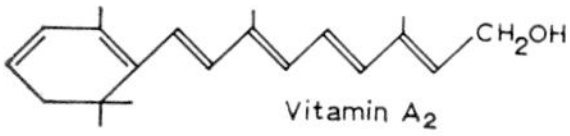 CH_2OH Vitamin A_2	287 351	820 1460	E	693	4,100
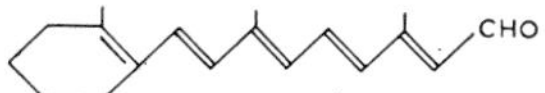 CHO Retinene$_1$	373 385 389	1548 1400 1303	CH E $CHCl_3$	664	3,400
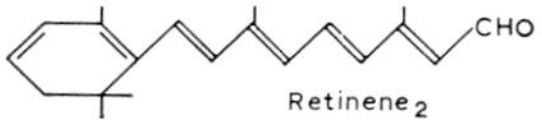 CHO Retinene$_2$	386 405	1440	CH $CHCl_3$	735–705	3,270
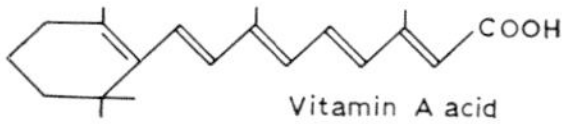 COOH Vitamin A acid	353	1510	E		

E = Ethanol CH = cyclohexane

reveals the presence of a product with well-resolved ultraviolet absorption λ_{max} 353, 372 and 393 mμ. This material can be made also by the action of anhydrous hydrogen chloride on vitamin A in ethanol; it is in fact anhydrovitamin A_1. It will itself, when purified, give a blue solution with the Carr–Price reagent, somewhat more intensely than vitamin A_1. Anhydrovitamin A_2 is similarly prepared. Vitamin A_1 methyl ether also gives λ_{max} *ca.* 620 mμ in the colour test.

References p. 131

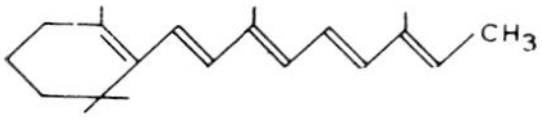

Deoxyvitamin A_1

Deoxyvitamin A_1 shows λ_{max} 577 mμ in the colour test and resolved absorption λ_{max} 331, 346 and 364 mμ in the ultraviolet, whereas purified anhydro-

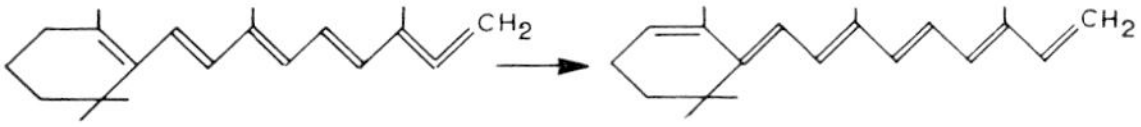

Anhydrovitamin A

vitamin A shows λ_{max} 620 mμ in the colour test and peaks at 351, 371 and 392 mμ in the ultraviolet.

TABLE XXIV

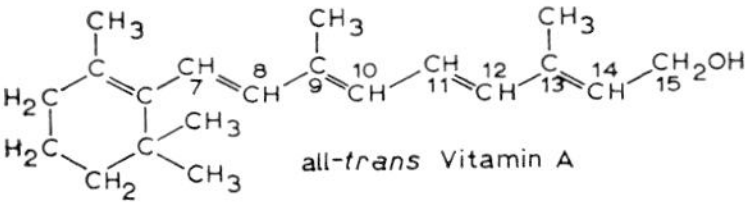

all-*trans* Vitamin A

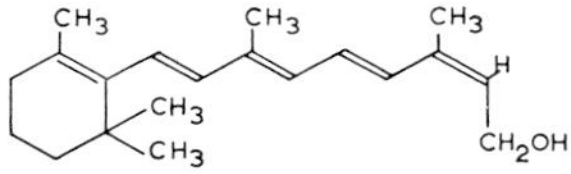

13-*cis* neovitamin A

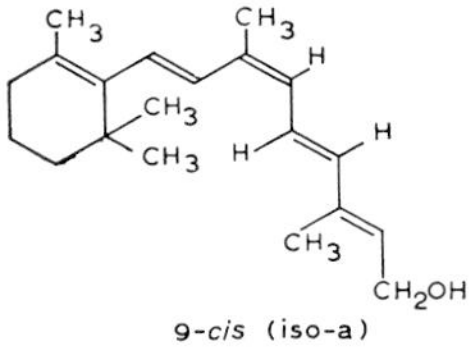

9-*cis* (iso-a)

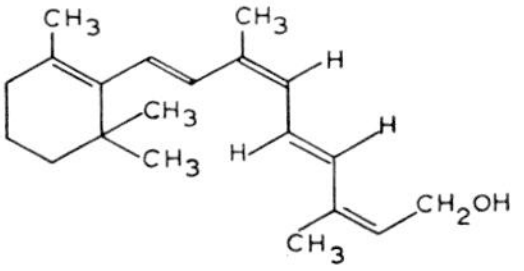

9,13 di-*cis*

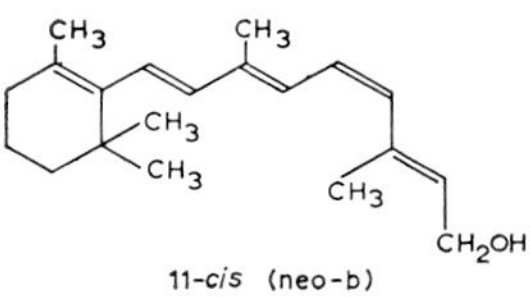

11-*cis* (neo-b)

Cis–trans isomerism in the vitamin A field has been important in the study of visual pigments and 11-*cis*-retinene plays a specific role in the formation of rhodopsin and iodopsin.

6. Absorption spectroscopy at low temperatures

Bowden and Morris[31] studied some biologically important molecules and measured the absorption spectra at the temperature of liquid air. The visible absorption of β-carotene was displaced in the direction of longer wavelengths (λ_{max} 406, 435, 467 and 499 mμ) and the ultraviolet peak near 270 mμ became sharper but was not displaced. The vitamin A maximum at 328 mμ was displaced to 335 mμ at the temperature of liquid air and weak bands at 290, 277, 258, 251 and 243 mμ appeared. Sinsheimer *et al.*[32] in Loufbourow's laboratory confirmed that at 77–74°K spectroscopic fine structure could be observed in the spectra of organic compounds in the visible and ultraviolet regions. The new detail can be valuable in structural studies; it represents of course vibrational transitions "smoothed out" at room temperature. These authors described techniques for low temperature spectroscopy. Among the useful points was the fact that a mixture of ether, isopentane and alcohol (EPA) or glycerol–water mixtures set to a glass-like mass suitable for transmitting light. They also used thin films prepared by vacuum sublimation. Later work by Wald and his colleagues[33] showed that cooling to −196°C (77°K) "relieves certain instances of steric hindrance" or intramolecular overcrowding with striking changes in absorption spectra.

All–*trans* retinene in the EPA solvent shows λ_{max} 373 mμ, ε_{max} 47,600, but at 88°K λ_{max} is at 387 mμ and ε_{max} is up by 10%. On the other hand the sterically hindered 11-*cis* shows λ_{max} 369 mμ, ε_{max} 26,400 at room temperature, the fall in molecular extinction coefficient *vis à vis* that of the all–*trans* isomer resulting from the twist in the structure. On cooling, λ_{max} reaches 385 mμ and ε_{max} 43,000, a rise of 62%. The temperature effects are reversible.

Retinene$_1$, undergoes photochemical isomerisation to a steady state in which the all–*trans* form is predominant. The 11-*cis* isomer changes readily even at 88°K. Neither the low temperature nor the rigid glassy solvent inhibits the isomerisation process.

The changes in spectra are well shown for all–*trans* β-carotene and 11, 11′-di-*cis*-β-carotene where there are striking improvements in resolution and changes in intensity of absorption.

7. Visual pigments

Retinene$_1$ and vitamin A$_1$ are concerned in both photopic (bright light, colour) vision and scotopic (dim-light) vision. The photopic luminosity curve

References p. 131

and recent measurements by Rushton[34] on the living human eye indicate that a pigment iodopsin is necessary for daylight vision (λ_{max} 560 mμ). This pigment appears to occur in the retina of the fowl. The scotopic luminosity curve shows λ_{max} 500 mμ (approx.) and the pigment rhodopsin can be prepared by suitable methods from retinas in a dim red light. In addition to the main absorption peak in the visible region there is a maximum, at 270 mμ. This is due to the protein moiety of the visual pigment. Rhodopsin can be regarded as a conjugated protein and the 270-mμ absorption is due to the aromatic amino acids. Impure preparations of rhodopsin usually contain other proteins and the lower the ratio E_{270}/E_{500} the "purer" the rhodopsin solution.

Fig. 14 shows the absorption spectrum of a solution of rhodopsin (in 1% aqueous digitonin) before and after irradiation.[35]

The bleaching of rhodopsin by light is a classical problem from which much can be learned. Wald[36] as far back as 1934–35 had shown that freshly "bleached" whole retinas yielded to chloroform the substances retinene$_1$ and retinene$_2$. These were later identified in the writer's laboratory as the aldehydes of vitamin A_1 and vitamin A_2. Vitamin A_2 is found in fish liver oils;

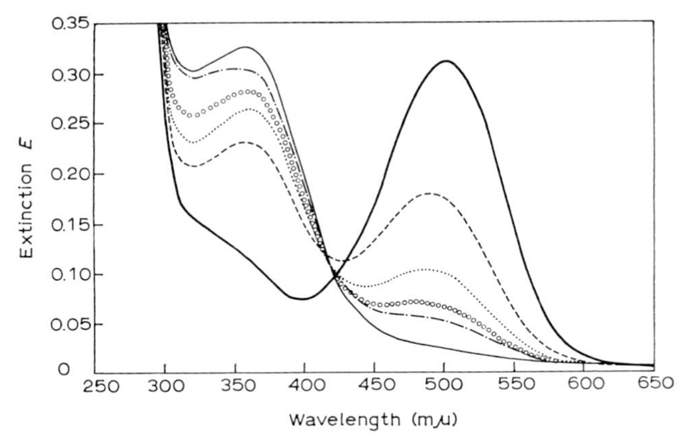

Fig. 14. Regeneration of rhodopsin. ——— curve representing fresh unbleached frog rhodopsin solution. – – – – – curve obtained after "irradiating" solution at — 70° and allowing it to reach equilibrium in the dark at room temperature. · · · · ·, ooooo and –·–·–· curves showing effects of repeating the above process three times. ——— curve obtained after complete "bleaching" at room temperature. Note that λ_{max} for rhodopsin differs from that for the regenerated product and that the initial curve does not pass through the isosbestic point.

the proportions of A_1 and A_2 are variable but in salt-water fishes the ratio A_1/A_2 is from 6–12 and in fresh-water fishes the ratio A_2/A_1 may often be 1, 2 or 3 and in some cases there is only A_2.

Lythgoe, as early as 1937 obtained evidence of a photochemical decomposition product of rhodopsin which he called "indicator yellow" because it exhibited λ_{max} 440 mμ in acid and 365 mμ in alkali. Actually retinene$_1$ combines with amino compounds to form indicator yellow analogues *e.g.*

$$C_{19}H_{27}CHO + H_2N\cdot CH_3 \longrightarrow C_{19}H_{27}CH{=}N{-}CH_2$$

(retinylidene methylamine)

This has the chromophoric properties of indicator yellow.

11-*cis* (neo-b) retinenes are required to make the pigments, but all–*trans*

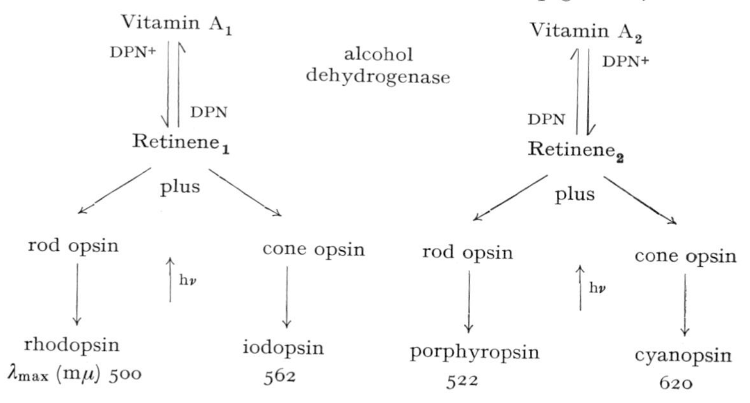

forms are produced on breakdown of pigments by light (Wald; for a fuller account and literature see ref.[38]).

TABLE XXV

RETINAL PIGMENTS

	λ_{max} (mμ)
Euphausiopsin	462
Rhodopsin	458–512 ? several
Porphyropsin	522 533 two ?
Iodopsin	562
Human cone pigment	570
Cyanopsin	620

Spectroscopic considerations

The multiplicity of visual pigments in which λ_{max} can be significantly different from say 500 mμ for rhodopsin or 522 mμ for porphyropsin emphasises the fact that the formation of Schiff's bases between the retinenes and the simpler amines does not provide a sufficiently great bathochromic shift. We do not know what the difference can be between rod opsin and cone opsin (both are proteins) which can account for the differences in λ_{max} in the conjugated proteins

$$\begin{array}{lcccc} & & \text{Pigment} & & \text{Pigment} \\ \text{cone opsin} & \xrightarrow{+\text{ retinene}_1} & 560\text{ m}\mu & \text{or} \xrightarrow{\text{retinene}_2} & 620\text{ m}\mu \\ \text{rod opsin} & & 500\text{ m}\mu & & 522\text{ m}\mu \end{array}$$

Spectroscopic methods applied to the study of photolabile pigments are described by Dartnall[37]. The use of difference spectra (ref.[38], p. 289) shows

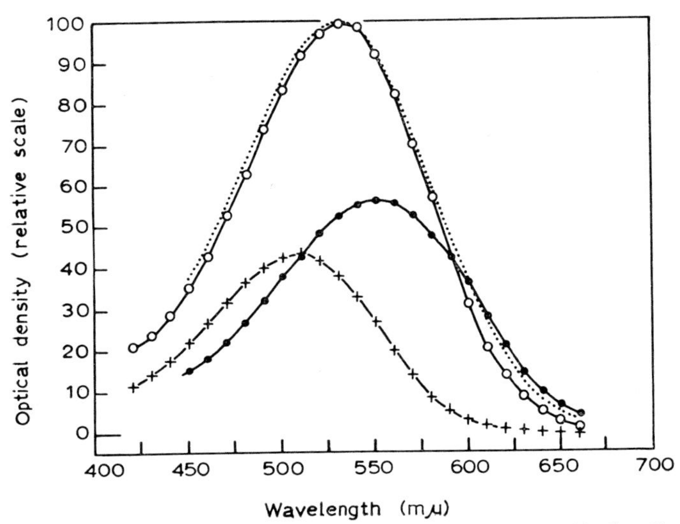

Fig. 15. Absorption spectra of three visual pigments present in bleak retinas in the proportions in which they occurred. +, visual pigment 510. ○, visual pigment 533. ●, visual pigment 550. The dotted curve is the sum of these three curves brought for comparison[37] to the same maximum (100) as that for visual pigment 533.

that there are probably two types of porphyropsin, one with λ_{max} 533 mμ and another with λ_{max} 523 mμ.

Partial bleaching by different wavelengths of monochromatic light is an even more effective tool[37].

8. Absorption spectra of purines and pyrimidines

The purine and pyrimidine bases have characteristic spectra which are not greatly changed in the corresponding nucleosides and nucleotides since the sugar residues and the phosphate groupings do not themselves contribute directly to the ultraviolet absorption. The absorption curves for the bases often differ for acid solutions and alkaline solutions. The effect of changing the pH from about 2 to 10–12 is not very large for adenine nor for guanine. This suggests that even in acid solution there is little tendency for the –OH group at position 6 to ketonise by migration of H to form NH at position 1. This is borne out in hypoxanthine where the change from an acid to an alkaline medium merely results in a slight bathochromic effect. In xanthine the bathochromic effect is much more marked and this may be attributed to the hydroxyl group at position 2. Uric acid shows even greater bathochromic effects in acid solution and a further shift in forming the trihydroxy-structure in alkali.

In uracil the change in pH from 2 to 12 moves the peak from 259 to 284 mμ but in uridine the hydrogen at position 1 has been replaced by ribose;

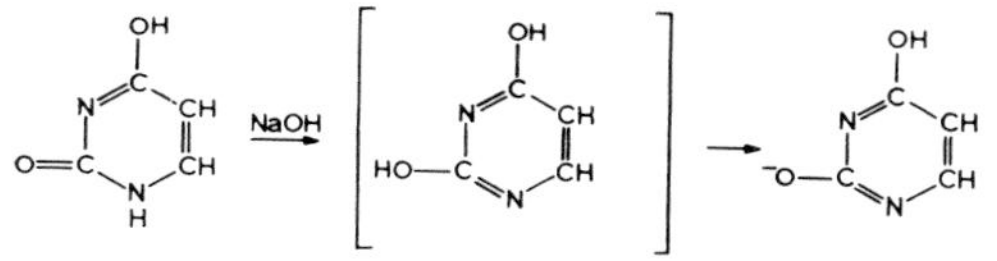

enolisation cannot occur at position 2 and the hydroxyl at position 4 seems not to ketonise. Similar effects are seen with thymine and thymidine. In the cytosines the effect of alkali is to depress the intensity of absorption at *ca.* 270 mμ and to increase it very considerably between 240 and 250 mμ.

Orotic acid (6-carboxyuracil) shows λ_{max} 205 and 280 mμ, ε_{max} 10,900 and

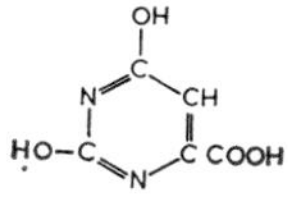

7,520 at pH 2 and λ_{max} 286 mμ, ε_{max} 5,980 at pH 10. As compared with uracil at pH 2 (λ_{max} 259 mμ) the COOH substituent is markedly bathochromic but at pH 12 uracil and orotic acid have very similar spectra.

There is no doubt that the selective absorption is due to the conjugated systems but the rather numerous possibilities of isomerism make it difficult to interpret all the data very strictly. Scrutiny of Table XXVI shows that the absorption of both purines and pyrimidines is maximal in the general neighbourhood of 260 mμ. Now the proteins in general owe their selective absorption (mainly around 280 mμ) to tyrosine, tryptophan and phenylalanine but there are few proteins which contain large amounts of these acids. In fact the contribution of the protein moiety to the absorption in the

References p. 131

TABLE XXVI

ABSORPTION SPECTRA OF PURINES AND PYRIMIDINES AND DERIVATIVES

Substance	*pH*	λ_{max} ($m\mu$)	$\varepsilon_{max} \times 10^{-3}$	λ_{min} ($m\mu$)	$\varepsilon_{min} \times 10^{-3}$
Adenine	2	263	13.1	229	2.5
	12	269	12.3	237	3.35
Adenosine	2	257	14.6	230	3.5
	11	260	1.9	227	2.25
Adenylic acid (5′)	2	257	15.1	230	3.5
	12	259	15.4	227	2.6
ATP	2	257	14.7	230	3.5
	12	259	15.4	227	2.5
Guanine	2	{248	11.4	267	7.15
		{275	7.35		
	11	{246	6.3	255	6.05
		{273	8.0		
Guanosine	1	256	12.2	228	2.4
	12	264	11.3	231	4.1
Guanylic acid	1	257	12.2	228	2.6
	12	256	11.1	230	4.3
Hypoxanthine	1	248	10.8	215	1.7
	11	258	11.0	232	3.75
Inosine	3	248	12.2	223	3.4
	12	253	13.1	224	2.5
Xanthine	2	267	10.2	239	2.7
	10	{240	8.9	257	5.0
		{277	9.3		
Xanthosine	2	{235	8.4	248	6.4
		{263	8.95		
	11	{248	10.2		
		{278	8.9	264	7.0
Uric acid	2	{231	8.5	255	3.6
		{283	11.5		
	9	292	11.6	260	2.7
Uric acid riboside	2	{240	8.4	259	3.6
		{286	6.1		
	12	{252	10.6	236	8.0
		{298	8.7		

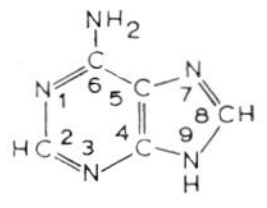
9-riboside

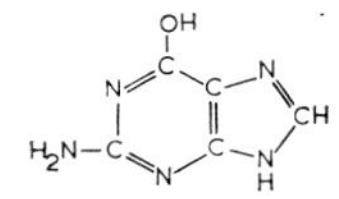
9-riboside

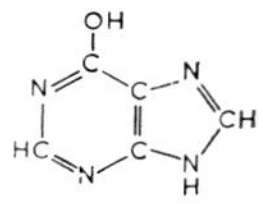
9-riboside

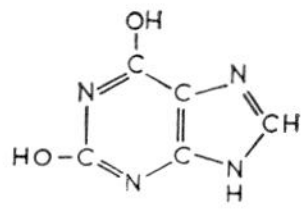
9-riboside

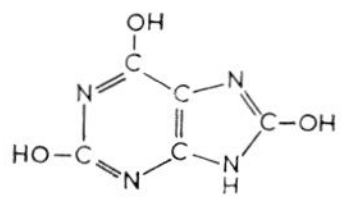
(enol)

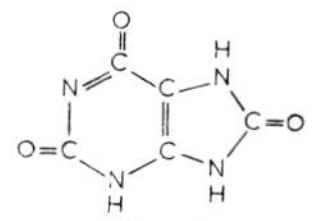
(keto)

9-riboside

TABLE XXVI (*continued*)

Substance	pH	λ_{max} (mμ)	$\varepsilon_{max} \times 10^{-3}$	λ_{min} (mμ)	$\varepsilon_{min} \times 10^{-3}$	
Uracil	2	259	8.2	227	1.8	
	12	284	6.15	241	2.15	
Uridine	2	262	10.1	230	2.05	
	12	262	8.5	236	4.5	
Uridylic acid (3′)	2	261	9.9	230	1.95	
	12	261	7.30	242	5.37	1-riboside
Thymine	2	{207 264	9.5 7.89	233	1.89	
	12	291	5.44	244	2.2	
Thymidine	2	{207 267	9.55 9.65	235	2.2	
	12	267	7.38	240	4.58	5-methvl-cytosine deoxyriboside
Thymidylic acid	2	267	9.6			
Cytosine	2	{210 274	9.7 10.2	238	1.2	
	10	2679	6.13	247	4.3	
Cytidine	2	{212 280	10.1 13.4	241	1.7	
	11	229 271	8.3 9.1	250	6.5	1-riboside
Cytidylic acid (5′)	2	281	13.6			
	12	274	7.3	250	6.6	
5-Methylcytosine	2	{210 283	12.0 9.8	242	0.9	
	10	{210 273	14.2 6.23	251	3.6	
5-Methyl-cytosine-deoxyriboside	2	{209 286	9.70 11.6	245	1.05	
	11	206 277	13.28 8.81	255	5.43	

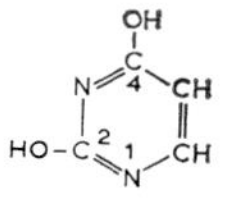

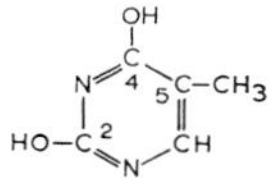

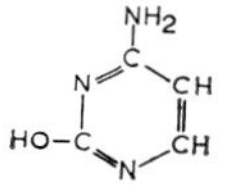

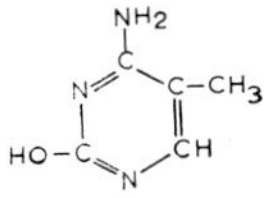

middle ultraviolet shown by a nucleoprotein is an almost negligible proportion of the whole. The predominant absorption is that of the purine and pyrimidine bases of the nucleic acids. Ultraviolet microphotography using radiations of wavelengths near to 260 mμ has been used to locate and even to determine nucleic acids in cells and in various tissues. Differential ultraviolet microphotography before or after the use of purified proteolytic enzymes or purified nucleases can assist in localising nucleic acids within cells.

Volken and Cohn[39] describe the preparation by various methods of tissue extracts capable of yielding trustworthy estimates of nucleic acid content by spectrophotometry. Webb and Levy[40] discuss the use of perchloric acid, which is transparent to ultraviolet light. Acid hydrolysis (using trichloracetic acid or perchloric acid) "depolymerises" nucleic acids and reproducibly

References p. 131

raises the intensity of absorption. This is expressed as ε, the extinction coefficient per g atom of nucleotide phosphorus per litre

$$\log I_0/I = \varepsilon C d$$

C = g atoms nucleotide P/l per cm; d = cell thickness in cm. At 268.5 mμ ε is 9850 for both DNA and RNA. Measurements can be made in 5% trichloracetic acid but it is important to put the "blank" solution through the same heating and dilution as the test solution. Perchloric acid is less exacting from the standpoint of compensation but it seems to form interfering protein degradation products.

9. Analytical procedures

(a) Determination of a single absorbing component

A simple example would be the determination of CS_2 in carbon tetrachloride. Here the solvent is transparent in the region (*ca.* 330 mμ) where the solute absorbs selectively. It is only necessary to determine $E^{1\%}_{1\,\mathrm{cm}}$ for carbon disulphide in carbon tetrachloride and then to assume a linear relationship between intensity of absorption at $\lambda_{\max}$ and concentration. It is, however, desirable with many biochemical problems to construct a calibration curve relating intensity of absorption to percentage concentration of pure solute (*i.e.* to test the validity of Beer's law).

(b) Determination of a two-component mixture

The standard method for analysing a two-component mixture was given by Vierordt[41]. It applies satisfactorily provided that there is no appreciable irrelevant absorption exerted by impurities. Goodwin and Morton[42] tackled the problem of the simultaneous determination of tyrosine and tryptophan where the absorption curves of the two amino acids overlap a good deal. When the curves are plotted with molecular extinctions against wavelength they intersect at isosbestic points. In a two-component system intensities of absorption at isosbestic points will obviously depend on the total molar concentration (*i.e.* the sum of the molar concentrations of the two components). Thus if at an isosbestic point (λ_1) where the molecular extinction of either component is ε, the total concentration when the observed optical density is A_1 will be

$$c\ (\text{moles/l}) = \frac{A_1}{\varepsilon} = m$$

Consider now a wavelength λ_2 where ε_x and ε_y are the molecular extinction coefficients of the two components. An observed reading A_2 will be made up as follows:

$$A_2 = n\varepsilon_x + (m - n)\,\varepsilon_y$$

where n = molar concentration of X and

$$m - n = \text{molar concentration of Y}$$

so that

$$n = \frac{A_2 - m\varepsilon_y}{\varepsilon_x - \varepsilon_y}$$

The major difficulty in using spectroscopic methods in practical problems arises from the occurrence of irrelevant absorption.

(c) Three point procedure of Morton and Stubbs[43]

The top curve in Fig. 16 is the sum of the two lower curves $LE_2'N$ due to a pure substance and ABC due to irrelevant absorption by impurity. It is assumed that the irrelevant absorption is linear from λ_1 to λ_3, two wavelengths on either side of the peak λ_2 but not very far removed. λ_1 and λ_2 have been chosen after study of the absorption spectrum of a pure sample

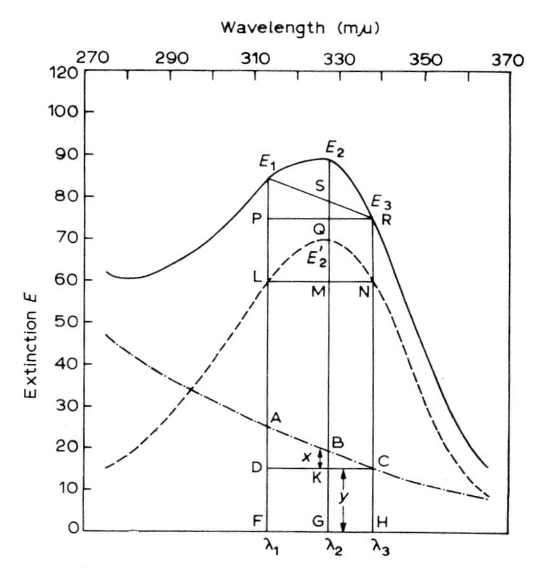

Fig. 16. The geometrical basis of the Morton–Stubbs' correction procedure[13].

References p. 131

of the substance under study so that the intensity of absorption E is the same at the two wavelengths and a known fraction of that at λ_2. Thus in Fig. 16 LMN is horizontal and LF = NH = $6/7\ E_2'$G. The three wavelengths are called fixation points. Careful readings are made on the sample at the three wavelengths λ_1, λ_2 and λ_3. Clearly the correction which has to be made at λ_{max} is BG = $E_2 - E_2'$ and E_2' is the corrected value. The total correction at λ_2 is made up of two parts BK (x) due to the slope of the irrelevant absorption line and KG (y) the height of the irrelevant absorption at λ_3 (CH). Comparing triangles

$$\mathrm{SQ} = \mathrm{BK} = x \qquad \mathrm{PR/QR} = E_1\mathrm{P/SQ} \qquad \mathrm{SQ}/E_1\mathrm{P} = \mathrm{QR/PR}$$

$$\mathrm{QR} = \lambda_3 - \lambda_2 \qquad \mathrm{PR} = \lambda_3 - \lambda_1 \qquad E_1\mathrm{P} = E_1 - E_3$$

hence

$$x = (E_1 - E_3)\cdot(\lambda_3 - \lambda_2)/(\lambda_3 - \lambda_1)$$

For the pure material

$$E_2'/\mathrm{LF} = E_2'/\mathrm{NH} = r \qquad (e.g\ 7/6)$$

$$\frac{E_2 - x - \mathrm{KG}}{E_3 - \mathrm{CH}} = r$$

but

$$\mathrm{CH} = \mathrm{KG} = y$$

so

$$\frac{E_2' - x - y}{E_3 - y} = r \quad \text{and} \quad y = \frac{E_3 r - E_2 + x}{r - 1}$$

Substituting for x and y

$$E_2' = \frac{r}{r-1}\left[E_2 - \frac{\lambda_2 - \lambda_1}{\lambda_3 - \lambda_1}E_3 - \frac{\lambda_3 - \lambda_2}{\lambda_3 - \lambda_1}E_1\right]$$

Morton and Stubbs found for esterified vitamin A λ_{max} 328 mμ and at 313 and 338.5 mμ, E was $6/7\ E_{max}$ in (cyclohexane). The correction procedure led to

$$E_{328\ \mathrm{m}\mu}\ (\mathrm{corr.}) = 7\ E_{328\ \mathrm{m}\mu} - 2.884\ E_{313\ \mathrm{m}\mu} - 4.116\ E_{338.5\ \mathrm{m}\mu}$$

The British Pharmacopeia, following Cama *et al.*[5] used

$$E_{327.5\ \mathrm{m}\mu}\ (\mathrm{corr.}) = 7\ E_{327.5\ \mathrm{m}\mu} - 2.835\ E_{312.5\ \mathrm{m}\mu} - 4.175\ E_{337.5\ \mathrm{m}\mu}$$

or for free vitamin A (in cyclohexane):

$$E_{326.5\ m\mu}\ (\text{corr.}) = 7\ E_{326.5\ m\mu} - 2.954\ E_{312.5\ m\mu} - 4.046\ E_{336.5\ m\mu}$$

The U.S. Pharmacopeia recognises tests in isopropyl alcohol on *free* vitamin A preparations, and follows a recent authorative co-operative study (Brunius[44]) which recommends the equation

$$E_{325\ m\mu}\ (\text{corr.}) = 6.815\ E_{325\ m\mu} - 2.555\ E_{310\ m\mu} - 4.260\ E_{334\ m\mu}$$

For the determination of vitamin A see also Embree *et al.*[45].

10. Spectroscopic determination of various substances

(a) Uric acid, hypoxanthine, xanthine (Dubbs et al.[46])

Uric acid absorbs strongly at 293 mμ but allantoin and other products formed from it under the action of uricase are transparent at that wavelength. The molecular extinction coefficient at 293 mμ is 12,200 so that $\Delta E = -0.0745/\mu$g/ml. The enzyme can be purchased. It is standardised (as a fine suspension in 0.15 *M* glycine) against lithium urate (1 g uric acid/l). Tissue extracts are deproteinised ($HClO_4$). Extinction readings are made at 293 and 320 mμ until they are constant; at 320 mμ there should be no change nor should there be change at 293 mμ in the control.

Hypoxanthine may be determined by using xanthine oxidase and converting to uric acid. Readings are taken at 248 and 290 mμ. The change is completed in half an hour and the changes in $E_{290\ m\mu}$ are $+0.08/\mu$g hypoxanthine/ml or in $E_{248\ m\mu}$ $-0.03/\mu$g/ml. Xanthine itself can be similarly determined by the enzymic formation of uric acid, and following the absorption at 248, 270 and 290 mμ:

$$\Delta E/\mu\text{g/ml, } 0 \text{ at } 248\ m\mu,\ -0.053 \text{ at } 270\ m\mu \text{ and } +0.066 \text{ at } 290\ m\mu$$

Plesner and Kalckar [47] show how the method can be used for determining a mixture of xanthine and hypoxanthine. The enzyme can also be used to determine xanthopterin which is converted to leucopterin, the greatest difference in absorption occurring at 330 mμ.

(b) Adenine

Klenow[48] determines adenine by a method which depends on the formation of 2,8-dihydroxyadenine under the action of xanthine oxidase. This is in some respects technically a simple case because the product has intense

References p. 131

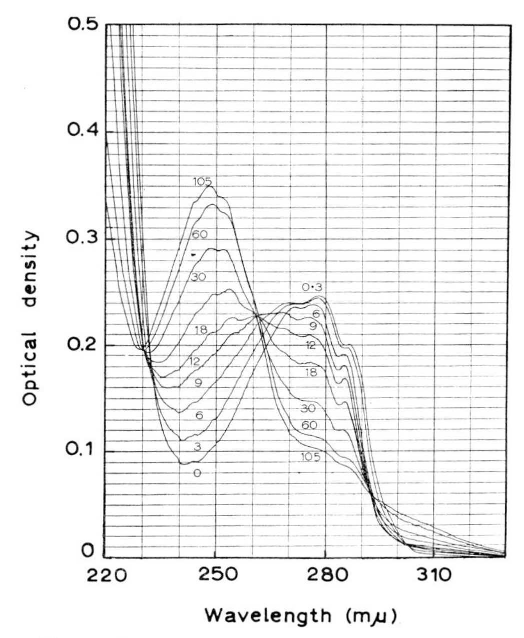

Fig. 17. Curves illustrating the changes in ultraviolet absorption which occur during enzymic oxidation of indoleacetic acid. Enzyme, 0.25 ml; IAA, 0.11 μmole; H_2O_2, 0.02 μmole in 2.62 ml citrate buffer. Records were begun at 330 mμ. Curve 0 was begun 15 sec after addition of H_2O_2; successive curves were begun at 3, 6, 9, 12, 18, 30, 60 and 105 min. Each record was completed in 55 sec[49].

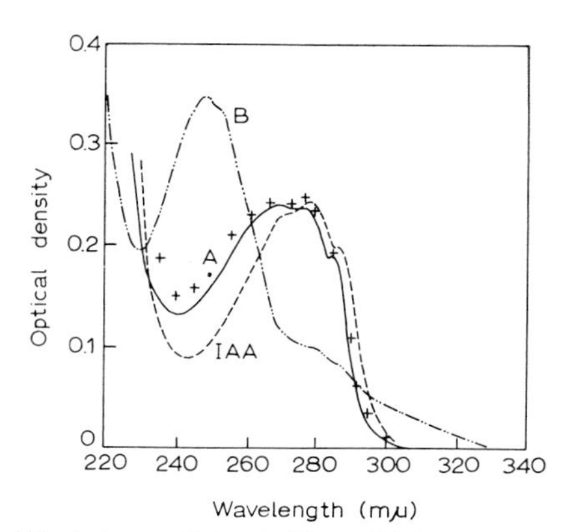

Fig. 18. Spectrum of the intermediate, A. The solid line shows the spectrum of A found by subtracting optical density due to B from the 9-min curve (B determined separately). + + spectrum of A determined from initial changes in optical density in a separate experiment. Each spectrum plotted to represent an amount of A equivalent to the amount of indoleacetic acid originally present[49].

absorption (λ_{max} 305 mμ) in a region where the absorption of adenine is negligible. In other respects it illustrates the need for standardising a method at a fixed pH:

pH	6.4	7.0	7.4	7.7
$\Delta E_{305\ m\mu}/\mu g$ adenine/ml	0.11	0.115	0.115	0.120

Because of the low solubility of 2,8-dihydroxyadenine in the recommended buffer the method works only up to 2 μg/ml adenine.

These examples illustrate a very important principle in the combination of enzymic and spectroscopic methods; this is that the *change* in absorption is the quantity to be measured, and given ingenuity and a suitable enzymic process, many analytical determinations can be devised which will work well on a micro scale without elaborate purifications and separations being necessary.

(c) *Indole derivatives*

Indole-3-acetic acid (IAA) may be destroyed enzymically or photochemically (Ray[49]). The enzyme acts neither on indole 3-propionic acid nor on indole-3-butyric acid. The final mixture contains at least four products among which is 3-methyldioxindole:

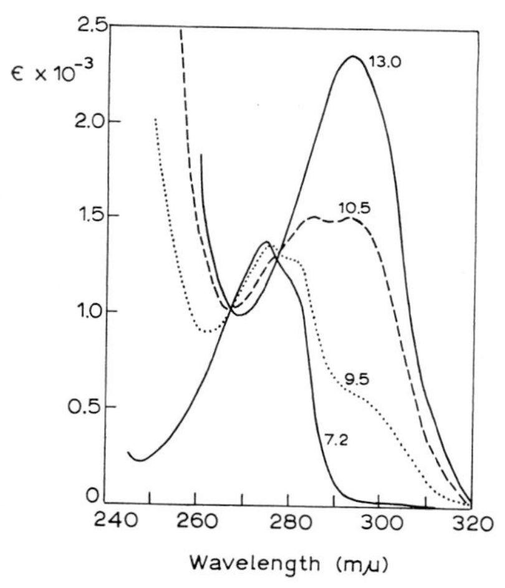

Fig. 19. Absorption spectrum of tyrosine at various pH values. Isosbestic points[50] at 267 and 277.5 mμ.

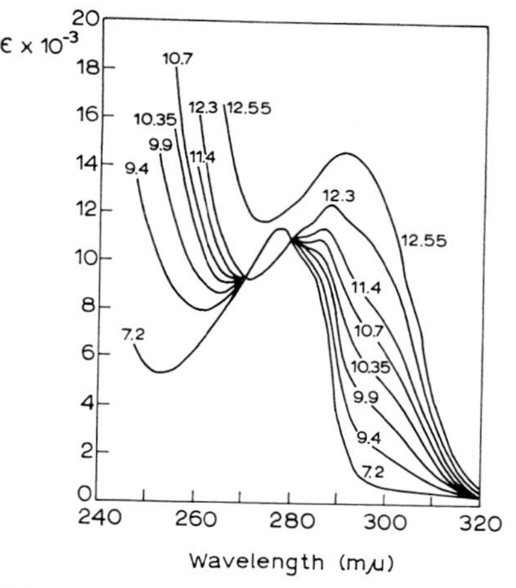

Fig. 20. Absorption spectrum[50] of ribonuclease at pH values indicated. Note isosbestic points at 270 and 280 mμ. Between these two wavelengths, at pH values between 9.4. and 11.4, the curves have not been drawn in, for the sake of clarity.

References p. 131

The absorption curve of indole-3-acetic acid at pH 3.7 shows peaks at 270 278 and 286 mμ. In the presence of hydrogen peroxide the enzymic oxidation proceeds smoothly to give a product with λ_{max} 247 mμ

$$\text{IAA} + O_2 \rightarrow CO_2 + \text{products} \quad \text{or} \quad \text{IAA} \rightarrow \text{A} \rightarrow \text{B} \rightarrow$$

but the curves for the early stages do not pass through the isosbestic points at 231, 261 and 292 mμ. Application of a colour test for IAA shows that isosbesticity is not established until all the IAA has been changed. The initial product must be A and the two components in the isosbestic system are A and B. Only the first step is enzymically catalysed.

The change in absorption at 261 mμ measures the disappearance of IAA and the second stage is measured by the change in absorption at 272 mμ (Figs. 17 and 18).

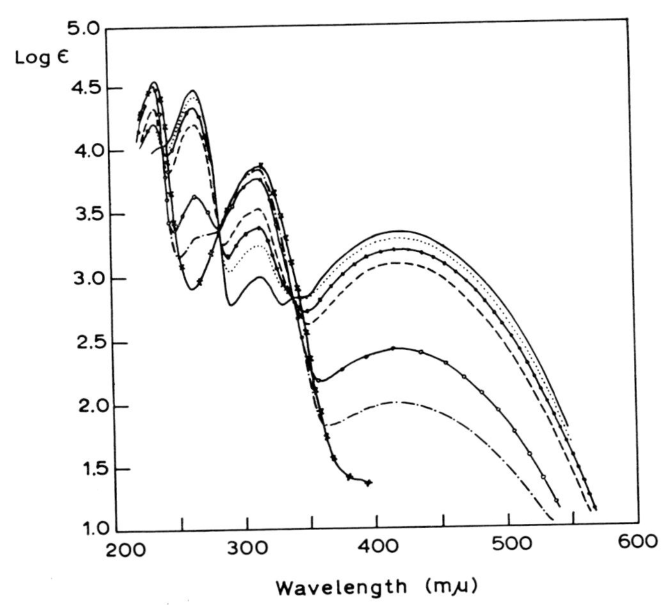

Fig. 21. Absorption spectra of 5-aminoquinoline in aqueous hydrochloric acid[51].

pH 2.965 ———— 1.105 – – – – –
1.562 · · · · · · 0.460 –o–o–o
1.140 –•–•–• 0.222 –·–·–·
Conc. HCl –x–x–x

(d) Proteins and enzymes

Many interesting problems arise with proteins, the selective absorption of which in the region near 280 mμ is due to the amounts of phenylalanine, tyrosine and tryptophan present. Fig. 19 (after Shugar[50]) shows the absorption spectrum of tyrosine at various pH values between 7.2 and 13.0. Two good isosbestic points are seen. The spectra of ribonuclease over the same pH range indicate similar effects[50] (Fig. 20).

11. Spectrophotometric determinations of dissociation constants[51]

The absorption spectra of 5- and 6-aminoquinoline in aqueous hydrochloric acid vary greatly with pH. In 2*N* hydrochloric acid the spectra resemble that of the quinolinium ion in 0.01 *N* acid.

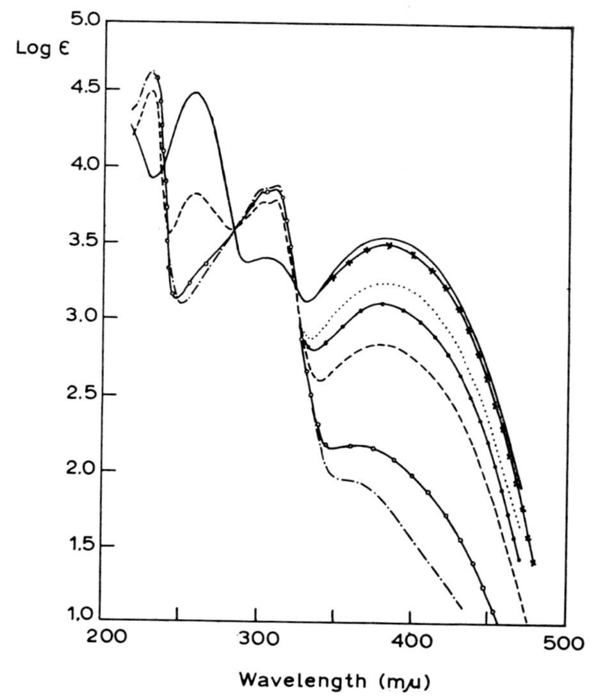

Fig. 22. Absorption spectra of 6-aminoquinoline in aqueous hydrochloric acid[51].

pH 2.965	———	1.105	– – – –
pH 2.165	–x–x–x	0.46	–o–o–o
1.562	······	0.222	–·–·–·
1.140	–•–•–•		

References p. 131

The equation $$pK_a = pH - \log [(\varepsilon_{BH^+} - \varepsilon)/(\varepsilon - \varepsilon_B)]$$

where ε_{BH^+} is determined at a low pH value at which the equilibrium is overwhelmingly in favour of the proton-donor BH^+ and ε_B is measured at some higher pH value at which the solute exists almost entirely as the proton acceptor B and ε is the molecular extinction coefficient at a defined or measured intermediate pH at which B and BH^+ co-exist. Not all wave-lengths are equally suitable because $\Delta_\varepsilon/\Delta_\lambda$ may be high, close to isosbestic points. The validity of the method depends of course on the existence of such crossing points. The pK_a values for the 5- and 6-amino quinolines are about 0.97 and 1.63 respectively for the monocation → dication change as

TABLE XXVII

	λ_{max} (mμ)	ε_{max}
Quinoline in 0.01*N* HCl	312	6,900
	235	35,000
6-Aminoquinoline in 2*N* HCl	315	6,610
	267	2,140
	234	34,300
6-Aminoquinoline in 2*N* HCl	362	87,6
	310	7,550
	232	42,600

against 5.5 and 5.6 for the first pK_a values due to the acceptance of a proton by the ring nitrogen atom (determined potentiometrically) (see also Sagar *et al.*[52], Vandenbelt *et al.*[53], for comparisons of pK_a values determined by electrometric titration and ultraviolet absorption).

BIBLIOGRAPHY

Books, Review articles, Collection of data, etc.

[1] G. F. LOTHIAN, *Absorption Spectrophotometry*, 2nd ed., Hilger and Watts, London, 1958.

[2] W. R. BRODE, Presentation of Absorption Spectra Data, *J. Opt. Soc. Am.*, 39 (1949) 1022.

[3] R. A. MORTON, *The Application of Absorption Spectra to the Study of Vitamins, Hormones and Co-enzymes*, Hilger and Watts, London, 1942.

[4] L. HEILMEYER (transl. L. JORDAN), *Spectrophotometry in Medicine*, Hilger, London, 1943.

[5] A. E. GILLAM AND E. S. STERN, *Electronic Absorption Spectroscopy in Organic Chemistry*, 2nd ed., Arnold, London, 1957.

[6] E. A. BRAUDE AND F. C. NACHOD (Eds.), *Determination of Organic Structure by Physical Methods*, Academic Press, New York, 1955, Chapter 4.

[7] F. A. MILLER, in H. GILMAN (Ed.), *Infrared and Ultraviolet Spectra, Organic Chemistry, an Advanced Treatise*, Vol. 3, Wiley, New York, Chapman and Hall, London, 1953, p. 122.

[8] M. PESTEMER AND D. BRUCK, *Absorptions-Spektroskopie im sichtbar und ultraviolet*, in HOUBEN-WEYL, *Methoden der organischen Chemie*, Vol. III, Part 2, Thieme, Stuttgart, 1955, p. 593.

[9] M. G. MELLON, *Analytical Absorption Spectrophotometry*, Wiley, New York, 1950.

[10] A. B. F. DUNCAN, *Electronic Spectra in the Visible and Ultraviolet Regions*, in *Technique of Organic Chemistry*, Vol. IX, *Chemical Applications of Spectroscopy*, Chapter V, Interscience, New York, 1956.

[11] F. A. MATSON, *Applications of Electronic Spectra in the Visible and Ultraviolet Regions*, in *Technique of Organic Chemistry*, Vol. IX, *Chemical Applications of Spectroscopy*, Chapter V, Interscience, New York, 1956.

[12] W. R. BRODE, *Chemical Spectroscopy*, 2nd ed., Wiley, New York, 1943.

[13] E. A. BRAUDE, in E. H. RODD (Ed.), *Chemistry of Carbon Compounds*, Vol. 1A, Elsevier, Amsterdam, 1952, pp. 71–99.

[14] J. GLOVER, *Colorimetric, Absorptiometric and Fluorimetric Methods*, in K. PAECH AND M. V. TRACEY (Eds.), *Modern Methods of Plant Analysis*, Vol. 1, Springer, Berlin, 1956.

[15] R. A. MORTON, *Molecular Spectra, Visible and Ultraviolet*, in THORPE's *Dictionary of Chemistry*, Vol. 8, 1949.

[16] J. F. SCOTT, *Utraviolet Absorption Spectroscopy*, in OSTER AND POLLISTER (Eds.), *Physical Techniques in Biological Research*, Vol. 1, Academic Press, New York, 1955.

[17] R. A. FRIEDEL AND M. ORCHIN, *Ultraviolet Spectra of Aromatic Compounds*, Wiley, New York, 1951 [A collection of absorption curves].

[18] H. M. HERSHENON, *Ultraviolet Absorption Spectra, Index for 1930–1954*, Academic Press, New York [Literature references].

[19] W. R. BRODE, Chemical Spectroscopy, *Am. Soc. Testing Materials, Proc.*, 50 (1950) 1–47.

[20] L. N. FERGUSON, Absorption Spectra and Chemical Constitution of Organic Molecules, *Chem. Revs.*, 43 (1948) 408.
[21] A. MACCOLL, Colour and Constitution, *Quart. Revs. (London)*, 1 (1947) 16.
[22] L. DORFMAN, Ultraviolet Absorption Spectra of Steroids, *Chem. Revs.*, 53 (1953) 47.
[23] R. N. JONES, Ultraviolet Absorption Spectra of Aromatic Hydrocarbons, *Chem. Revs.*, 32 (1943) 1.
[24] G. A. J. PITT AND R. A. MORTON, *Ultraviolet Spectroscopy of Fatty Acids*, in *Progress in the Chemistry of Fats*, Vol. 4, Pergamon, London, 1957, p. 227.
[25] L. ZECHMEISTER, Cis–trans Isomerism in Carotenoids, *Chem. Revs.*, 34 (1944) 267.
[26] R. A. MORTON AND G. A. J. PITT, *Visual Pigments*, in *Fortschritte der Chemie Organischer Naturstoffe*, Vol. XIV, Springer, Vienna, 1957, p. 244.
[27] K. DIMROTH, *Angew. Chem.*, 52 (1939) 545.
[28] G. N. LEWIS AND M. CALVIN, *Chem. Revs.*, 25 (1939) 273.
[29] R. A. MORTON, *Ann. Repts. on Progr. Chem. (Chem. Soc. London)*, 38 (1942) 7
[30] P. L. SINSHEIMER, in A. HOLLAENDER (Ed.), *Radiation Biology*, Chapter 5, McGraw-Hill, New York, p. 2.
[31] M. J. KAMLET (Ed.), *Organic Electronic Spectral Data*, Vol. I, 1946-1952; H. E. UNGNADE (Ed.), *Organic Electronic Spectral Data*, Vol. II, 1953-1955, Interscience, New York.

REFERENCES

[1] A. E. Gillam and R. A. Morton, *Proc. Roy. Soc. (London), A*, 124 (1929) 604.
[2] N. Q. Chako, *J. Chem. Phys.*, 2 (1934) 644.
[3] T. Förster, *Z. Elektrochem.*, 45 (1939) 557.
[4] G. W. Haupt, *J. Res. Natl. Bur. Standards*, 48 (1952) 414.
[5] H. R. Cama, F. D. Collins and R. A. Morton, *Biochem. J.*, 50 (1951) 48.
[6] K. S. Gibson, *Spectrophotometry (200–1000 mμ)*, Circular Natl. Bur. Standards, No. 484, 1949.
[7] E. A. Braude, J. S. Fawcett and C. J. Timmons, *J. Chem. Soc.*, (1950) 1019.
[8] W. R. Brode, *J. Opt. Soc. Am.*, 39 (1949) 1022.
[9] A. Burawoy, *J. Chem. Soc.*, (1939) 1177; (1941) 20.
[10] R. B. Woodward, *J. Am. Chem. Soc.*, 63 (1941) 1123; 64 (1942) 72, 76.
[11] L. K. Evans and A. E. Gillam, *J. Chem. Soc.*, (1941) 815; (1943) 432, 465.
[12] E. A. Braude, *Ann. Repts. on Progr. Chem. (Chem. Soc. London)*, 42 (1945) 105.
[13] A. E. Gillam and D. H. Hey, *J. Chem. Soc.*, (1939) 1170.
[14] R. A. Morton and A. L. Stubbs, *J. Chem. Soc.*, (1939) 1321; (1940) 1347.
[15] W. M. Asouz, D. V. Parke and R. T. Williams, *Biochem. J.*, 55 (1953) 146.
[16] R. A. Morton, A. Hassan and T. C. Calloway, *J. Chem. Soc.*, (1934) 883.
[17] A. K. Lunn and R. A. Morton, *The Analyst*, 77 (1952) 718.
[18] L. Dorfman, *Chem. Rev.*, 53 (1953) 47.
[19] P. Bladon, H. B. Henbest and G. W. Wood, *Chem. & Ind.*, (1951) 866; *J. Chem. Soc.*, (1952) 2537.
[20a] I. M. Heilbron, E. D. Kamm and R. A. Morton, *Biochem. J.*, 21 (1927) 78.
[20b] A. J. Kandutsch, E. D. Murphy and M. E. Diesbach, *Arch. Biochem. Biophys.*, 61 (1956) 450.
[21] L. Velluz, G. Amiard and A. Petit, *Bull. soc. chim. France*, 16 (1949) 501; L. Velluz, G. Amiard and G. Goffinet, *ibid.*, 22 (1955) 1341.
[22] E. Havinga, A. L. Koevoet and A. Verloop, *Rec. trav. chim.*, 74 (1955) 1230; 76 (1957) 689.
[23] G. A. J. Pitt and R. A. Morton in *Progress in the Chemistry of Fats*, Vol. 4, Pergamon, London, 1957, p. 227.
[24a] E. A. Braude and F. C. Nachod (Eds.), in *Determination of Organic Structures by Physical Methods*, Academic Press, New York, 1955, p. 131.
[24b] L. Zechmeister, *Chem. Revs.*, 34 (1944) 267; *Experientia*, 10 (1954) 1; *Fortschr. Chem. org. Naturstoffe*, 15 (1958) 31.
[25a] P. Karrer and E. Jucker, *Carotenoids*, Elsevier, Amsterdam, 1950.
[25b] H. J. Bielig, *Handbuch der physiologisch und pathologisch-chemischen Analyse*, Vol. III, Springer, Berlin, 1955, p. 954.
[25c] T. W. Goodwin in K. Peach and M. V. Tracey (Eds.), *Modern Methods of Plant Analysis*, Vol. 3, Springer, Berlin, 1955, p. 272.
[25d] R. A. Morton and T. W. Goodwin, *Brit. Med. Bull.*, 12 (1956) 37.
[26] F. D. Collins, *Nature*, 165 (1950) 817.
[27] Association of Official Agricultural Chemists, *Official Methods of Analysis*, 8th ed. 1955.
[28] Analytical Methods Committee, Society of Public Analysts, *The Analyst*, 75 (1950) 568.
[29] E. M. Bickoff, in D. Glick (Ed.), *Methods of Biochemical Analysis*, Vol. 4, Interscience, New York, 1957, p. 1.
[30] G. Karmakar and L. Zechmeister, *J. Am. Chem. Soc.*, 77 (1955) 55.
[31] F. P. Bowden and S. D. D. Morris, *Proc. Roy. Soc. (London), B*, 115 (1934) 274.
[32] P. L. Sinsheimer, J. F. Scott and J. R. Loofbourow, *J. Biol. Chem.*, 187 (1950) 299.
[33] L. Jurkowitz, J. N. Loeb, P. K. Brown and G. Wald, *Nature*, 184 (1959) 614.
[34] W. A. H. Rushton, *J. Physiol.*, 134 (1956) 11; *Nature*, 179 (1957) 571.
[35] F. D. Collins and R. A. Morton, *Biochem. J.*, 47 (1950) 3, 10, 18.
[36] G. Wald, *Nature*, 134 (1934) 65; *J. Gen. Physiol.*, 18 (1935) 905; 19 (1935) 351, 781.
[37] H. J. A. Dartnall, *J. Physiol.*, 128 (1955) 131.

38 R. A. MORTON AND G. A. J. PITT, *Fortschr. Chem. org. Naturstoffe*, 14 (1957) 244.
39 E. VOLKEN AND W. E. COHN, in D. GLICK (Ed.), *Methods of Biochemical Analysis*, Vol. 1, Interscience, New York, 1954, p. 294.
40 J. M. WEBB AND H. B. LEVY in D. GLICK (Ed.), *Methods of Biochemical Analysis*, Vol. 6, Interscience, New York, 1958, p. 19.
41 K. VIERORDT, *Die Anwendung des Spektral-Apparates zur Photometrie der Absorptions-Spektren*, Tubingen, 1873.
42 T. W. GOODWIN AND R. A. MORTON, *Biochem. J.*, 40 (1946) 628.
43 R. A. MORTON AND A. L. STUBBS, *The Analyst*, 71 (1946) 348.
44 E. BRUNIUS, *J. Ass. Off. Agric., Chem.*, 42 (1959) 657.
45 N. D. EMBREE, S. R. AMES, R. W. LEHMAN AND P. L. HARRIS, in D. GLICK (Ed.), *Methods of Biochemical Analysis*, Vol. 4, Interscience, New York, 1957, p. 43.
46 C. A. DUBBS, F. W. DAVIS AND W. S. ADAMS, *J. Biol. Chem.*, 218 (1956) 497.
47 P. PLESNER AND H. M. KALCKAR in D. GLICK (Ed.), *Methods of Biochemical Analysis*, Vol. 3, Interscience, New York, 1956, p. 101.
48 H. KLENOW, *Biochem, J.*, 50 (1951) 404.
49 P. M. RAY, *Arch. Biochem. Biophys.*, 64 (1956) 193.
50 D. SHUGAR, *Biochem. J.*, 52 (1952) 142.
51 J. M. HEARN, R. A. MORTON AND J. C. E. SIMPSON, *J. Chem. Soc.*, (1951) 3318.
52 E. E. SAGAR, M. R. SCHORLEY, A. S. CARR AND S. F. ACREE, *J. Res. Natl. Bur. Standards*, 35 (1945) 521.
53 J. M. VANDENBELT, C. HENRICH AND S. G. VAN DEN BERG, *Anal. Chem.*, 26 (1954) 726

Chapter V

Infrared Spectra of Compounds of Biological Interest

L. J. BELLAMY

Ministry of Aviation, Waltham Abbey, Essex (Great Britain)

1. Introduction

(a) The origins and uses of infrared spectra

The infrared region of the electromagnetic spectrum extends from just above one micron (= 10,000 Å = 10,000 cm^{-1}) to about 500 microns (= 20 cm^{-1}) where the microwave region begins. Only a relatively small part of this range is of any direct interest to the organic or biochemist; this is the region 10,000 to 400 cm^{-1} in which molecular vibrations occur. The remainder of the infrared region is very difficult of access and is primarily of importance to physicists who are interested in the rotational spectra of small molecules.

When infrared radiation is passed through a molecule a number of individual frequencies are selectively absorbed, so that when the radiation is dispersed and analysed a complex series of absorption bands emerges. This is due to the fact that the vibrational frequencies of the various linkages present lie in the infrared region and these absorb energy in being raised to higher vibrational levels. In theory all these bands arise from molecular motions involving the molecule as a whole, but in practice it is found that many structural units are sufficiently insulated from the rest to give rise to characteristic absorptions of their own. These can be assigned to specific motions of the link such as for example to a stretching motion of an XH bond and always recur in the same general region of the spectrum whenever the individual group is present. In the spectrum of a complex organic compound there are of course many other bands which do arise from coupled motions involving several atoms and the origin of these cannot be decided with any certainty. Nevertheless the final spectrum is a very highly characteristic physical property of the compound and comparisons between the spectra of natural and synthetic samples are widely used as a final proof of structure. Only two reservations need to be made in regarding the infrared spectrum

References p. 167

as a unique characterisation of the molecule. The spectrometer cannot distinguish between *d* and *l* isomers although there are differences between these and the *dl* mixtures. However, when more than one asymmetric centre is present it is possible to distinguish between normal and *allo* forms. The other limitation is in respect of large polymeric materials containing repeating chain units. As the spectrum is so largely derived from the vibrations of small groups of atoms, the spectra tend towards a common pattern when a large number of common units make up the chain. The differences between the spectra of two similar polymers of different molecular weight are therefore very small.

The fact that characteristic group frequencies occur, leads directly to the most widespread application of infrared work in the study of large molecules, *i.e.* to the determination of the presence or absence of a variety of different structural units in an unknown compound. However, as these group frequencies often show some sensitivity to the nature of their internal or external environment it is also possible to obtain much valuable information on such topics as hydrogen bonding and chelation, crystal forces, steric arrangements etc. Through the use of polarised radiation it is also possible to obtain data on the relative orientation of bonds in crystals or in fibres.

So far infrared techniques have not been as fully exploited in the biochemical field as they have in basic organic chemistry, and this is probably partly due to the difficulties of working in aqueous solutions. However, within certain specialised fields a number of distinct advances have been made. The discussion which follows will concentrate primarily upon applications of I.R. spectroscopy in structural work on natural products as this has been the main application so far. Some account will also be given of quantitative studies, and applications to studies on the chemistry of bacteria will also be discussed. Within the scope of a broad review of this kind it is not possible to quote every individual reference and these have frequently been omitted where a reference to a detailed review is available. One of the most interesting sources in this field is the recent symposium on Biological Applications of Infrared Spectroscopy held by the New York Academy of Sciences at which a wide range of interesting papers was presented[1]. This should be consulted for further details on specific uses.

(b) Techniques and limitations of infrared spectroscopic methods

It is not intended that this section should deal in any detail with instrumentation, as this topic has been briefly reviewed in two previous articles on biological applications[2,3], and is very well covered in the standard texts[4,5]. In general the biochemist is very much more concerned with the significance of the spectra than with the details of the manner in which they were obtained. However, there are a number of limitations of the method which are imposed partly by the instrumental techniques and partly by external factors such as solubility effects etc. It is important that the biochemist should be aware of these in order that he may select his experimental conditions to the best advantage, and to ensure that the subsequent interpretation of the spectrum is not invalidated by extraneous factors.

(i) Frequency measurements

Glass is opaque over most of the infrared region and it is therefore necessary to use alternative materials for prisms, windows, cells etc. Unfortunately no single material is both transparent and highly dispersive over the whole range required, and for some purposes it is necessary to use a range of different materials. The commonest choice is sodium chloride which makes excellent prisms transmitting over the range 10,000 to 650 cm^{-1}, and this is used in nearly all commercial instruments. The dispersion in the low frequency range is excellent and these frequencies can be obtained with high precision. However, in the high-frequency region the dispersion is relatively poor and for detailed work on such problems as hydrogen bonding where one is often concerned to measure relatively small frequency shifts, it is necessary to employ either a lithium fluoride prism or preferably a grating/prism combination. Gratings give excellent dispersive characteristics, but must always be used in combination with prisms or filters to remove the overlapping higher orders. Similarly for work on such problems as the strengths of metal carbon bonds in chelate compounds it is necessary to employ a potassium bromide or caesium bromide prism which is capable of transmitting longer wavelengths than the rocksalt prism.

For most general purposes a single rocksalt prism instrument will suffice but it should be appreciated that the precision with which the higher frequencies can be measured is limited. Attention must also be paid to the instrument temperature. The refractive index of the prism is sensitive to changes of temperature and this can lead to inaccurate frequency measurements. This becomes particularly important when studying small points of difference between two similar spectra as in work on bacteria and viruses. Finally it should be noted that the solvent or phase in which the specimen is studied will often alter the precise frequencies found, so that it is important in comparison work to keep such factors constant.

(ii) Intensity measurements

Comparative intensity measurements for such purposes as quantitative analysis can be made with reasonable precision, provided the same instrument is used throughout. Wherever possible, it is desirable also to use the same cells and ancillary equipment. However, due to instrumental factors such as

References p. 167

the quality of optics, their alignment and the finite slit widths, the measurement of absolute intensity values is extremely difficult. It is not therefore possible to transfer concentration calibration curves from one instrument to another even if it is of the same make and design. Absolute intensities have not been of very great interest in the past, but recent work suggests that in some cases they may be of equal, or even greater value for structural diagnosis than the frequencies themselves. When sufficient data of this kind is available the biologist will wish to measure this factor also. For this purpose the simplest approach is through a very high resolution instrument. It now seems likely that reproducible values will be obtained in general when the spectral slit width is about one fifth of the width of the band to be measured. This can now be obtained using prism/grating instruments, and it is likely that these will gradually supersede the present conventional types of spectrometer.

(iii) The effects of solvents and of change of phase

Ideally all infrared spectra should be measured in the vapour phase where the compounds studied are free from the effects of interactions with other molecules. With large molecules this is rarely possible, and these must be studied in solution or in the liquid or solid states. This at once introduces serious limitations. All solvents absorb in the infrared so that some parts of the spectrum will inevitably be obscured by solvent absorptions. At the cost of some trouble this can be overcome by studying the spectra in two different solvents such as carbon tetrachloride and carbon bisulphide which absorb in different regions. However, the number of solvents which are transparent over wide regions is small, and the most suitable materials are all nonpolar. When a compound is insoluble in anything but a polar solvent one is usually limited to relatively small spectral regions in which the solvent has a window. In such cases also, interactions between solvent and solute can cause appreciable frequency shifts of the bands due to the more polar linkages. The OH stretching absorption of phenol for example occurs at 3654 cm^{-1} in hexane solution, at 3559 cm^{-1} in benzene and at 3344 cm^{-1} in ether, where strong hydrogen bonding occurs. Tables of the absorption bands of all the common solvents have been given by several authors[6-8] and are valuable in the selection of suitable ones.

When the compound is studied in the liquid or solid phases, the same problems of molecular interaction arise. Phenol for example is strongly associated in the liquid state, and this must be allowed for in any interpretation of the spectrum. Solids are normally studied as mulls in paraffin oil or as pressed discs in potassium bromide. The first suffers from the disadvantage that parts of the spectrum are obscured by the strong CH absorptions of the paraffin oil, but this can be overcome by running a second spectrum in perfluoroparaffins. The pressed disc technique is superficially very attractive in having none of these disadvantages but has real difficulties of its own. Such discs are remarkably difficult to keep free from adsorbed water which can associate with the compound being studied. Differences in the spectra also occur in some cases due to variations in the degree of grinding of the specimen. In carboxylic acids for example, the spectra change when one passes from discs made from coarsely ground material to those prepared from very finely divided products. In the first case the acids remain as small aggregates in their normal dimeric form, but in the second each molecule of acid is surrounded by the KBr lattice and this leads to frequency shifts in some bands.

Aqueous solutions present a particularly difficult problem for infrared studies because of the very intense solvent absorptions. Some useful work has nevertheless been done in this field through the combined use of normal and heavy water which absorb in different regions. For work of this kind the usual materials of cell construction such as sodium chloride are of course unsuitable and one must use alternatives such as silver chloride or for more limited frequency ranges calcium fluoride or synthetic sapphires.

(iv) Difference spectroscopy

Almost all modern commercial spectrometers operate on a double beam principle in which atmospheric absorptions due to carbon dioxide and water vapour are cancelled out by measuring the difference between two beams which have identical atmospheric path lengths. In principle this arrangement can also be used to cancel solvent absorptions where these give rise to interference[9,10]. This is best done through the use of a variable path length cell in the reference beam adjusted to give an identical path length in both beams. This very useful device must be used with understanding or it will give misleading results. With difference spectroscopy the detector is measuring the differences in energy between the two beams, and in the region of the strong solvent bands the total energy emerging may be very small indeed. It is then possible to obtain spectra in which bands appear to be absent because the energy available is too small to activate the recorder. Wherever possible it is wise to run a single beam recording of the sample in the solvent at the chosen thickness, using a standard known signal in the other beam. It is then possible to evaluate the actual energy available in any spectral region and to decide the instrumental conditions required if informative spectra are to be obtained.

2. Infrared methods of structure determination

(a) General

It has been found experimentally that some linkages vibrate at frequencies which are essentially independent of the residual structure to which they

References p. 167

are attached. These produce the characteristic group frequencies which are so widely used in the study of organic compounds. The most useful of these vibrations are those involving the stretching or bending motions of hydrogen atoms or those from the stretching of multiple bonds. The first give invariant frequencies because of the light mass of the hydrogen atom in relation to the element to which it is joined. The second group do so because the short bonds involved lead to high frequencies well away from those of other bonds; they are therefore less subject to coupling effects. These two classes comprise the major effective group frequencies. However this is by no means as restrictive as might at first appear. Not only are there characteristic frequencies for each type of XH link, (OH, NH, CH, etc.) but further subdivisions allow the separation of different valency states. Olefinic and acetylenic CH groups can be recognized separately from alkyl groups for example, and it is usually possible in this way to identify the various types of double bonds or to recognise the presence of strained structures. Further subdivisions allow the differentiation of alkyl groups attached to different elements. By making use of the XH deformation modes it is also possible to identify the substitution pattern in aromatic or heterocyclic compounds. Similarly the multiple bond range includes not only the various subdivisions of carbonyl and olefinic bonds but also such groups as P=O, S=O, SO_2, N=O, NO_2 etc. along with azides, isocyanates, acetylenes and similar structures.

The frequency ranges in which these various group frequencies fall can only be roughly defined. Thus, although most tertiary amides show their carbonyl absorption near 1660 cm^{-1} it is possible to devise structures in which the electronic environment is so altered that the frequency rises to 1790 cm^{-1} which would be more appropriate for a vinyl ester or strained ring lactone[11]. Correlation charts and tables therefore refer to the usual positions and divergences from them must be expected. In order that one may be in a proper position to assess the likelihood of abnormal frequencies it is necessary to have some understanding of the origins of group frequencies and of the reasons for their displacement. For this reason this topic is discussed in the following section before any attempt is made to illustrate the many applications of group frequency work.

Apart from the vibrations referred to above, nearly all of which occur in the high frequency region, there are a number of correlations available for single bond modes which have some more limited usefulness. Thus the C—O stretching mode is sensitive to the masses of the attached substituents so that the frequency varies widely. However, when these masses are kept constant the frequencies also become more stable. It is therefore possible to recognise the band arising from this vibration in primary, secondary, and tertiary alcohols, as it occurs in a different position in each. This principle can be further extended to the study of specific groups in an invariant environment within a specialised series. Thus many individual bands can be recognised in steroid or carbohydrate structures which could not safely be identified in materials which were completely unknown. Some examples of limited but very valuable correlations of this type will be given in later sections.

(b) The origins of group frequencies and the influence of the internal environment

(i) XH vibrations

The approximate position of an absorption band can be estimated from Hook's law of simple harmonic motion. This states that the frequency

$$\nu = \frac{1}{2\pi c}\sqrt{\frac{f}{\mu}}$$

where c is the velocity of light, f is the force constant (which measures the springiness of the bond) and μ is the reduced mass given by the formula

$$\frac{m_1 \times m_2}{m_1 + m_2}$$

where m_1 and m_2 are the effective masses of the atoms constituting the link. If it is assumed that all XH links have about the same force constants, a frequency of about 3000 cm^{-1} for the CH stretching band can be derived in this way and this agrees well with the experimental findings. However, if f is constant, variations will arise only from alterations in μ, the reduced mass. It is obvious that a change of H for D will alter ν by a factor of $1/\sqrt{2}$ and this provides a most useful way in which XH bonds can be identified. However, it is also clear that changes in the mass of the X element will have only a small effect. On passing along the top row of the periodic table for example $\sqrt{\mu}$ changes from $\sqrt{12/13}$ to $\sqrt{19/20}$ which will have only a slight lowering effect upon the frequency. In fact as one passes from CH through NH and OH to HF the observed frequency rises sharply from 3000 cm^{-1} to nearly 4000 cm^{-1}. This must therefore be due to changes in the force constant f arising from the different chemical nature of the elements rather than from any mass effect.

The sharp shortening of the XH bonds in this series and the consequent rise in the frequencies, contrasts with the reasonably constant values for the F—F, O—O, N—N and C—C bond distances. It arises from the inductive effects due to the differences in nuclear charge. In the series CH, NH, OH, and FH the X element is in each case in a state of sp^3 hybridisation with the

References p. 167

four electron pairs tetrahedrally disposed about the nucleus. That pair which forms the XH link is therefore subject in the case of fluorine to a nuclear attraction corresponding to +7 units, whereas in the CH link the corresponding electrons are attracted by only +4 units. It is not therefore surprising that the link shortens in HF, whereas in the F—F to C—C series the links are of similar lengths because the bonding electrons are now subjected to attraction from both sides, and the charge alterations play no part.

Very similar effects operate as one passes down a column of the periodic table. Although the nuclear charge is now constant the nucleus is progressively screened from the bonding electrons by successive filled shells. The effective charge is therefore reduced. The result of these two effects is shown in Fig. 1, in which the changes in bond lengths and of frequencies as

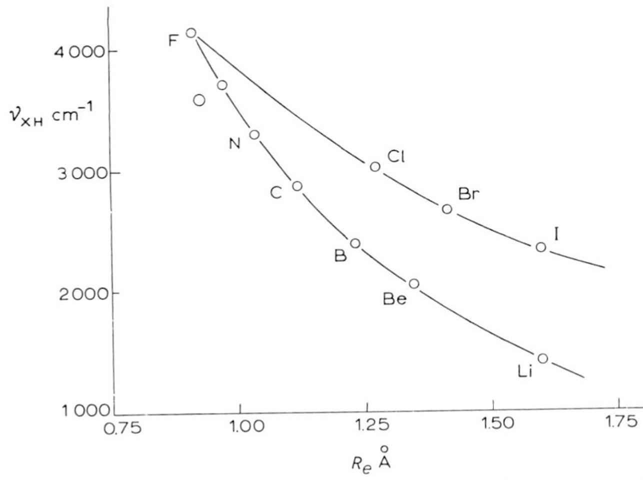

Fig. 1. Relationship between radii and stretching frequencies of XH-links.

one passes either across or down the periodic table are illustrated. The frequencies used are uncorrected values for the radicles but suffice for this comparison. It follows therefore that each element will show its own characteristic XH stretching frequency, determined by its position in the periodic table and the consequent electronegativity; the inductive effect rather than any influence of mass being the controlling factor.

The basic XH frequency range will then be determined by the element X, but as the nuclear charge of X also varies slightly with the valency state a further subdivision of this range is to be expected which will characterise the separate states. In CH compounds for example there are sufficient differences between the stretching frequencies of alkyl, olefinic and acetylinic

CH bonds to enable each type to be identified readily. This can be most easily pictured in terms of the hybridisation changes which occur. As the bonding orbital from the carbon atom to the hydrogen changes in character from sp^3 in alkyl compounds to sp in acetylenes, the orbit shortens due to the change of shape. As the hybridisation of the hydrogen atom remains essentially pure s, it must move towards the carbon atom to achieve maximum overlap. The CH link then shortens and the frequency rises.

Finally, as a second order effect, the CH frequencies of alkyl groups change with the electronegativity of the element to which they are attached. In CH_3X compounds for example the carbon orbital directed towards the X atom is not a pure sp^3 hybrid as the proportions of s and p character are slightly modified by the electronegative properties of X. In consequence the orbits directed towards the hydrogen atoms are modified also. Thus if the CX orbit acquires an increased p character the CH links shorten as the carbon hydrogen orbits must then take on a slightly increased s character. This effect finds useful applications in the recognition of $C—CH_3$ groups etc. and in the differentiation of CH_2 groups adjacent to carbonyl links.

(ii) Multiple bonds

Multiple bond frequencies are also sensitive to the inductive effects of the substituents. However, the overall direction in which these operate depends upon the initial polarity of the bond. With linkages such as the carbonyl group and others with an $^+X{=}O^-$ dipole, an increase in the electronegativity of the substituents raises the stretching frequency because the initial polarity of the bond is reduced. However, with C=C links and other non-polar structures an electronegative substituent increases the bond polarity and the frequency falls.

These effects are often accompanied by conjugation and mesomeric effects. The presence of an $\alpha\beta$ double bond or of an element such as nitrogen or oxygen carrying a suitably oriented lone pair of electrons leads to some delocalisation of the π-electrons of the initial double bond with a consequent increase in polarity and a fall in frequency. The final frequency of a carbonyl group is thus the resultant of two opposed effects. In esters the inductive effect predominates over the mesomeric so that they absorb about 20 cm^{-1} above the frequencies of the corresponding ketones. The influence of the mesomerism is, however, shown by a comparison with the frequencies of vinyl esters in which this factor is much reduced. These absorb near 1790 cm^{-1}. In amides the opposite is true; mesomerism predominates over induction and the carbonyl frequencies are low. The final values depend upon the degree of substitution of the nitrogen atom as this determines to some extent the availability of the lone pair electrons for delocalisation. However, they nearly always show the C=O frequency below 1700 cm^{-1}.

References p. 167

It is the interplay of these electrical effects which is responsible for the distinctive frequency ranges of the various classes of carbonyl compounds and which allow us to differentiate between esters, ketones, anhydrides, amides etc. However, it is important to realise that in an abnormal electrical environment these same factors will cause the group frequencies to move well out of the usual range. It is possible for example to prepare amides such as N-acetyl tetrazole in which the normal mesomeric influence of the nitrogen atom is very largely suppressed because of the heterocyclic ring resonance. The frequency of the carbonyl group then rises to 1790 cm^{-1} under the influence of the electronegativity of the nitrogen atom. This is of course well outside the published range for an amide frequency. Similarly abnormally low carbonyl frequencies occur in compounds such as 4-pyridone in which the mesomeric effect is enhanced by contribution from an aromatic type canonical form. These then absorb below 1600 cm^{-1}. These examples stress the need for the careful use of group frequencies. The environment of the group present must be considered in the light of these factors so that the likelihood of any abnormalities can be assessed; otherwise the indiscriminate use of group frequency tables and charts can only lead to serious errors.

(iii) Ring strain

Strained ring systems are often found in natural products, and the infrared frequencies of the normal vibrations are then found to be changed. This is valuable in enabling such systems to be identified. The frequency changes arise in part from the mechanical consequences of angle change but are also to be ascribed to the hybridisation changes. Thus in a six membered ring system C=C absorptions occur at their normal frequency near 1650 cm^{-1}. As the ring angles are closed down in smaller rings the carbon–carbon bonding orbits take on an increased p character and the stretching frequency falls sharply. The corresponding CH stretching frequencies rise as a result of the increase in s character of the remaining carbon orbits. When the double bond is exocyclic, as in methylene cyclopentane or in cyclopentanone, the frequency rises with ring strain as it is the ring C—C links whose orbits take on an increased p character, and the s character of the orbits of the exocyclic double bond is therefore increased.

(iv) Field effects

Smaller changes in carbonyl and similar frequencies are sometimes found in situations in which a polar oxygen atom is near in space to some other element such as chloride. A mutual induction of charges then leads to a frequency rise in both the C=O and C—Cl vibrations. This effect is principally of use in the identification of structural isomers. It is for example possible to use it in the differentiation of equatorial and polar α-halogen substitution in the sterol series. Equatorial α-halogen substituents cause the carbonyl frequency to rise above the normal value whereas no change occurs with axial substituents which are further removed in space from the oxygen atom.

(v) Mechanical effects

The above are the main electrical effects which are responsible for the small differences which allow one to detect and interpret the exact position of an absorption band in terms of the surrounding structure. In addition to these, and overlaying them, we have the effects of mechanical coupling and of electrical interaction. Insofar as the XH and multiple bond frequencies are concerned these are not often very important. However, certain of these frequencies are coupled so that the X=Y=Z type group frequencies for example are due to symmetrical and asymmetrical motions of the whole group. Carbonyl frequencies are also influenced by coupling effects in amides, whilst mass effects which are small with most substituents become significant with hydrogen. There is therefore a carbonyl frequency shift on going from a normal to a deuterated aldehyde which is directly due to the mass effect. However, mass effects play a major part in determining the frequency shifts of many single bonded vibrations and the correlations for these should only be used for larger units of structure where the mass effect is eliminated by the constancy of the surroundings.

Other disturbing effects such as Fermi resonance can result in the splitting of a single band into twin peaks. With polar bonds this can often be recognised for what it is by a change of solvent which will often shift the fundamental away from the band with which it is interacting. A marked change in the relative intensities follows.

Some splitting effects can be turned to good account as in the case of methyl substituents on a carbon atom. A single methyl group on a carbon gives a sharp absorption band at 1375 cm^{-1}. This splits into a doublet of equal intensities when an isopropyl group is present and shows a further change when a third methyl group is placed upon the same carbon atom.

3. The interpretation of infrared spectra

The factors which control group frequencies have been discussed at some length in the preceding section because it is essential that these be properly understood before any reliance can be placed upon the empirical correlation data on which structural diagnosis is based. It will be seen that a great deal of data of variable reliability is presented within an infrared spectrum and in unknown compounds some discrimination is required in deciding what

References p. 167

weight is appropriate for any individual assignment. This involves a consideration of the type of vibration involved and of the probable nature of its immediate environment, along with a knowledge of the general reliability of the correlation data on which the identification is made. This data has been fully documented in a number of textbooks[12, 13] and is also summarised in many correlation charts. It cannot be described at length here but many examples of the more important correlations in biological compounds will be given in the following pages. It will be found that many of the correlations are based on the study of widely different types of compound and these are generally reliable. Others are often put forward for specific classes only and should not be trusted too far outside the series for which they were designed. In hydrocarbons for example many of the skeletal frequencies of groups such as the isopropyl unit can be recognised but it would be dangerous to use these with overmuch confidence in the field of natural products. Any initial data which is available as to the general class of compound under study or even a knowledge of the elemental composition will help considerably in improving the reliability of identifications.

This point is perhaps best illustrated by an example. Fig. 2a shows the infrared spectrum of the sodium salt of pyruvic acid. If this represented an entirely unknown material only a very limited amount of reliable deductions would be possible. Starting at the high frequency end of the spectrum it can be seen that only weak bands appear in the CH stretching region and that these occur below 3000 cm^{-1}. It follows with reasonable certainty that there are only saturated CH links present and that the compound does not contain OH, NH or other XH links. Also the low intensity of the CH band in relation to the remainder of the spectrum suggests that the alkyl groups are few in number. In the 1700 cm^{-1} region a carbonyl band appears at 1720 cm^{-1}. This is certainly a carbonyl absorption and it is in the appropriate position for a ketone. However, this is less certain as it could equally well be due to some other type of C=O whose frequency has been shifted into the 1720 cm^{-1} region by electrical effects. It could for example equally well be an $\alpha\beta$ unsaturated ester. Some support for the ketonic assignment is given by the absence of CH aldehyde bands and by the absence of the strong bands in the 1250 and 1000 cm^{-1} region which also appear in esters. This then is likely but not certain. Finally there are strong bands near 1600 and 1450 cm^{-1}. Pairs of this type are given by ionised carboxylic acids and by nitro groups when attached to carbon atoms. No certain differentiation between these is possible from the spectrum alone. No other bands in the spectrum provide any further information, as that at 1460 cm^{-1} only confirms the alkyl CH assignment.

On the basis of these data it might be possible to make an intelligent guess that a pyruvic acid salt was a likely possibility but no certain identification

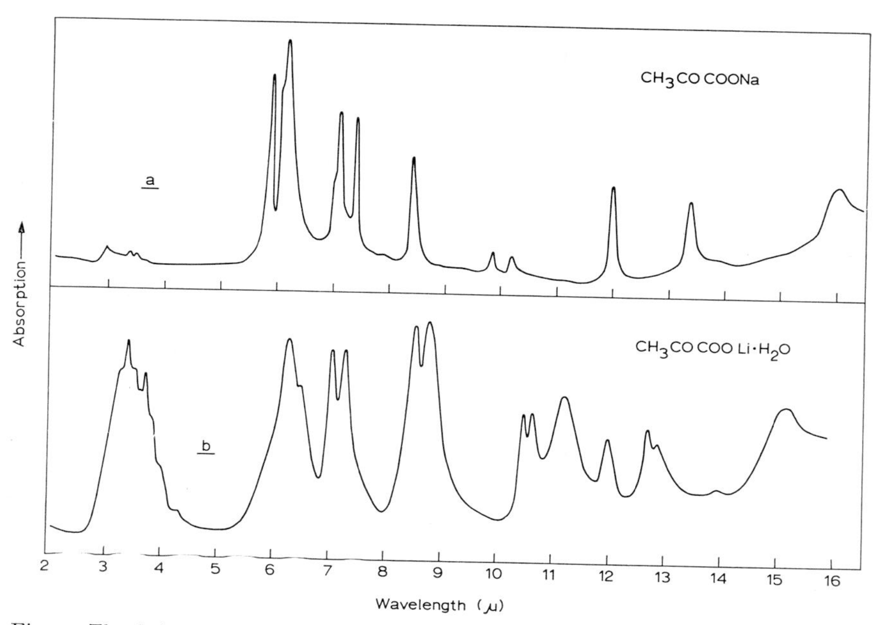

Fig. 2. The infrared spectra of sodium pyruvate (a) and lithium pyruvate monohydrate (b).

could be made until the spectrum was compared with an authentic specimen.

Spectrum (2b) is that of hydrated lithium pyruvate and illustrates a different type of use of spectral diagnosis. In this case the composition is known, and one is seeking instead to find out why its chemical behaviour is so different from that which would be expected. A comparison of the two spectra shows at once that the ketonic carbonyl band has disappeared from the spectrum of the hydrate and that a new strong band has appeared in the 3300 cm^{-1} region. This shows that OH groups are present which must have been formed by the addition of water across the carbonyl double bond. This can be confirmed by a comparison with the low frequency region which is now much more useful as the groups present are known. Thus it is possible to recognise the appearance of the C—O stretching band at 1150 cm^{-1} and of the OH bending absorptions at 1551 and 897 cm^{-1}. These could not be identified with such certainty were it not known that many other groups which could absorb in these regions were absent.

This example is of some biological interest as the lithium salt of hydroxy pyruvic acid behaves similarly[14]. In the discussion which follows on special classes of biologically important compounds many other applications of group frequencies are illustrated. However, it is important to realise that

References p. 167

the reliability of identifications depends in part on the type of vibration involved, and in part on how much is known of the basic structure. In carbohydrates, and in sterols for example, it is often possible to make positive assignments for absorption bands which in an entirely unknown material could at best be only tentatively recognized.

If the material studied is already known it is of course possible to resolve any doubts as to the correctness of the assignments by a comparison with an authentic spectrum. Large commercial collections of spectra are available from a number of sources and there are of course many others scattered throughout the literature. A particularly useful compilation is that of Clark[15] which lists references to published spectra of biologically important compounds. Other useful compilations are the Beilstein type indices, supplied with the various volumes of spectrographic abstracts prepared by the British Ministry of Supply[16] and the publication of Hershenson[17] which gives literature references for some 10,000 spectra.

4. Correlation work on biologically important materials

(a) Carbohydrates

A number of useful reviews are available on the application of infra-red methods to carbohydrate chemistry. In particular that of Barker, Bourne and Whiffen[18] discusses this subject in considerably greater detail than is possible here. Other useful papers and reviews are those of Kuhn[19] which gives the spectra of 79 carbohydrates, Whiffen[20], Neely[21] and Konkin *et al.*[22].

Carbohydrates are normally studied as mulls or as potassium bromide discs, and the spectra need special care in their interpretation for this reason. Thus in mulls some marked differences are found between polymorphic forms of the same material due to crystal lattice interactions whilst in discs interactions with the alkali halide lattice also lead to spectral changes. Despite these limitations a number of extremely useful chemical applications have been worked out.

Applications of standard group frequency methods are not very informative in this series. All compounds contain OH and C—O—C links leading to very intense absorptions in the 3300 cm^{-1} and 1200–1000 cm^{-1} regions, and these are not of much value except in special cases such as in the study of the strengths of hydrogen bonds which lengthen the OH link and lead to frequency shifts. However, these correlations become more valuable with sugar derivatives. Unionised carboxylic acids show characteristics bands due to the carbonyl group near 1735 cm^{-1} and a complex pattern in the 3000–2000 cm^{-1} range derived from the carboxylic OH groups. Ionised acids behave differently and absorb near 1600 cm^{-1}. Similarly, characteristic features of acetyl, acetamido, and benzoyl derivatives, enable such substituents to be recognised. Other useful correlations are available for oxime links, acetals, amino groups, and for sulphonated polysaccharides.

However, the most useful applications of infrared in this field are those utilising special limited correlations which have been worked out specifically for carbohydrates and which are not otherwise generally applicable. In the glucopyranoses for example there is a deformation vibration of the hydrogen atom at C_1 which is sensitive to the steric arrangement but insensitive to the nature of the other substituents. In α-glucopyranoses it occurs at 844 cm^{-1}, but in the β compounds it shifts to 891 cm^{-1}. Parallel but slightly different correlations exist for other pyranose sugars. α-Galactopyranoses absorb at 825 cm^{-1} and α-mannopyranoses at 833 cm^{-1}. The corresponding β derivatives absorb at 983 and 895 cm^{-1}. These latter two sugars can also be differentiated from glucopyranoses by the presence of an absorption at 875 cm^{-1} which is due to a deformation of the hydrogen atoms at positions 2 and 4 in galactopyranose and in mannopyranose. It is independent of configuration or of substitution but is of course absent from the spectra of glucopyranoses. Other useful absorptions of this type are those arising from breathing modes of the tetrahydropyran ring system. α-Glucopyranoses give a band of this type near 818 cm^{-1} and it is likely that derivatives of galactopyranose and of mannopyranose do so too. However, this correlation is best applied only to unsubstituted sugars, partly because of the proximity of the CH bands referred to above, and partly due to the fact that methyl esters and ethers also absorb hereabouts. A second band of similar origin is found near 766 cm^{-1} in α-glucopyranoses, which diminishes in intensity and moves to 774 cm^{-1} in the β-derivatives. In the α-xylopyranones the band is at 750 cm^{-1} and is wholly absent in the β-series. Similar correlations have been studied for the hexoses arabino, galacto and mannopyranoses.

These correlations are extremely useful for the detection of some of the finer points of structural detail within the sugars. However, these bands along with others also provide a pattern of bands in the 950–700 cm^{-1} range which can be used as a whole for the differentiation of the different polymer types. It is therefore directly possible to recognise from the spectra each of the six major polymer types by the overall pattern in this range. Thus dextrans can be differentiated from cellulose or from any of the other main polymer types such as nigeran or luteose.

This aspect has proved particularly valuable in the identification of polysaccharides isolated from bacteria. 57 samples of pneumococcal polysaccharides were isolated by Levine *et al.*[23] who showed that the organisms could be typed in this way, and that the polysaccharides could be divided into four main classes on the basis of their chemical composition. Many specific

References p. 167

identifications such as the identification of D-glycero-D-galactoheptose in the somatic antigen of *Chromobacterium violaceum* have also been achieved by infrared techniques. Dextrans from bacterial sources have also been studied and can be further sub-classified on the basis of an infrared estimation of the proportion of 1:3 links.

Many other examples could be quoted in this field, and further references are available in the review by Norris of infrared applications to bacterial chemistry[24].

(b) Steroids

The infrared spectra of the steroids have been more intensively studied than those of any other organic family with the possible exception of the hydrocarbons. Over 3000 individual steroids have been examined and characterised in this way and two volumes of an atlas of steroid spectra are already available[25]. The invariant steroid skeleton containing a limited number of polar groups offers an almost ideal field for the application of group frequencies and these can be refined within the series to allow of the differentiation of stereoisomeric compounds. The low-frequency fingerprint region between 1350 and 650 cm^{-1} has also been studied in some detail and it has been shown that most of the strong bands in this region can be assigned either to polar groups or to vibrations of C—C and CH links immediately adjacent to the active substituents. It is therefore possible to make very much more use of this region in diagnostic work than is normally possible. These specialised correlations are summarised in the atlases referred to above[25], and in a paper by Jones and Herling[26]. Cole has also written a valuable review[27].

Because of the great selectivity of the method within the series, frequency differences of even a few wave numbers become significant and can be employed in differentiating between alternative possibilities. This of course makes it all the more important that the solvents used should be the same as those on which the correlation is based and Jones *et al.* have actually provided separate carbonyl frequency correlation tables for both solutions in carbon tetrachloride, and in chloroform.

In the high frequency region a study of absorptions in the 3650 to 3200 cm^{-1} region allows the identification of hydroxyl groups and the nature and extent of any hydrogen bonding can be evaluated. Bands in the 3100 to 3000 cm^{-1} range denote the presence of unsaturated CH groups in olefines, or in aromatic rings, whilst saturated CH links in methyl or methylene groups show up just below 3000 cm^{-1}. The region of carbonyl absorption stretches from 1793 cm^{-1} in the case of certain lactones to about 1650 cm^{-1} in doubly conjugated ketones. Within this overall range correlations for 150 different types of carbonyl situations are available. Many of these of course overlap so that for any given frequency a number of possibilities are given. Some progress has been made in the further differentiation through intensity measurements, but usually this is done by the examination of other regions of the spectrum. Esters for example are differentiated from ketones by the characteristic C—O stretching bands in the range 1250 to 1000 cm^{-1} and these also are closely subdivided so that a good deal of further detail as to the position of the ester group and its environment can be obtained. Similarly the "scissoring" motions of methylene groups which normally appear in the 1465 cm^{-1} region have been studied in relation to small alterations in the immediate environment. When adjacent to a ketonic group this band falls within the range 1440 to 1400 cm^{-1} and its precise position can then be related to the location of the carbonyl group. Thus the 2-methylene group of 1-ketones appears at 1438 cm^{-1}, but that of a 23-methylene-22-ketone at 1406 cm^{-1}. The frequencies of the methyl group bending bands are also slightly sensitive to their position so that for example angular methyl groups can be differentiated from ring or side chain substituents. In the case of C=C double bonds of olefinic links or of aromatic rings a parallel series of correlation tables is available listing nearly 70 different absorption types within the range 1697 to 1490 cm^{-1}.

These correlations are those which are most commonly employed in identification work but they are capable of a much greater degree of refinement in relation to the significance of small shifts as long as it is known that the material is a member of the steroid series. This reflects the mass of background data available in this series. In addition to these, the fingerprint region below 1350 cm^{-1} which is normally of limited use, can now be extensively employed. Substantial tables of correlations are available for this region which list characteristic band patterns for various substituents even though the actual vibrations involved are themselves complex and cannot be assigned to any specific molecular motion. As an example of this, 17-keto,5-α steroids show a series of 9 characteristic bands between 1208 and 700 cm^{-1} all of which fall within narrow ranges.

One of the most important uses of the fingerprint region is in the differentiation of stereoisomers. The spectral changes in this region resulting from even small alterations in the relative arrangements of polar substituents are very remarkable as can be seen from Fig. 3. This shows the changes which result from the inversion of the OH configuration at the C_3 position in 3-hydroxyandrostan-17-one, and also from a change in the relative configuration of rings A and B. The correlations mainly used for this purpose are those involving either the O stretching motions of either CH or ester groups. In acetates for example a band at 1240 cm^{-1} is split into a number of components in certain steroids and it has been shown that the band is single when the acetate group is attached equatorially but complex when the attachment is axial. Similar differences between equatorial and axial

References p. 167

hydroxyl groups are found near 1000 cm^{-1}. It is also possible to obtain information on stereochemical factors in the cases of α-halogen substituted ketones, as in equatorial arrangements the carbonyl frequency is raised about 25 cm^{-1} as a result of the field effect described earlier. This does not operate in axial conformations and the frequency is then normal. Some

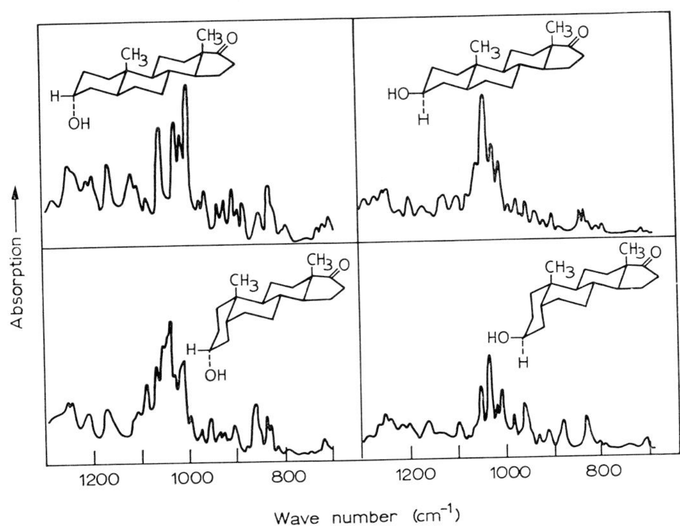

Fig. 3. Spectra in the fingerprint region of various conformations of the same basic sterol structure (This drawing is reproduced through the courtesy of Dr. R. N. Jones).

tentative correlations are also available which relate the C-halogen stretching frequencies and CD stretching frequencies to the particular conformation present, but these are less well established.

The commonest application of all these correlations is of course in the study of the structures of pure single sterols isolated from natural products. However, a great deal of work of more direct biological interest has also been done on the identification of steroids produced in animals, and in studies of the possible relationships between the pattern of steroids present in the urine and the incidence of specific diseases. Indeed much of the impetus for early studies of sterols was provided by the work of Dobriner and his colleagues who carried on very extensive studies on the relationship between steroid metabolism and pathological conditions. This work was basically aimed at a study of any possible relationship between the presence of any abnormal steroids in urine and the presence of carcinomas of various types, but it has since expanded in many different ways. Such studies are of course very dependent upon the availability of efficient concentration and purification techniques which will allow the isolation of individual steroids in a pure state. Such methods as countercurrent distribution and various forms of chromatography have been widely used and have been reviewed in relation to their usefulness in infrared work by Rosenkrantz[28]. Special techniques for handling the very small samples produced have also been worked out. Despite the formidable difficulties of work of this kind, some very substantial achievements have already resulted. Studies on the presence of aldosterone in urine are of importance in such fields as the persistent elevation of blood pressure. Infrared studies have successfully shown this material to be present in cases of cardiac failure in pregnant women, and in the urine of a nephrotic boy. The nature of excreted ketosteroids has also been much studied. Urine contains something like 42 different ketosteroids in very small amounts, each of which has a characteristic spectrum. Even 11 years ago Dobriner was able to demonstrate the presence amongst these of pure androsterone and much progress has been made since that time. A good example of current techniques of this kind is their use in following the changes in the pattern of neutral ketosteroids in the urine of arthritic patients which follows upon the administration of adrenosterone[29]. From the various chromatographic fractions the following metabolites were specifically identified; $\Delta^{9(11)}$ androsten-3α-ol-17-one, $\Delta^{9(11)}$ etiocholen-3α-ol-17-one, 11β-hydroxyandrosterone, etiocholan-3α-ol-11,17-dione, androstan-3α-ol-11,17-dione and etiocholane-3α-11β-diol-17-one.

(c) Antibiotics and drugs

Antibiotics usually present an entirely different problem to the cases considered above, in that they cover a very wide range of chemical types and initially little or nothing is known of their basic structure. The spectroscopist is then limited to the determination of the presence or absence of those structural units which give reliable group frequencies in all circumstances. However, when this approach is applied also to the products of chemical degradations the total information obtained is often very considerable and has led in a number of instances to a very much more rapid identification of the structure than would have otherwise been possible. In this connection the fact that so many antibiotics contain very remarkable chemical groupings has made this a particularly fertile field for infrared work.

A classic example of the use of infrared in this field is of course the identification of the β-lactam structure of penicillin. Earlier formulations of the structure of penicillin could not be reconciled with the appearance in the spectrum of a high-frequency carbonyl band which could only be due to a highly strained lactam ring. Syntheses of model compounds showed that these same frequencies were given consistently by β-lactam rings when

References p. 167

fused to other rings. This led to particular attention being directed at the β-lactam structure which of course proved to be correct[30].

Other examples of the use of infrared in this field are the identification of nitro groups and of aromatic rings in chloramphenicol, of allenic and acetylenic links in mycomycin, of the recognition of the chelated β-hydroxy $\alpha\beta$-unsaturated ketonic structure of tetracycline, and of the azo ester grouping in the tumor inhibiting material azaserine. The infrared identification of the hydrolysis product of this last compound as serine, led to its very rapid identification as O-diazoacetyl serine and this was confirmed by synthesis and a direct comparison of the spectra of the products. In this field infrared is best regarded as one of a number of tools available to the structural chemist but reviews of recent publications in this field show that it is one of the most valuable tools available for this purpose[31].

In addition, infrared finds many applications in pharmaceutical laboratories in the assay of antibiotic preparations, and many such uses have been described[32,33].

In the field of alkaloids and drugs the situation is again different. Here the broad chemical classification is usually known or can be confirmed by simple chemical tests such as the Koppanyi reaction for barbiturates. More often the problem is that of identification by a complete matching of the spectrum with that of some known product. In alkaloids, infrared has demonstrated the identity of the substances rhombine, monolupine and anagyrine which were isolated from different plant sources[34], and has for example been used in the stereochemical correlation of indole alkaloids. For the purposes of direct matching of spectra, several collections are available. Jones *et al.*[35] have published a comprehensive selection and this has been supplemented by a very full set of spectra issued by the World Health Organisation as an aid to rapid identification in connection with the suppression of the illicit drug traffic[36]. Numerous quantitative applications such as the determination of strychnine and quinine in elixirs have been described, many of which are listed in the reviews quoted above.

Comprehensive collections of the spectra of antihistamines and of barbiturates are also available so that once the class is known, positive identification is usually possible. In the case of the barbiturates, methods of analysis applicable to body fluids have been described. The spectrum obtained can then be classified as belonging to one or other of three major and six minor groups on the basis of the presence or absence of series of characteristic bands. The final identification is then relatively straightforward.

(d) Lipids and allied substances

Early attempts to study lipids in biological media by infrared methods met with little success. Thus Blout[37] was unable to distinguish any bands from lipids in a film of dried serum, owing to the masking effect of the strong protein absorptions. Attention was therefore turned to the analysis of degradation products, particularly in the characterisation of fatty acid residues, triglycerides etc. Here the technique can make a most useful contribution as can be seen from the amount of spectroscopic data presented in papers such as those of Crombie on the chemistry of lipids[38].

Saturated fatty acids themselves give remarkably similar spectra but there are differences in the spectra of the crystalline acids which arise from the rocking or twisting motions of the methylene groups. When these are in an all-*trans* arrangement as in crystals, the number of bands appearing between 1350 and 1180 cm^{-1} depends upon the chain length, which can thus be approximated in this way[39]. It is also possible to detect chain branching provided it is reasonably near to the carbonyl group. With unsaturated acids the presence of *trans* double bonds is shown by strong absorption near 965 cm^{-1}. Moreover the precise position of this absorption is sensitive to the extent and nature of any conjugation which is present. The situation here has been fully reviewed by O'Connor[40], and there seem to be reasonable possibilities for differentiating for example *cis,trans* (984 cm^{-1}) from *trans, trans* (980 cm^{-1}) or *trans, trans, trans* (995 cm^{-1}) systems.

The identification of *cis* double bonds is more difficult although in the absence of *trans* unsaturation they can be estimated from the intensities of the CH band at 3020 cm^{-1}.

Important differences also occur in the spectra of the various types of pure lipids. Sphingolipids for example contain a fatty acid amide group. This gives strong characteristic bands at 1655 and 1550 cm^{-1} which allows this group to be differentiated from other types of lipid. Similarly cephalins and lecithin have fatty acid ester groups which absorb at 1740 cm^{-1} by which they can be recognised. They can also be differentiated from each other by the presence of a band in cephalins at 1020 cm^{-1} which is not found in lecithins, whilst the latter have a characteristic band of their own at 970 cm^{-1}. These differences offer possibilities for the quantitative estimation of lipid mixtures and preliminary studies along these lines have given promising results. However, before they can be generally applied to unknown materials more information must be obtained on the possible variations of the extinction coefficients of these bands within the parent series.

The recognition that large spectral differences exist between various types of lipid has stimulated further work on the spectra of biological extracts themselves although a preliminary chromatographic separation is first required. Papers have recently appeared on lipids in tissues, in serum, and in bacteria which illustrate the great potentialities of this combined approach. In tissue work Schwarz[41] has described the infrared analysis of chromato-

References p. 167

graphic fractions of brain lipids. The first group was identified as containing mainly free cholesterol, the second as being galactose-containing sphingolipids, the third as cephalins and the fourth as lecithins. Parallel studies have been made by Freeman[42] on serum lipids. He emphasises the importance of I.R. analytical methods for the lipids of blood sera pointing out that the concentrations of lipoproteins for example, have been correlated statistically with the development of coronary artery disease and of atherosclerosis. Whilst at the present stage it cannot be claimed that infrared provides the rapid and accurate method which would be required for diagnostic work, these preliminary studies are at least highly encouraging in this respect.

In bacteria, Randall *et al.*[43] have concentrated on a study of the lipids from various strains of mycobacteria. After chromatographic separation characteristic spectral differences begin to appear which are related to the strain of the organism from which they were derived. Whilst all strains contain some common components it appears that some are specific to the strain itself and even to the sub-strains. It is thus possible to differentiate by spectral methods atypical tuberculosis from the normal human strain or from avian or bovine tuberculosis. There are also differences in for example the virulent and BCG strains of bovine tuberculosis. These separative and spectroscopic techniques are of course very time consuming and are still far from finding any general application in clinical diagnosis. Nevertheless the possibilities both for this and for the study of the basic changes in the chemistry of bacteria which follow mutation or changes in the basic nutritional pattern are clearly very great.

(e) Amino acids, polypeptides and proteins

(i) Amino acids

It would be foolish to suggest to the biochemist that spectroscopy can in any way compete with the ninhydrin reaction for the simple recognition of amino acids. However, it does afford a convenient method whereby any particular member of the class may be positively identified. Several collections of amino acid spectra are available for this purpose[44-47] but it is usually possible to narrow the field from a study of the details of the spectrum. Thus the characteristic CH_3 and CH_2 stretching and deformation frequencies will usually afford a lead as to the chain length and to the extent of any branching.

All amino acid spectra show characteristic bands due to the NH_3^+ or NH_2 structure along with those due to the ionised carboxyl group, and the characteristic zwitterion structure can be conclusively demonstrated in this way. These bands are modified by salt formation as in the hydrochlorides. Thus in salts, there are changes in the 3000–2000 cm^{-1} region in which the complex pattern of bands due to the NH_3^+ structure disappears and is replaced by the simpler higher frequency bands of the NH_2 group. Corresponding changes occur in the 1600 cm^{-1} region where the NH_3^+ deformation modes are responsible for the appearance of the characteristic amino acid I and II bands. On the formation of hydrochlorides the two bands due to the COO^- group vanish and a normal carbonyl absorption appears. These changes can also be observed in solution using water and heavy water as complementary solvents.

One interesting feature of the spectra of amino acids is the differences which occur between optically active and racemic forms. Whilst the spectrum of a pure *d* isomer is identical with that of a pure *l* form there is a change on going over to the *dl* form. This is primarily associated with differences in the crystal packing which lead to modifications in the positions and intensities of the NH_3^+ deformation modes in the 1600 cm^{-1} region. This accounts for some of the discrepancies found in the past in this region by workers using different forms of the same amino acids.

(ii) Polypeptides

When a small number of amino acids are linked in a peptide chain the spectrum retains the characteristic features of the zwitterion form. The spectral differences between, for example, di-, tri- or tetraglycine are still sufficient to enable them to be differentiated from each other or from any similar peptide containing mixed acids[47]. However, when the chain length becomes longer, the spectra take on more and more a uniform pattern, as is to be expected from the fact that the absorptions are derived from small individual units and are not therefore particularly sensitive to the numbers of such units in the repeating chain. However, it is also found that the spectra of different polypeptides also tend towards a common "protein pattern" so that whilst some differences often remain, the individuality of the spectrum is largely lost. Application of infrared work in this field has therefore tended more towards the elucidation of orientation and configurational problems than to the more direct use in recognition. A number of detailed reviews are available on the spectra of proteins and polypeptides and these supply extensive bibliographies on all aspects of this work[48–51].

Spectroscopy offers two important techniques which are of particular value in this field. Firstly it is possible in suitable cases to differentiate between intermolecular hydrogen bonds between two separate molecules, and intramolecular bonds which link two different parts of the same molecule. When intermolecularly bonded compounds are dissolved in non-polar solvents the association is progressively broken by dilution. It is therefore possible to observe the gradual disappearance of the associated NH bands

References p. 167

near 3300 cm^{-1} and their replacement by bands at a higher frequency due to free NH groups.

With intramolecular bonds the NH frequency is, however, unaffected by dilution and the internal hydrogen bonds remain unbroken. Studies on polypeptides which are soluble in non-polar solvents have shown that the hydrogen bonds are invariably of this type, indicating the presence of coiled structures. However, the same polypeptides can also be prepared in different orientations which are then insoluble in non-polar solvents. The method cannot now be directly applied, but parallel studies on acetylated peptides have been made[49] which show that intermolecular hydrogen bonds can also occur. This is consistent with the X-ray data which assigns chain structures to these insoluble β-modifications. Some workers have suggested that specific frequency differences exist between inter- and intra-molecular hydrogen bonds by which they can be differentiated[52]. If substantiated, this could be of the greatest value in protein studies, but at present the general applicability of this finding must be accepted with some reserve. The frequency depends primarily upon the initial environment of the NH link, and upon the strength of the hydrogen bond. It is therefore possible to envisage conditions under which internal and external bonds would give rise to identical NH frequencies.

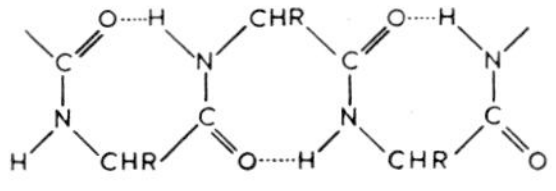

The second and perhaps more important technique is that which uses polarised radiation to measure the different orientations of specific groups. This depends upon the simple principle that radiation which enters a molecule along the line of a given linkage will be absorbed, whereas that which enters at right angles will not. By studies of the changes in the intensities of NH or C=O bonds which occur in crystals or oriented fibres when the angle of incidence of the polarised light is rotated through 90°, it is possible to evaluate the relative angles which these links make in relation to the main chain. With compounds such as nylon in oriented fibres, the dichroic results show that both the NH and C=O bonds are at right angles to the main chain axis, thereby confirming the X-ray picture of parallel chains cross-linked by intermolecular hydrogen bonds. With synthetic polypeptides such as poly *l*-benzyl glutamate two different forms exist depending on the method of preparation of the film. One of these (the β-form) behaves similarly to nylon and is therefore thought to be linked in chains or sheets, but the other form has its NH and C=O bonds in a plane parallel to the chain axis. This suggested a folded structure such as that shown below[53]. This result was later supported by the finding that the material, unlike the β-form, was soluble in non-polar solvents, and that the bonded NH links in solution were not broken on dilution, indicating that they were indeed intramolecular[54].

This folded structure was subject to some criticism as not conforming with the X-ray data and it was later shown that this particular fold was based on an oversimplified interpretation of the dichroic ratios. Because of the strong resonance in the amide link, the CN bond has some double bond character, and its vibration is to some extent coupled with that of the carbonyl group. One result of this is that the transition moment of the carbonyl group does not lie directly[55] along the line of the C=O link but is twisted towards the CN bond. When allowance has been made for this, the dichroic ratios are found to agree well with those which would be expected for the improved folded structure, the α helix, which was put forward by Pauling *et al.*[56] on the basis of X-ray data. The results from studies of this kind must clearly be interpreted with caution, particularly when they are extended into the field of the natural proteins, but the technique does offer a very valuable supplementary approach to the interpretation of the X-ray data and is particularly useful in instances in which the degree of crystallinity is low.

When these differences between folded (α) and extended (β) structures in polypeptides were first recognised it was assumed that all folded forms would conform to the α-helix pattern. This, coupled with the observation that there were distinct differences in the carbonyl and NH deformation frequencies of the two forms, suggested a possible basis on which the structures of proteins and similar materials might be classified. In synthetic polypeptides which are known from X-ray work to take the α-helix form, the carbonyl absorption occurs near 1655 cm^{-1} whilst the NH deformation is usually found near 1550 cm^{-1}. The same compounds in the extended β-form show these bands at 1630 cm^{-1} and 1530 cm^{-1}. These frequencies were used by many workers as a basis for classification, although it was realised that the NH frequencies at least were occasionally somewhat erratic and liable to mislead. However, whilst all polypeptides which contain the α-helix appear to absorb at 1655 cm^{-1}, it is now realised[51,57,58] that other folded forms are possible which may also absorb at this frequency. Polyproline and polysarcosine for example absorb here but are certainly not folded in a normal α-helix. Recently there has even been some evidence that disordered chains can absorb here also. Whilst the precise frequencies in this region are clearly an excellent measure of the extent of hydrogen bonding, more work will therefore be needed before they can be used to differentiate the type of hydrogen bond present.

(iii) Proteins

Infrared studies of natural proteins have followed closely the lines outlined

References p. 167

above for the simpler polypeptides. However, in making use of this earlier work it should not be forgotten that there are certain fundamental differences between the two classes which may well lead to some differences in the spectra. Most proteins are water-soluble or water-absorbing materials which even in the folded forms are insoluble in non-polar solvents. Polypeptides on the other hand are often insoluble in water and, if folded, appreciably soluble in non-polar solvents. This indicates a difference in the ability to associate with water. Pauling has calculated that the strength of the amide–amide bond is greater than that of the water–amide bond by about 3 kcal so that these links should persist in aqueous solutions. However, the attachment of water molecules to the bonded atoms would be expected to lead to a further frequency displacement and possibly to some adjustments in the configuration. This possibility must be borne in mind in any discussion of the spectra of dried protein films in relation to their structure in the natural state. This is well illustrated by recent studies of the water-soluble sodium poly α-*l*-glutamate, which show that the β-configuration is preferred at relative humidities of less than 70% but that conversion to the α-form occurs at higher humidities[57].

(iv) Fibrous proteins

Silk fibroin has been shown by X-ray work to consist of long polypeptide chains lying parallel to the fibre axis and cross-linked by intermolecular hydrogen bonds. In confirmation of this the carbonyl frequency appears near 1630 cm^{-1} and the dichroism shows that the C=O and NH bonds are at right angles to the fibre axis. The infrared findings for β-keratin are essentially similar. In this last case it seems likely that a slightly puckered sheet is present (Pauling and Corey's "pleated or rippled" sheet) but this does not affect the dichroism as the effect is due to the fact that the polypeptide chain is able to adopt a slightly folded configuration without altering the planarity of the amide group or the relative orientations of its components. α-Keratin shows dichroism of the opposite kind as would be expected from the folded form[60]. The α- and β-forms of myosin of the muscle contracting fibre have also been studied and show similar results. For many years there has been reason to suppose that the special contraction properties of this protein were in some way related to its ability to assume a folded form. Recently there has been some evidence to suggest that a specially contracted form consisting of β-chains cross-linked into a folded "jumping cracker" arrangement[61] may exist, but there is insufficient data as yet available to enable this idea to be fully evaluated.

The spectra of collagen fibres have also been extensively studied. The results are qualitatively but not quantitatively similar to those of extended chain systems such as β-keratin. The observed dichroism can be correctly predicted on the basis of the current structural models for this compound based on X-ray studies. It is interesting to note, however, that collagen is another compound in which the carbonyl frequency is near to that which at one time was specifically associated with the α-helix structure although it is now quite clear that this is not present.

(v) Crystalline and globular proteins

The compact structure of globular proteins, as shown by the ultracentrifuge, originally suggested the presence of some specially folded forms such as the cyclol structure in which interlocking lactam rings would exist on the surface of a polyhedron[62]. Infrared data has shown, however, that lactam forms are not present and that the NH groups are hydrogen bonded. On denaturation by boiling, fibrous structures are produced which show similar dichroic and X-ray patterns to typical chain compounds such as β-keratin. It therefore seems likely that globular and crystalline proteins exist normally as folded forms of similar long chain structures. Many of them show a carbonyl band near 1660 cm^{-1} and this was originally thought to indicate the presence of typical α-helices. However, these would be expected to pack in crystals in a parallel way and should show extensive dichroism. Studies on single crystals of haemoglobin, ribonuclease and insulin[63], have shown, however, only weak dichroism, and although this is of a kind which would be consistent with the α-helix it is doubtful whether more than a small proportion of the protein exists in this form. It would seem therefore that folded forms other than the normal α-helix are present in these cases.

5. Quantitative analysis

(a) Methods

The absolute intensity of an absorption band in the infrared depends upon the rate of change of the bond dipole during the vibration. This in turn depends upon a number of factors including the type of dipole, its polarity, and its internal and external environment. In principle, however, each absorption band has a unique absolute absorption intensity when measured under standard conditions. These intensities vary widely with different types of band so that some absorptions are as much as 1500 times as strong as others.

The measurement of these absolute intensities is a matter of considerable difficulty and quantitative analyses are usually based on the more readily accessible molecular extinction coefficient (ε). This is a function of the peak height as measured by I_0/I, the concentration (c) and the cell thickness (l), and is given by the expression

$$\varepsilon = (1/cl) \log I_0/I$$

References p. 167

which is known as Beer's law. This relation is the basis of all quantitative analysis in the infrared as in the ultraviolet. Given a supply of the pure material which it is desired to estimate, it is a relatively simple matter to prepare a calibration curve relating the optical density of a chosen band to the concentration in a standard cell. This can then be used to measure the concentration of this component in mixtures provided no other component absorbs at the same point. This broad generalisation is, however, subject to certain limitations which must be properly understood if analysis is to be carried out with any precision. These are as follows.

(1) It is desirable that the band selected for quantitative measurements should be reasonably strong and that it should occur in a region of the spectrum in which none of the other components of the mixture absorb. It is not always possible to achieve this, and it is often necessary to work on bands which are at least partially overlapped by others. A number of devices have been worked out which will allow the appropriate corrections to be applied in such cases. One of the best of these involves a separate estimation of the interfering component using some other strong band elsewhere in the spectrum. A second calibration curve is then measured. This relates the concentration of the interfering impurity and its contribution to the optical density at the frequency chosen for the main determination. In this way the extraneous optical density due to the second component can be evaluated and corrections made. Some typical values showing the magnitudes of corrections of this kind for the estimation of the mixed *o*-, *m*- and *p*-xylenols are given by Brugel[5] who also discusses other ways in which this difficulty can be overcome.

Sometimes it is even necessary to make measurements on a band which appears only as a shoulder on the side of a stronger one. The height of the band must then be measured against the sloping background so introduced and some errors are introduced in this way. However, it is sometimes possible to refer such measurements to a fixed point in the spectrum such as an isosbestic point and to prepare the calibration curve on this basis. Isosbestic points are those at which the absorption intensities are independent of the relative proportions of either of the two components and are therefore particularly well suited for this purpose.

An alternative, and in many ways a more attractive solution is through the use of difference spectroscopy, the principles of which have already been outlined briefly. In this method a solution of the pure interfering component is placed in the reference beam in a variable path length cell. The spectrometer is then set at a point at which this component absorbs strongly and the cell thickness adjusted until the band disappears. The concentration of this component in the reference beam is then the same as that in the unknown sample in the primary beam. Direct measurements can then be made on the main component without interference. This method is capable of high sensitivity but is difficult to adapt to mixtures in which interference is due to a number of different components.

(2) The absolute intensity of an infrared absorption is very dependent upon the physical state in which the measurement is made and upon the nature of any solvent employed. Preferably all measurements should be made on dilute solutions in carbon tetrachloride or carbon disulphide, but this is not always possible on account of solubility difficulties or of solvent absorptions. It is, however, essential that the calibration curve is prepared from measurements made in the particular solvent which is to be used for the estimation.

Solids which have no suitable solvents present special difficulties. Techniques for preparing nujol mulls of known film thicknesses have been devised but are difficult to operate with high precision. Internal standards of some other substance are also employed in special cases, and these allow the film thicknesses to be estimated. These techniques have however, limitations of their own, particularly in relation to the problem of obtaining completely uniform homogeneous mixes. Pressed disc methods can also be used although these also are liable to mixing errors unless special care is taken. Whilst such analyses are therefore possible and indeed are widely used, the accuracy obtainable is necessarily less than in solution studies.

(3) Due to the optical limitations of most commercial instruments the observed extinction coefficients of absorption bands are to some extent concentration-dependent so that Beer's law is not strictly obeyed. This imposes the limitation that the calibration chart prepared for an analysis can only be used on the particular machine from which it was made. Even another identical model from the same manufacturer would probably differ sufficiently in such characteristics as optical alignment and scatter, to lead to inaccurate results. This is a limitation only in respect of the transferability of the data and the results from any one instrument are valid, provided regular checks are made on the calibration curve to ensure that no change has taken place in the alignment. For similar reasons it is desirable, if possible, that the same cell should be used for the actual estimation as was employed in the calibration.

(4) Deviations from Beer's law also arise from association effects. In dilute solutions in non-polar solvents the OH band of an alcohol or phenol corresponds to the monomeric form. At higher concentrations polymerisation leads not only to a frequency shift but to changes in the absolute intensity which can be as great as ten fold. The pitfall is obvious in this case, but it can often lead to error in circumstances when the compound studied is capable of association with some other component of the mixture or with

References p. 167

some impurity present in the solvent. Special care is therefore required in the analysis of groups liable to such effects.

(b) Applications

The above discussion has concentrated largely on the various limitations of quantitative analysis in the infrared. It is important that these should be properly appreciated but it must also be stated that a very large number of complicated and difficult analyses can be carried out in this way at high speed, and often with high precision. The fact that only small samples are required which can be recovered unchanged is also a great advantage. It is not possible within the scope of this review to list any large numbers of practical examples but excellent reviews by Price[32] and by Carol[33] give detailed references for many typical analyses in the fields of drugs and pharmaceuticals. Details of specific estimations are also given each month in a special section of *Analytical Chemistry*.

Most methods aim to carry out the estimation without the necessity of any preliminary separation. The analysis of mixtures of aspirin, phenacetin and caffeine for example is made directly on the original specimen and collaborative tests by a large number of different laboratories have shown that highly reliable results can be obtained. In the case of very complex mixtures such as the estrogens in pregnant mare's urine, some preliminary separation is essential and it is also necessary to convert the components into a form in which they will be soluble in a non-polar solvent. In this instance the phenolic ketosteroids are separated from the others using Girards reagent and are then converted into their benzene sulphonates. The equilin, equilenin and estrone can then be estimated directly in the same mixture. Estradiol-17β can be estimated separately as the benzene sulphonate. Whilst therefore the method requires some manipulative work, the overall analysis is still much simpler, much faster and more accurate than any other.

Quantitative measurements can also be applied to such problems as the determination of crystallinity in cellulose and in polypeptides. The method has been reviewed by Elliot[51] who summarises the relevant references. Basically it consists in an estimation of the proportion of hydroxyl groups which are available for association with water. It has been found that isotopic exchange between deuterium and OH groups proceeds rapidly in the non-crystalline portions of cellulose or polypeptide films but does not normally proceed to completion. This is due to the fact that the OH(NH) groups in the crystalline regions are involved in strong hydrogen bonding and are not readily accessible for deuterium exchange. Measurements on the intensity of the OH(NH) bands before and after exposure to heavy water therefore afford a means of estimation of the crystalline/amorphous ratios.

Isotopic substitution is sometimes used in a different connection as a means of improving the precision of analyses which are otherwise difficult. A good example of this is the estimation of the γ-isomer of the insecticide hexachlor-hexahydrobenzene. The direct estimation of this isomer in the presence of all the others is difficult and insensitive, as only a weak band is available for measurement and this is partially overlapped by others. However, if a known amount of pure γ-D-derivative is added to the mixture and a specimen of the component is then isolated by conventional chromatography it is possible to carry out an accurate estimation of the H/D ratio from which the original γ-content can be determined.

6. The infrared spectra of bacteria and viruses

The possibility that one might be able to differentiate rapidly between different species or strains of bacteria by spectroscopic methods is an attractive one and has prompted a great deal of work. In a recent review of this topic by Norris[24] over 100 references are quoted dealing with this subject. Initially efforts were made to characterise microorganisms by the spectra of the whole cells and the findings were somewhat sceptically received by most spectroscopists as it was considered that the large number of components present including carbohydrates, proteins and nucleic acids would obscure any minor differences in composition. As will be seen the spectra of whole cells can be used to obtain valuable data, provided sufficient care is taken in the standardisation of conditions, but the more promising line from the point of view of studies of the chemistry of microorganisms is undoubtedly through preliminary separation methods into cell fractions.

(a) The spectra of whole cells

Many different methods have been used for the study of whole cells. The earliest workers used smears of a bacterial colony on silver chloride plates. Others have used the standard technique of grinding in paraffin or the potassium bromide disc method. This last approach is applicable to freeze dried specimens which can be incorporated directly into the disc. Spectra have also been obtained in aqueous suspensions using normal and heavy water alternatively.

As is to be expected, the spectra obtained in this way show many common features as will be seen from Fig. 4. Nevertheless, significant differences can also be seen between the spectra, particularly in the shapes and intensities of many of the small bands, and there has been much controversy as to how far the overall pattern can be justifiably used for characterisation of any

References p. 167

given bacterium or strain. It now seems clear that real differences can be established in this way but only if a very detailed analysis of the relative intensities of all the bands is made and only if the bacteria are grown and treated in a standard way. Thus Riddle *et al.*[64] examined the spectra of 650 strains of 201 species of bacteria, and compared the minor spectral changes in detail using a punched card system. They were able to show that real differences do exist in the spectra of many bacteria although they did encounter some species which could not be differentiated in this way.

Greenstreet and Norris[65] followed this with an even more elaborate treatment using 136 strains of 29 species of bacteria and subjecting the results

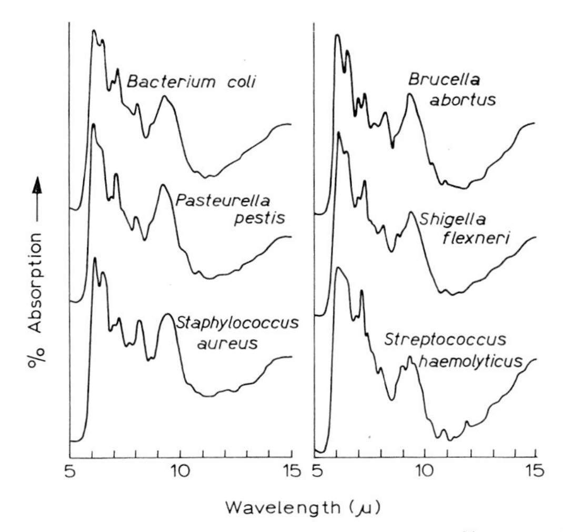

Fig. 4. The spectra of whole bacteria (reproduced from ref.[24] by kind permission of the author and of the editor of *J. Hyg.*).

to statistical analysis. They showed clearly that the differences between genera were significantly greater than the differences between species but that differentiation of the latter was also possible in many cases provided sufficient care was taken to grow and prepare the specimens in a standard way.

The question of sample preparation is of course fundamental, and is one of the limiting factors in the use of the spectra of whole cells for rapid identification of bacteria. In many preparations, such as the method of culture smears, the medium on which the organism is grown will also be present and will contribute to the overall spectrum. Even were it possible for this to be totally removed, the actual chemical composition of the organisms would be expected to depend to some extent upon the nature of the food supplies available for growth so that the spectra of identical organisms grown on different media will not be the same in all the fine details. For the purpose of positive identification it is therefore essential for the spectra to be compared with that of the standard organism grown at the same time and under the same conditions, and this is only practicable where the general broad classification of the organism is already known. For the more limited purpose of differentiating between two different bacteria or subspecies, however, the spectra can provide rapid and reliable answers which can be of great assistance to the practical microbiologist.

The technique is, however, not sufficiently sensitive to allow the detection of very small differences in composition. Kull and Grimm[66] for example were unable to find any difference between the spectra of penicillin sensitive and penicillin resistant strains of *Staphylococcus aureus* or in the corresponding pair of streptomycin resistant and sensitive strains of *E. coli*. However, current approaches to this problem by such methods as difference spectroscopy may well lead to more positive results.

Studies on viruses in whole cells are in many ways parallel to those for bacteria. Benedict[67] was able to separate the spectra of the viruses listed below into four groups, but was unable to find any real differences between the members of any one group. The groups were as follows: Group A, Influenza strains A, A[1] and B, mumps and normal host component; Group B, Newcastle disease virus; Group C, Psittacosis, meningopneumonitis, lymphogranulo mevenereum, and feline and mouse pneumonitis; Group D, vaccina and fowl pox. Here again some useful differentiation is possible but not positive identification.

(b) *The spectra of cell fractions*

The differences between one bacterium and another are minimised in the spectra of the whole cells because of the presence of so many common components, and it is to be expected that these differences will be much more clearly seen in the spectra of selected cell constituents. Randall *et al.*[43] have had considerable success in this way from studies on the lipid residues of tubercule bacteria. These are obtained by methanol–chloroform extraction and purified and separated by chromatography. 18 genera were studied and shown to be capable of clear differentiation on the basis of the spectra of the liquid extracts, which showed very much greater differences than the spectra of the original whole cells. Further, the lipid composition of avirulent and virulent human strains are different and either can be differentiated from bovine or from avian strains. The isolation of single pure chemical components in this way and the recognition that there are compositional changes which relate to the change of species is of the first importance and

References p. 167

may be the beginning of a new field of study in the chemistry of bacteria.

Bacteria have also been successfully typed on the basis of the spectra of the capsular polysaccharides which are fairly easily separated from the other cell components. Here again a significant improvement in diagnostic power over the whole cell technique is apparent.

Spectroscopy has of course also played an important part in the identification of chemical extracts of bacteria. In the polysaccharide field in particular many examples could be given in which the particular sugar present has been positively identified in this way. For example it has been shown that the cellulose produced when *A. xylinium* is grown on various sugars is independent of the nature of the carbon source[68].

Acid components of bacteria have also been studied. A new sulphur containing amino acid isolated from yeast has been shown spectroscopically to be an isomer of β-methylxanthionine, whilst the accumulation of β-hydroxybutyric acid polymers in certain cells has been measured and related to the morphology of the cells.

This field is one in which progress has been slow in the past, partly because of the non-availability of spectroscopic equipment in most microbiological laboratories. This situation can be expected to alter rapidly in the next few years. Now that it has been established that it is possible to follow in this way small alterations in the chemical composition of bacteria on passing from one strain to another, it is likely that the great potentialities of this tool will be more fully employed in detailed studies on the relation of bacterial behaviour to the basic chemical composition.

REFERENCES

[1] Symposium on Biological Applications of Infrared Spectroscopy, *Ann. N.Y. Acad. Sci.*, 69 (1957).
[2] C. Clark, in G. Oster and A. W. Pollister (Eds.), *Physical Techniques in Biological Research*, Vol 1, Academic Press, New York, 1955, p. 206.
[3] R. C. Gore and E. S. Waight, in E. A. Brande and F. C. Nachod (Eds.), *The Determination of Organic Structures by Physical Methods*, Academic Press, New York, 1955.
[4] G. G. R. Harrison, R. C. Lord and J. R. Loofborough, *Practical Spectroscopy*, Blackie, London, 1948.
[5] W. Brugel, *Einführung in die Ultrarotspektroskopie*, 2nd ed., Steinkopff, Darmstadt, 1957.
[6] R. N. Jones, The Selection of Solvents for I.R. Spectroscopy, *N.R.C. Bulletin No. 3*, Ottawa, 1953.
[7] P. Tokington and H. W. Thompson, *Trans. Faraday Soc.*, 41 (1945) 184.
[8] F. Pristera, *Appl. Spectroscopy*, 6 (1952) 29.
[9] L. J. Bellamy, *J. Appl. Chem. (London)*, 3 (1953) 421.
[10] H. Powell, *J. Appl. Chem. (London)*, 6 (1956) 488.
[11] L. J. Bellamy, *Spectrochim. Acta*, 13 (1958) 60.
[12] L. J. Bellamy, *The Infrared Spectra of Complex Molecules*, 2nd ed., Methuen, London, 1958.
[13] R. N. Jones and C. Sandorfy in P. W. West (Ed.), *Chemical Applications of Spectroscopy*, Interscience, New York, 1956.
[14] L. J. Bellamy and R. L. Williams, *Biochem. J.*, 68 (1958) 81.
[15] C. Clark and M. Chianta, *Ann., N.Y. Acad. Sci.*, 69 (1957) 205.
[16] *Spectrographic Abstracts, British Ministry of Supply, H.M.S.O.*, Vols. 1–5, 1954–1959.
[17] H. M. Hershenson, *Infrared Absorption Spectra 1945–1947*, Academic Press, New York, 1959.
[18] S. A. Barker, E. J. Bourne and D. H. Whiffen, in D. Glick (Ed.), *Methods of Biochemical Analysis*, Vol. 3, Academic Press, New York, 1956, p. 213.
[19] L. P. Kuhn, *Anal. Chem.*, 22 (1950) 275.
[20] D. H. Whiffen, *Chem. & Ind., (London)*, (1957) 129.
[21] W. B. Neely, *Advances in Carbohydrate Chem.*, 12 (1957) 13.
[22] A. A. Konkin, D. N. Shigorin and K. I. Novikova, *Zhur. Fiz. Khim.*, 32 (1958) 894.
[23] S. Levine, H. R. J. Stevenson and P. W. Kabeer, *Arch. Biochem. Biophys.*, 45 (1953) 65.
[24] P. K. Norris, *J. Hyg.*, 57 (1959) 326.
[25] R. N. Jones *et al.*, *The Infrared Absorption Spectra of Steroids*, Vols. I and II, Interscience, New York, 1953, 1958.
[26] R. N. Jones and F. Herling, *J. Org. Chem.*, 19 (1954) 1252.
[27] A. R. H. Cole, *Fortschr. Chem. org. Naturstoffe*, 13 (1956) 1.
[28] H. Rosenkrantz, *Ann. N.Y. Acad. Sci.*, 69 (1957) 5.
[29] K. I. Savard, S. Burstein, H. Rosenkrantz and R. I. Dorfman, *J. Biol. Chem.*, 202 (1953) 717.
[30] *Chemistry of Penicillin*, Princeton University Press, Princeton, 1949.
[31] N. G. Brink and R. E. Harman, *Quart. Revs. (London)*, 12 (1958) 93.
[32] W. C. Price, *J. Pharm. and Pharmacol.*, 7 (1955) 103.
[33] J. Carol, *Ann. N.Y. Acad. Sci.*, 69 (1957) 190.
[34] R. N. Jones, *Chemistry in Canada*, June (1950) 3.
[35] L. Marion, D. A. Ramsey and R. N. Jones, *J. Am. Chem. Soc.*, 73 (1951) 305.
[36] L. Levi, C. E. Hubley and R. A. Hingle and J. J. Manning, *Bull. Narcotics U.N. Dept. Social Affairs*, 7 (1955) 42, 85.
[37] E. R. Blout and R. C. Mellors, *Science*, 110 (1949) 137.
[38] L. Crombie and A. G. Jacklin, *J. Chem. Soc.*, (1957) 1622; 1632.
[39] R. N. Jones, A. F. McKay and R. G. Sinclair, *J. Am. Chem. Soc.*, 74 (1952) 2575.
[40] R. T. O'Connor, *J. Am. Oil Chemists Soc.*, 33 (1956) 1.

[41] H. P. Schwarz, L. Dreisbach, R. Childs and S. V. Mastrangels, *Ann. N.Y. Acad. Sci.*, 69 (1957) 116.
[42] N. K. Freeman, *Ann. N.Y. Acad. Sci.*, 69 (1957) 116.
[43] D. W. Smith, H. M. Randall, M. M. Gastambide-Odier and A. L. Koevoet, *Ann. N.Y. Acad. Sci.*, 69 (1957) 145.
[44] H. M. Randall, R. G. Fowler, N. Fuson and J. R. Dangl, *The I.R. Determination of Organic Structures*, Van Nostrand, Princeton, 1949.
[45] R. J. Koegel, J. P. Greenstein, M. Winitz, S. M. Birnbaum and R. A. McCallum, *J. Am. Chem. Soc.*, 77 (1955) 5708.
[46] R. J. Koegel, R. A. McCallum, J. P. Greenstein, M. Winitz and S. M. Birnbaum, *Ann. N.Y. Acad. Sci.*, 69 (1957) 94.
[47] H. W. Thompson, D. L. Nicholson and L. N. Short, *Discussions Faraday Soc.*, 9 (1950) 222.
[48] G. B. B. M. Sutherland, *Advances in Protein Chemistry*, 7 (1952) 291.
[49] S. Mizushima, *The Structure of Molecules and Internal Rotation*, Academic Press, New York, 1954.
[50] E. J. Ambrose in W. Klyne (Ed.), *Progress in Stereochemistry*, Vol. 1, Butterworths, London, 1954, p. 250.
[51] A. Elliott in H. W. Thompson (Ed.), *Advances in Spectroscopy*, Vol. 1, Interscience, London, 1959, p. 214.
[52] N. V. Mikhailov, D. N. Shigorin and S. P. Makar'eva, *Doklady Acad. Nauk S.S.S.R.*, 87 (1952) 1009; 94 (1954) 711.
[53] E. J. Ambrose and W. E. Hanby, *Nature*, 163 (1949) 483.
[54] E. J. Ambrose and A. Elliott, *Proc. Roy. Soc.*, (*London*), A205 (1951) 47.
[55] R. B. D. Frazer and W. C. Price, *Nature*, 170 (1952), 490.
[56] L. Pauling, R. B. Corey and H. R. Branson, *Proc. Natl. Acad. Sci., U.S.*, 37 (1951) 205.
[57] A. Elliott, W. E. Hanby and B. R. Malcom, *Discussions Faraday Soc.*, 25 (1958) 167, 228.
[58] G. B. B. M. Sutherland, *Discussions Faraday Soc.*, 25 (1958) 227.
[59] H. Lenormant, A. Baudras and E. R. Blout, *J. Am. Chem. Soc.*, 80 (1958) 6191.
[60] E. J. Ambrose, A. Elliott and R. B. Temple, *Nature*, 163 (1949) 859.
[61] W. T. Astbury, *Discussions Faraday Soc.*, 25 (1958) 80.
[62] D. Wrinch, *Proc. Roy. Soc.*, (*London*), A161 (1937) 505.
[63] A. Elliott, *Proc. Roy. Soc.*, (*London*), A211 (1952) 490.
[64] J. W. Riddle, P. W. Kabler, B. A. Kenner, R. H. Bordner, S. W. Rockwood and H. J. R. Stevanson, *J. Bacteriol.*, 72 (1956) 593.
[65] J. E. S. Greenstreet and K. P. Norris, *Spectrochim. Acta*, 9 (1957) 177.
[66] F. C. Kull and M. R. Grimm, *J. Bacteriol.*, 71 (1956), 392.
[67] A. A. Benedict, *Ann. N.Y. Acad. Sci.*, 69 (1957) 158.
[68] H. G. Shirk and G. A. Greathouse, *Anal. Chem.*, 24 (1952) 1774.

Chapter VI

Fluorescence

ANDERS EHRENBERG AND HUGO THEORELL

Nobel Medical Institute, Biochemical Department, Stockholm (Sweden)

1. Historical introduction

The word fluorescence originates from fluorite which as a natural mineral contains fluorescent impurities and was studied early in the 19th century. The pure fluorite, CaF_2, does not fluoresce but has nevertheless given its name to the phenomenon. The first established observations of what we today call fluorescence were made about 300–400 years ago on biochemical materials, namely blue sandalwood and horse chestnut (*cf.* Förster[1]). In 1852 Stokes demonstrated that absorbed light of one wavelength is emitted at a longer wavelength, and it is this which distinguishes fluorescence from simple light scattering. Another characteristic property of fluorescence is that the light emission persists only for a very short time after excitation has ceased. In most cases the decay time of the emission is of the order of 10^{-9}–10^{-8} sec, but in extreme cases it may be up to 10^{-4} sec. A closely related phenomenon is phosphorescence, which, however, differs from fluorescence by having a much longer decay time which may be from 10^{-4} to several seconds.

Photoluminescence is used as a collective term for these two phenomena, indicating that in both cases photons are used to excite the light emission. In its widest sense photoluminescence also includes Rayleigh and Raman scatterings, but they will not be dealt with here. Another branch of luminescence consists of chemi- and bioluminescence in which chemical energy is transformed into light emission. In this chapter we shall mainly deal with the fluorescence phenomenon but will also pay some attention to phosphorescence. No attempt will be made to "cover the field" in this restricted space, and frequent reference will be made to more detailed reviews[1–5]. The basic principles will be outlined, and we shall discuss some details of the theory and the practical applications that we think might be of value to the rapidly growing group of biochemists who take an interest in applying fluorescence techniques to their problems.

References p. 187

2. Theory

(a) Excitation and emission mechanisms

At room temperature the thermal energy is insufficient to excite more than a fraction of the molecules of a substance into higher vibrational states. Since the energy corresponding to an electronic transition is so much larger than the vibrational energies, the thermal excitation of electrons can clearly be neglected under these conditions. All the molecules of a normal organic substance are thus at room temperature in the ground state, *i.e.* the electrons are distributed so that the molecular energy is at a minimum. In a normal molecule with an even number of electrons the ground state is a singlet, here denoted S_0, *i.e.* the electrons are in pairs so that the resultant spin is zero.

When visible or ultraviolet light is absorbed by an organic substance, the absorbing molecules are excited to higher electronic states. Among the absorption bands of appreciable strength, the one at longest wavelength usually corresponds to the excitation from the singlet ground state S_0 to the lowest excited singlet state S_1 (Fig. 1). Depending on the energy of the photons, the transition may end up in any of the vibrational sublevels of S_1. In a dense system (solids, liquids or gases at higher pressure) the vibrational energy is effectively dissipated to the surroundings so that the

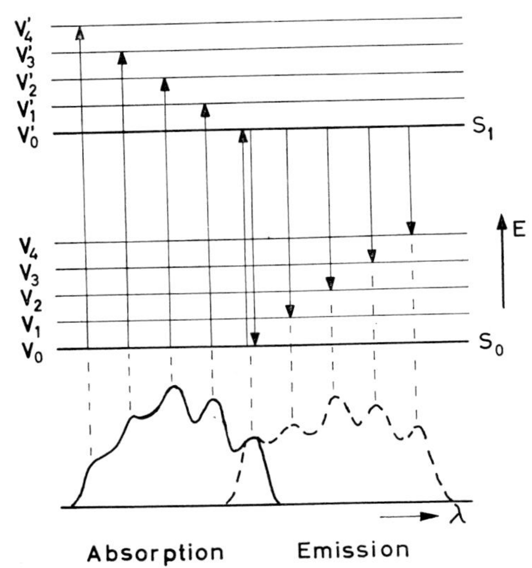

Fig. 1. Schematic representation of the transitions between two electronic states with vibrational sublevels and their relation to the absorption and emission spectra (*cf.* Reid[3], p. 64).

excited molecule rapidly, within 10^{-13}–10^{-12} sec, reaches the lowest vibrational state of S_1. The way back to S_0 may now either be a direct transition accompanied by light emission in the form of fluorescence, or it may be "radiationless", in which case the excitation energy is transformed into thermal energy which is eventually emitted as radiation at much longer wavelengths. The mechanism of fluorescence emission is thus the reverse to that of excitation and may end up in any of the vibrational states of S_0. The emission therefore occurs at longer wavelengths than the absorption (Stokes' law), and the emission spectral band resembles a mirror image of the absorption band, as shown in Fig. 1.

Other important properties of the transition mechanism are illustrated in Fig. 2. The potential energy of the molecule, vertical axis, is shown as a function of the coordinate *r*.

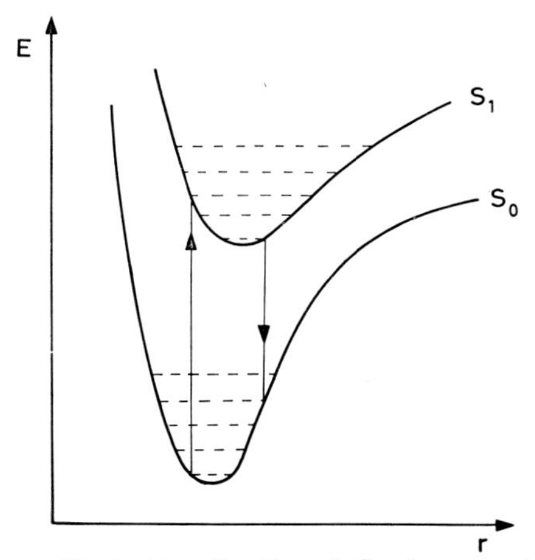

Fig. 2. Energy diagram illustrating the Franck-Condon principle for the transitions between the ground state S_0 and the first excited singlet S_1 (*cf.* Reid[3], p. 65). For explanation see text.

For a diatomic molecule, *r* is the internuclear distance. In the case of a more complex molecule, the potential energy has to be represented by a surface in a polydimensional space. The two-dimensional representation is then obtained by a suitable cross section through this surface, and *r* becomes a generalized coordinate related to the whole structural configuration. The *r*-values of the minima of the different curves represent the equilibrium configurations of the vibrating atoms in the corresponding electronic states. The horizontal lines inside the potential curves depict the vibrational states, the end points representing the vibrational turning points where the kinetic energy is zero. The transition of an electron from one state to another is

References p. 187

a very rapid process that is performed in about 10^{-15} sec. The time between two molecular collisions in solution or of a period of nuclear vibration are both about 10^{-12} sec. This implies that the configuration of nuclei cannot change very much during an electronic transition, a rule known as the Franck–Condon principle[6]. The most probable transitions are those for which the vibrational kinetic energy is not altered. Transitions of this type are represented by vertical arrows connecting the potential curves of Fig. 2, and give rise to intense absorption or emission bands. Other transitions are called "forbidden". However, due to perturbations of different sorts they can still occur but the transition probabilities are small and the corresponding absorption bands relatively weak. Considerations of this sort will, in general, explain the shape of the absorption and emission bands.

If no other processes compete with the radiational reversal from the excited state, the quantum yield of fluorescence will be unity and the natural lifetime, τ_N, of the excited state obtained under these circumstances will depend only on the transition probability, *i.e.* whether the transitions are allowed or to some extent forbidden. The same probability determines the strength of the corresponding absorption band, so that τ_N and the integrated absorption will be related according to eqn. (1).

$$\int \varepsilon \mathrm{d}\bar{\nu} = \frac{N}{2{,}303 \times 8\pi c} \times \frac{1}{\bar{\nu}^2} \times \frac{g_u}{g_l} \times \frac{1}{\tau_N} \qquad (1)$$

ε is the molar extinction coefficient, $\bar{\nu}$ is the wave number of the absorption center in cm^{-1}, and N is Avagadro's number. g_u and g_l are the multiplicities of the upper and lower electronic states respectively, being 1 for singlets, 3 for triplets etc. For an allowed singlet transition the absorption is intense and the lifetime τ_N is 10^{-9}–10^{-8} sec. Under special conditions a singlet transition can have a much longer lifetime, for example $3.3 \cdot 10^{-5}$ sec, corresponding to a weak absorption band in naphthalene.

(b) *Intramolecular quenching*

As already mentioned there are mechanisms that revert the excited molecules to the ground state without any accompanying light emission. In this way the number of excitations giving fluorescence emission is decreased, *i.e.* the fluorescence is quenched.

When intramolecular quenching processes compete effectively with the radiational transition, the lifetime of the excited state will be shortened and the quantum yield of the fluorescence decreased. How the mechanism of this internal conversion is imagined can be seen from the potential energy diagram of Fig. 3. The energy curves of the different electronic states have crossing points at which the vibrational modes of the two states have common turning points and where the electronic energy of S_1 can switch over to the vibrational energy of S_0, either directly at P_1 or at P_2 via another excited state S_2. Increasing the temperature increases the rate of passing the crossing

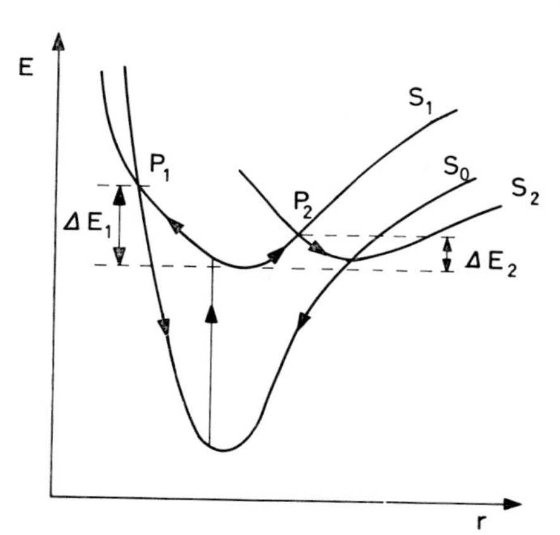

Fig. 3. Energy diagram illustrating the mechanism of radiationless internal conversion between crossing energy levels.

barrier, ΔE_1 or ΔE_2, and hence will generally weaken the fluorescence. The chances of crossing and the height of the barrier depend on the chemical structure. When crossing points are common and the barriers are low, the internal conversion will be so rapid that the compounds will never fluoresce as, for example, in the case of saturated hydrocarbons. More loosely bound electrons in heteroatoms such as oxygen and nitrogen, or in double bonds, especially when conjugated or in ring-systems, seem to give distributions of energy levels that favour the appearance of fluorescence. It is striking that so many compounds of great biologic importance are fluorescent, see for example Duggan *et al.*[7,8]. The appearance of fluorescence in different classes of compounds has also been treated systematically by West[2] and by Pringsheim[5].

(c) Intermolecular quenching

Colliding molecules of the solvent itself or of another solute may quench the fluorescence of a substance by perturbing the energy curves so that they cross or so that the barrier at the crossing point is decreased. The time of contact, *i.e.* perturbation, between two molecules that come close enough is dependent on the amount of chemical interaction involved. For a purely "elastic" collision the contact time is shorter than 10^{-12} sec. In this case the

References p. 187

quenching interaction must take place with the already excited molecules. This is called *dynamic* quenching. In the other limiting case, *static* quenching, a collision leads to the formation of a long-lived complex that has its own fluorescence properties, and may undergo intramolecular quenching by internal conversion. Examples of both types of quenching are furnished by the reactions of the strongly fluorescent riboflavin 5′-phosphate. At low pH values this combines with hydrogen ions to form an acid with a pK of —0.2 as determined from the change in light absorption. Fluorescence studies, however, have indicated a much higher pK of 2. In an interesting study on the fluorescence of flavins, Weber[9] has shown that this large difference is due to collisional quenching by hydronium ions. This quenching is effective at pH values for which the acid flavin form is dissociated to more than 99%. The quenching collisions might well be pictured as a rapid formation and redissociation of the nonfluorescent acid form.

Static quenching is concentration-dependent in such a way that the degree of quenching is proportional to the amount of nonfluorescent complex formed. Increasing temperature will, in most cases, promote the dissociation of this complex and hence cause a decrease of the quenching. The lifetime of the fluorescent state is, of course, not influenced by the addition of a quencher of this type, nor is the fluorescence depolarization influenced, *cf.* p. 179.

In the case of dynamic quenching, the concentration-dependence of the degree of quenching is, at low concentrations of the quencher, the same as for static quenching. At higher concentrations, however, the efficiency of the dynamic quencher is, at least in some cases, increased[9]. Increasing temperature will now act in the opposite way and enhance the degree of quenching. These effects are explained in terms of more frequent and more effective collisions. The lifetime of the excited state will decrease at the same time as the intensity of fluorescence decreases. As a consequence of the decreased lifetime, the fluorescence depolarization will decrease as will be described later, p. 179. In many cases, the effect of a quencher must be explained in terms of both of these mechanisms. These quenching mechanisms have also been treated in detail by Förster in his monograph[1].

When riboflavin 5′-phosphate is bound to the apoprotein of the old yellow enzyme to form the holoenzyme, the strong flavin fluorescence completely disappears. That only rather small perturbations in the energy levels are necessary for this drastic change in fluorescence can be seen from the light absorption spectra of riboflavin 5′-phosphate and of the holoenzyme[10]. The absorption maxima of the coenzyme are only slightly shifted towards longer wavelengths as a consequence of the reaction with the apoenzyme[10]. It can be concluded that in cases like this, measurements of fluorescence are better suited for quantitative work than are measurements of light absorption.

Other examples are given by the pyridine nucleotides, the reduced forms of which are strongly fluorescent. Upon combination with apoenzymes the absorption and fluorescence maxima are sometimes shifted slightly, and the fluorescence intensity increased manyfold[11] due to the inhibition of an internal conversion operating in the free reduced nucleotide or to sensitized fluorescence (pp. 176–177). Data on some pyridine nucleotide dependent enzymes are shown in Table I.

TABLE I

ACTIVATION AND EMISSION MAXIMA OF REDUCED PYRIDINE NUCLEOTIDES, FREE AND BOUND TO SOME APOENZYMES

The data have been corrected for instrumental characteristics

Compound	*Wavelength of maximum absorption (activation)* in mμ*	*Wavelength of maximum emission* in mμ*	*Fluorescence intensity as compared with free DPNH*
Reduced diphosphopyridine nucleotide (DPNH)	340 (37)	462 (38, 39)	—
Liver alcohol dehydrogenase–DPNH	325 (40)	440 (corr. value from Fig. 8)	more
Acetylpyridine DPNH analogue (APDPNH)	365 (41)	478 (41)	less
Liver alcohol dehydrogenase–APDPNH	—	440 (41)	more
Yeast alcohol dehydrogenase–DPNH	340 (38)	443 (38)	more
Lactic dehydrogenase–DPNH	330 (42)	440 (20, 43)	more
Malic dehydrogenase–DPNH	351 (44)	447 (44) 454 (45)	more
Triosephosphate dehydrogenase–DPNH	340 (20)	462 (20)	less
Reduced triphosphopyridine nucleotide (TPNH)	340 (37)	462 (46)	same
Isocitric dehydrogenase–TPNH	335 (46)	440 (46)	more

* Reference numbers between brackets.

An important point to consider when discussing these mechanisms is that the excited state of a molecule in many respects has a different chemical reactivity than that of the ground state. The dissociation of aromatic acids has been shown to be increased in the excited state. If both the acid and the cation are fluorescent, the result is a shift of the fluorescence towards longer wavelengths for those hydrogen ion concentrations (*i.e.* close to the dissociation constant) that allow the excited acid to dissociate before emission takes place[1,3]. The increased reactivity of the excited state is often manifested in photoreactions that quench the fluorescence, *e.g.* photodecomposition or photooxidation (as in the case of riboflavin).

Related to this photooxidation and to the collisional quenching discussed above is the *reversible redox quenching* outlined by Weiss (see *e.g.* ref. [4]). As is shown in Fig. 4 the excited state is first thought to be oxidized by the quencher. While still in contact with each other, the oxidized molecule and

References p. 187

reduced quencher are, by partial internal conversion, brought to a position where the reverse electron transfer takes place to yield the original molecular species. The quenching of the fluorescence of chlorophyll by oxygen and nitric oxide, or by transition element ions that easily change valence, has been thought to be an example of this mechanism. However, all these

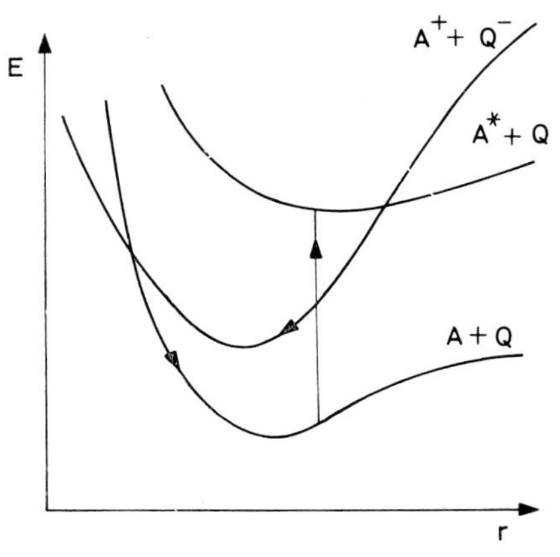

Fig. 4. Energy diagram illustrating the mechanism of the Weiss redox quenching.

quenchers are small molecules with strong electric and magnetic fields which make it difficult to distinguish between Weiss' redox mechanism, and quenching by collisional perturbation. The latter may catalyze singlet–triplet conversions as discussed under phosphorescence (pp. 180–181).

(d) Excitation transfer

A quenching mechanism of considerable interest and increasing importance in biochemistry and biophysics is the *excitation transfer*[12,13] between molecules without the accompanying emission and reabsorption of photons. The mechanism of this nonradiative or "resonance transfer" of electronic excitation energy is best treated in quantum mechanical terms. The main requirement is found to be the same as in the trivial reabsorption case, *i.e.* a good overlap between the emission band of the primary absorbing molecule, which is called the sensitizer, and the absorption band of the quenching molecule which accepts the excitation. Calculations have shown[14] that the excitation transfer between the fluorescent amino acids phenylalanine, tyrosine and tryptophan, and the prosthetic groups such as the pyridine and riboflavin nucleotides and heme will be effective up to distances of the order of 10 to 50 Å. The mean distance between the mentioned groups in most proteins is within this effective range. When the quenching molecule emits the transferred excitation as light, we call it sensitized fluorescence.

Excitation transfer reactions are of obvious importance in the biochemistry of vision and photosynthesis and in radiobiology. The energies released in ordinary biochemical reactions are, however, far too small to cause any excitations of the sort discussed here (see, however, the reactions leading to bioluminescence). Nevertheless, the very existence of excitation transfer in a system implies that a special interaction occurs between different molecules, or between parts of a larger molecules, as discussed by Szent-Györgyi[15,16]. Further consequences of, and factors influencing this interaction are now being explored.

(e) Excitation at shorter wavelengths

As described above, the fluorescence emission from a normal organic molecule is due to a direct electronic transition from the lowest excited singlet state to the ground state. Only the excitation by light absorption in the band corresponding to this particular electronic excitation has been discussed so far. Light absorption in bands of shorter wavelengths results in higher electronic excitations. Through internal conversion, an excitation of this kind might dissipate some energy and end up in the lowest excited singlet state, and thus have the same chance of giving fluorescence as a direct excitation to this state. The internal conversion might, however, operate in such a manner that the lowest excited singlet is bypassed. In this way, the quantum yield of fluorescence by absorption at shorter wavelengths becomes smaller than the quantum yield in the longer wavelength region. When light of shorter wavelength is used for the excitation, one must remember that the chance for photolysis and other interfering photoreactions increases with the energy of the photons used.

(f) Polarized fluorescence

The basic phenomena connected with polarized fluorescence are easiest to describe if we consider a fluorescent sample placed in a cubic cell which has the origin of a Cartesian coordinate system at its center with the coordinate axes perpendicular to the cell walls, as illustrated in Fig. 5. The exciting light travels in the y-direction and the observations are made on the fluorescent light leaving the sample in the x-direction. The detailed theory of the electronic transition mechanism[1,3,5] shows that the absorption or emission of light corresponding to a certain transition is associated with a certain direction within the molecule. This direction is, in the classical theory, visualized as the direction of a linear electronic oscillator. In quantum

References p. 187

mechanical language, this corresponds to the transition moment vector. If the exciting light is linearly polarized with its electric vector in the z-direction, molecules oriented with their transition moments in this direction will preferentially be excited. The more the transition moment of a molecule deviates from the z-direction, the smaller is the excitation probability. If the

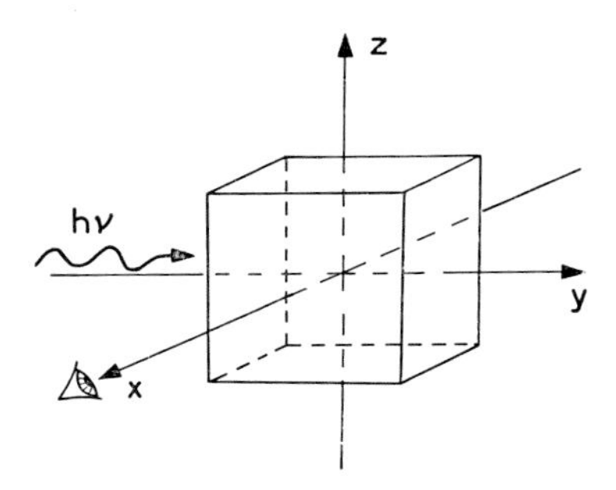

Fig. 5. Schematic drawing of a cubic sample centered at the origin of a Cartesian coordinate system. The exciting light is entering in the y-direction. The fluorescent light is observed in the x-direction.

rotary motion of the fluorescent molecules is slow enough, the excited molecules will not change their orientation appreciably until they have emitted the fluorescence light. In this case the emitted light will be partly polarized when observed from the x-direction. This will be the case for fluorescent molecules of any size in very viscous media such as glycerol or solid solutions, or for many macromolecules in ordinary aqueous solutions.

Light is a transverse wave, which means that unpolarized exciting light in the y-direction has electric vector components only in the z- and x-directions. Molecules with their transition moments in the xz-plane will preferentially be excited, and if their rotary motion is slow enough, the fluorescent light observed in the x-direction (or in any direction in the xz-plane) will be partly polarized in this case also.

The degree of polarization (p) of the fluorescent light is defined by the equation

$$p = \frac{I_z - I_y}{I_z + I_y} \tag{2}$$

where I_z and I_y are the amounts of the fluorescent light having its associated electric vector in the z- and y-directions respectively. When molecular rotation is facilitated by decreasing viscosity or decreasing molecular size, p is diminished and eventually becomes zero, *i.e.* the fluorescence is completely depolarized. For a spherical molecule, these relationships are described by the following equation derived by Perrin[17,18]:

$$\frac{1}{p} \mp \frac{1}{3} = \left(\frac{1}{p_0} \mp \frac{1}{3}\right)\left(1 + \frac{RT}{\eta V}\tau\right) \quad (3)$$

where R is the gas constant, T the absolute temperature, η the viscosity of the solvent, V the molar volume of the fluorescent component and τ the lifetime of the excited state. p is the observed polarization and p_0 is the limiting polarization when no depolarizing rotations are operating. The minus signs are valid when linearly polarized light is used for the excitation, and the plus signs when unpolarized light is used. Theoretical considerations[1] give for p_0 a value of $\frac{1}{2}$ in the former case and $\frac{1}{3}$ in the latter.

Excitation at shorter wavelengths usually corresponds to transition moment vectors with other directions than the fluorescence transition moment. This causes the p_0-values to decrease, and for certain angles between the transition moments the values of p_0 will even be negative.

Weber[19] has derived the alterations of the formula that are necessary when systems with several fluorescent components are investigated, or when the molecular shape of the fluorescent molecules deviates considerably from the spherical shape. He also treated the case where a small fluorescent molecule is bound to a macromolecule by a single point of attachment so that a certain freedom of rotation is conserved and can act depolarizingly.

The relatively small coenzyme DPNH is mobile enough in water solution to give a fluorescence that is largely depolarized. When DPNH is bound rigidly to an apoenzyme, the depolarization will be negligible and $p = p_0$. Detailed studies of such effects were first carried out by Velick[20] in 1958.

Excitation transfer, leading to sensitized fluorescence, will also act depolarizingly on the emitted light. The use of this phenomenon has become an important experimental tool in the study of excitation transfer. The concentration depolarization occurring at higher concentrations of a single fluorescing solute is of the same nature, *i.e.* excitation transfer between molecules of the same kind.

(g) Phosphorescence

It has been shown, especially through the work of Lewis and coworkers[21,22], that the slowly decaying light emission of phosphorescence is due to transitions from the lowest excited triplet state down to the singlet ground state. This triplet state is energetically lower than the lowest excited singlet, as is shown in Fig. 6. Hence the phosphorescence appears at a longer wavelength than would a fluorescence emission from the same compound. According

References p. 187

to eqn. (1) the long lifetime of phosphorescence corresponds to a very weak absorption. Hence the singlet–triplet absorption bands are usually very difficult to determine by common absorption spectrophotometry. These properties of the transition are due to the spin conservation principle which makes the transition probability very low between a singlet state in which

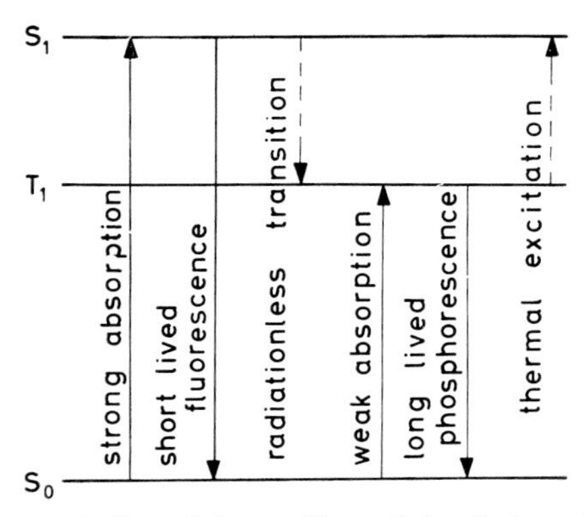

Fig. 6. Schematic representation of the position of the first excited triplet T_1 and its relation to the first excited singlet S_1.

all the electrons in the molecule have their spins paired, and a triplet state with two of the spins unpaired. The lowest excited triplet state is easiest populated by illumination in the region of strong absorption, leading, to the lowest excited singlet state. A portion of these excitations will, through a radiationless transition, be converted into the triplet state as is schematically shown in Fig. 6.

A consequence of the long lifetime of the triplet state is that the radiationless deactivation at room temperature is allowed to compete effectively with the phosphorescence emission process. Hence, only few organic and biochemical compounds are phosphorescent at room temperature. At a low enough temperature, for example that of liquid nitrogen, the internal conversion process is generally slowed down to such a drastic extent that phosphorescence now becomes a very common property. The low energy and the long lifetime of the lowest excited triplet state makes it especially interesting from the biochemical point of view, since this will be the excited electronic state that will be energetically the easiest one to reach by use of ordinary reaction energies. With this in mind, Szent-Györgyi has used results from phosphorescence experiments for very stimulating discussions of biochemical systems[15,16].

The lowest excited triplet (T_1 of Fig. 6) has been suggested to be involved in the process of fluorescence quenching by small paramagnetic molecules such as oxygen or nitric oxide. They are supposed to catalyze the conversion of the singlet S_1 into the triplet T_1 which then, at room temperature, will be deactivated without emission (*cf.* p. 176).

3. Methods

(a) Instrumentation

A simple photofluorometer is obtained by focusing the light from a suitable light source, *e.g.* a mercury lamp, on the sample contained in a cell with square cross section and observing the fluorescence at a 90° angle with a sensitive photocell coupled to a meter or a recorder. A simple spectral resolution might be obtained by placing interference filters before and after the sample. Constructional details of such instruments will be found in many places. One type especially suited for kinetic work has been described by Theorell and Nygaard[23].

A recording spectrophotofluorometer, which for some years has been in continuous use in our laboratory, is described in Fig. 7. The cheap mercury lamp has the disadvantage of giving a spectrum with many lines of varying intensity. A xenon lamp is better suited as a light source since it emits a

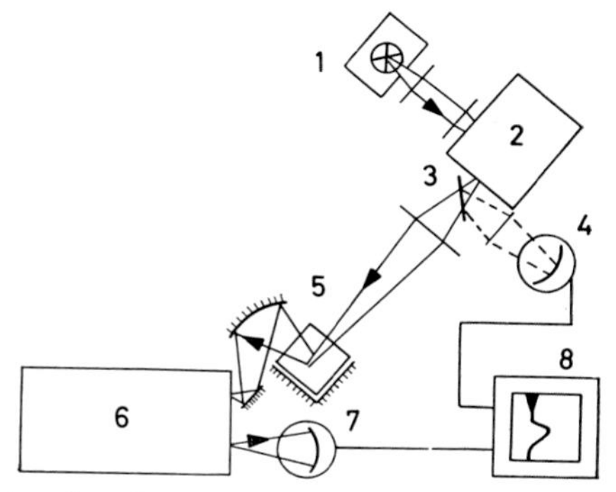

Fig. 7. Recording spectrophotofluorometer constructed by the authors. (1) Xenon lamp, 300 Watts (Osram XBO 301) with water cooled lamp house. (2) Grating monochromator (Bausch and Lomb 250-mm focal length) for excitation wavelength, equipped with synchronous motor for scanning. (3) 45° quartz plate which via a suitable filter, slit and (4) photomultiplier gives a reference voltage. (5) Sample in a thermostated sample holder replacing the lamp of a (6) second monochromator (Beckman DU). The latter is equipped with a synchronous motor for scanning as well as a manual wavelength indicator. (7) Photomultiplier giving signal voltage. (8) Recorder and electronic equipment by which the reference voltage monitors the sensitivity, after a design by Lomakka as schematically shown by Caspersson[24]. A commercial servomultiplier might alternatively be adapted for this purpose. Strongly absorbing or scattering solutions can be studied by turning the sample close to 45° and measuring the fluorescence light merging from the surface layer[25, 26].

References p. 187

very intense spectrum with smoothly increasing intensity from below 250 mμ up to 400 mμ where it flattens off, and has several lines between 450 and 500 mμ, followed by a slow decrease in intensity. Improved stability and long life of the lamp is best achieved by feeding it with highly stabilized direct current. Some fluctuations in the fluorescent light will be due to the remaining instability of the lamp. For some work, especially kinetic studies and quantitative analysis, it is a great advantage to employ some system for compensation of this disturbing effect. For this purpose a fraction of the excitation light is fed to a photocell 4, the voltage from which is used to control the sensitivity of either the photocell 7 or the recorder 8, as shown in Fig. 7. A well thermostated sample is also essential for this type of work, not only because the velocity constants change with temperature, but also because the fluorescence yield is temperature dependent.

High intensity of the excitation light is essential in order to obtain high sensitivity. Since a narrow spectral band width is usually of minor importance, a low-dispersion grating monochromator is suitable if the exciting wavelengths used are not too long. In the case of the longer wavelengths passing through the analyzing unit, the smaller aperture of a prism monochromator is compensated for by its smaller dispersion. If here a grating monochromator is used instead, scattered excitation light must sometimes be filtered away to avoid disturbances from its appearance in the overlapping second order spectrum.

It must be emphasized that the recorded excitation and emission spectra are functions of the components of the spectrophotofluorometer used. In order to compare spectra obtained by different instruments, it is necessary to find the natural shape and position of the spectral bands by correcting for the wavelength characteristics of the instruments[27]. The calibration might be achieved by positioning a bolometer or chemical actinometer in front of the sample cell (between 3 and 5 in Fig. 7), and measuring the excitation light. In this way, the characteristics of the lamp plus excitation monochromator are obtained. The characteristics of the reference photocell plus filter can be obtained by a simultaneous recording of the reference voltage. Next, a mirror throwing the light directly into the analyzing monochromator should be placed in the sample holder. By using small slits and adjusting both monochromators to the same wavelength, it is possible to determine the characteristics of the analyzing monochromator plus its photocell, since the entering intensity is known from the first calibration step.

Since very small light intensities are measured by a photofluorometer, the noise generated in the photomultiplier will sometimes be the factor that limits the sensitivity. Cooling of the photomultiplier will then be helpful. The highest sensitivity is probably obtained by a photon-counting system operating in the same way as a counting rate meter for measuring radioactivity. At this extreme sensitivity, however, it will be a serious problem to avoid interference from chemical impurities or dust particles.

The spectrophotofluorometer is easily adapted for polarization measurements by inserting one polarizer in front of the sample cell and another one as analyzer after the cell[19,20]. Polarizers made of films coated with polarizing crystals have wide openings and will operate above 350 mμ with a transmission better than 10%. Glan-Thompson prisms of calcite have smaller openings, but can be used down to 250 mμ. Below 250 mμ, airspaced prisms must be used, and the transmission becomes poor. All monochromators will to some extent polarize the passing light. If necessary, special corrections must be made on the measured values, or else depolarizators must be inserted after the first and before the second monochromator[28].

Several spectrophotofluorometers, which are especially useful for qualitative work[29], are commercially available today. More elaborate instruments have been developed for special purposes. The microfluorometer of Chance and Legallais[30] was constructed for localizing fluorescent materials in living cells. French[30a] has described a most effective spectrophotofluorometer with automatic compensation for the wavelength characteristics of the instrument components. The instrument has so far mainly been used for studies of photosynthetic pigments *in vitro* and *in vivo*.

In absorption spectrophotometry, the practical limit of dilution of the sample is usually set at the order of 10^{-6} M because of the difficulties of accurately measuring a small decrease in a comparatively high light intensity. In photofluorometry, the situation is more favourable because a given light intensity is compared with a light intensity of zero. One can thus reach a limit of sensitivity of about 10^{-9} M. On the other hand, the concentration quenching often sets a practical upper limit of the concentration at about 10^{-5} M. The two methods are thus in a way complementary.

(b) Chemical precautions

Because of the low concentrations of solutes often used in fluorescence studies, it is obvious that fluorescent impurities must be carefully avoided. One p.p.m. of impurities in the water used for the solutions or in the chemicals used for the buffers might give as much fluorescence as the sample. Quartz distilled water is recommended, and all chemicals should be purified. The purity of the water and the chemicals is easily checked by measuring their fluorescence in a blank under the same conditions to be used in the experiment.

Special attention must be paid to the quenching properties of the buffer components. The quenching potentiality of dissolved atmospheric oxygen must also be considered.

References p. 187

4. Applications

Some applications of fluorescence in biochemistry have already been mentioned in connection with the brief outlining of the theoretical principles. A few further points may be emphasized.

(a) Analysis

A fluorescent compound is characterized by both its excitation and emission spectra and it is this fact that makes the spectrophotofluorometer a very selective tool for qualitative analysis. 10^{-2} or 10^{-3} μg of a low molecular weight fluorescent compound can often be easily identified. The accuracy of the quantitative estimates is largely dependent on the stability of the light source or on the efficiency of the system employed to compensate for its instability, as well as on the control of the sample temperature. Valuable data concerning the spectra and practical concentrations of many compounds are listed in the papers of Duggan *et al.*[6,7]. Examples of nucleotides, vitamins, hormones, steroids and other important compounds are found in these tables. The fluorescence properties of the aromatic amino acids have been investigated in detail by Teale and Weber[31]. Many references on applications in analysis are found in the review by White[32].

The fluorescence properties of the flavin and pyridine nucleotides are of special importance. Free FMN and FAD are both strongly fluorescent in the oxidized form. When they are bound to apoenzymes, the fluorescence is in

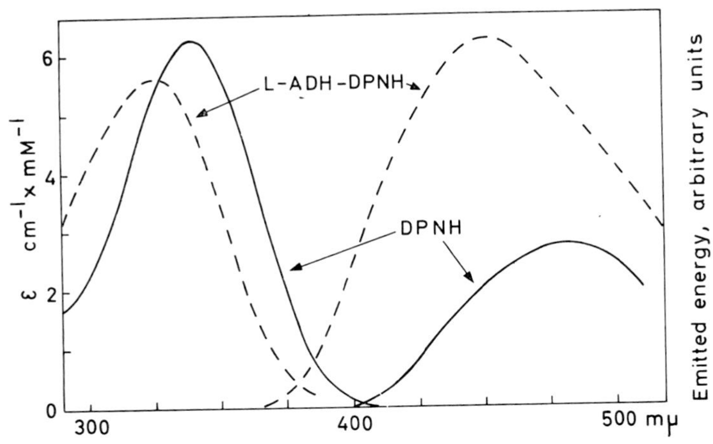

Fig. 8. Absorption (*i.e.* excitation) and emission spectra of reduced diphosphopyridine nucleotide, both free (DPNH) and bound to liver alcohol dehydrogenase (L-ADH–DPNH). The absorption spectrum of L-ADH–DPNH has been corrected for the absorption of L-ADH. The emission spectra have been corrected for blank fluorescence but not for the characteristics of the instrument components.

some cases quenched completely[11]. As a matter of fact, this distinguishing property between free FMN and FMN bound to the old yellow enzyme made it possible to follow by eye the first reversible splitting of an enzyme into its apoprotein and coenzyme[33]. The rate constants for this splitting and recombination have been determined under various conditions.

Similar measurements are possible on the pyridine nucleotide enzymes, and the examples are numerous[11]. The high sensitivity of the fluorescence method makes it possible to investigate the equilibrium in such dilute solutions, that dissociation constants as low as $5 \cdot 10^{-9}$ M can be measured[47]. In this case, the reduced form is the fluorescent one, and the excitation and emission spectra are usually changed when the coenzyme is coupled to the apoprotein. Some data on DPNH- and TPNH-enzymes have been collected in Table I. The excitation and emission spectra of DPNH, both free and bound to alcohol dehydrogenase, are shown in Fig. 8, and offer a clear demonstration of the great selectivity of the fluorescence method. By suitable choice of activating and recorded emission wavelengths, different compounds in a solution can be studied more or less separately. For example (see Fig. 8), recording of a mixture of L-ADH–DPNH and DPNH at 410 mμ will give a nearly negligible fluorescence contribution from DPNH as compared with that of L-ADH–DPNH. Selection in this direction will be still more increased by activation below the isosbestic point (328 mμ) of the light absorption curves.

(b) Kinetics

The strong fluorescence of the reduced pyridine nucleotides and its absence in the oxidized forms makes the fluorescence technique very suitable for kinetic studies on DPN- and TPN-linked enzymes both *in vitro*[11,34,35] and *in vivo*[25,26,30]. The rate of binding of DPNH or TPNH to an apoenzyme and the speed of the reverse dissociation can be measured. The high sensitivity of the technique is again helpful, since the reaction velocity of a second order reaction with a high velocity constant is slowed down enough to be easy to follow at high dilutions. Binary and ternary complexes have been revealed, and their dissociation constants determined[35]. In some cases it has been possible to obtain very detailed information concerning complicated enzymatic reaction mechanisms[47].

(c) Various applications

The monitoring of chromatography on paper or on columns by the fluorescence excited by ultraviolet light is a routine method in most biochemical laboratories. By fluorescence microscopy, the localization of fluorescent compounds in histological preparations can be observed. The method has been extended to other compounds by staining with fluorescent dyes.

References p. 187

Certain metals can be identified and measured in minute amounts by the fluorescent X-rays emitted from the metal atoms when they are irradiated by X-rays of higher energy. The method has for example been used to determine cobalt in the adenyl–cobamide coenzyme[36].

5. Concluding remarks

In the last ten or fifteen years, the biochemist has found fluorometry to be a very useful tool. Its high sensitivity and selectivity makes it in suitable cases go far beyond the limits of spectrophotometry. It has already given information on enzyme–coenzyme systems which would not have been available with any other method, and the literature in this field is increasing rapidly. The same is true for the interesting results already obtained by the study of the polarization properties of fluorescent systems. It begins to lead to a better understanding of excitation transfer within and between molecules.

This method of illuminating problems by irradiating molecules and letting them shed light into the darkness brings great hope for the future.

REFERENCES

[1] T. Förster, *Fluorescenz Organischer Verbindungen*, Vandenhoeck and Ruprecht, Göttingen, 1951.
[2] W. West in A. Weissberger (Ed.), *Technique of Organic Chemistry*, Vol. IX, Interscience, New York, 1956, pp. 707–758.
[3] C. Reid, *Excited States in Chemistry and Biology*, Butterworth, London, 1957.
[4] R. Lumry and H. Eyring in A. Hollaender (Ed.), *Radiation Biology*, Vol. III, McGraw-Hill, New York, 1956, pp. 1–69.
[5] P. Pringsheim, *Fluorescence and Phosphorescence*, Interscience, New York, 1949.
[6] J. Franck, *Trans. Faraday Soc.*, 21 (1926) 536.
[7] D. E. Duggan, R. L. Bowman, B. B. Brodie and S. Udenfriend, *Arch. Biochem. Biophys.*, 68 (1957) 1.
[8] S. Udenfriend, D. E. Duggan, B. M. Varta and B. B. Brodie, *J. Pharmacol. Exptl. Therap.*, 120 (1957) 26.
[9] G. Weber, *Biochem. J.*, 47 (1950) 114.
[10] H. Theorell and Å. Åkeson, *Arch. Biochem. Biophys.*, 65 (1956) 439.
[11] S. Shifrin and N. O. Kaplan in F. F. Nord (Ed.), *Advances in Enzymology*, Vol. 22, Interscience, New York, 1960, p. 337.
[12] Energy transfer with special reference to biological systems, *Discussions Faraday Soc.*, 27, Aberdeen, 1959.
[13] L. G. Augustine (Ed.), *Bioenergetics Radiation Res.*, Suppl. 2 (1960).
[14] G. Karreman, R. H. Steele and A. Szent-Györgyi, *Proc. Natl. Acad. Sci. U.S.*, 44 (1958) 140.
[15] A. Szent-Györgyi, *Bioenergetics*, Academic Press, New York, 1957.
[16] A. Szent-Györgyi, *Introduction to a Submolecular Biology*, Academic Press, New York, 1960.
[17] F. Perrin, *J. Phys. radium*, 7 (1927) 390.
[18] F. Perrin, *J. Phys. radium*, 7 (1936) 1.
[19] G. Weber, *Biochem. J.*, 51 (1952) 145.
[20] S. F. Velick, *J. Biol. Chem.*, 233 (1958) 1455.
[21] G. N. Lewis and M. Kasha, *J. Am. Chem. Soc.*, 66 (1944) 2100.
[22] G. N. Lewis, M. Calvin and M. Kasha, *J. Chem. Phys.*, 17 (1949) 804.
[23] H. Theorell and A. Nygaard, *Acta Chem. Scand.*, 8 (1954) 877.
[24] T. Caspersson, *Mikrochim. Acta*, 1–6 (1956) 1.
[25] B. Chance and H. Baltscheffsky, *J. Biol. Chem.*, 233 (1958) 736.
[26] L. N. M. Duysens and J. Jamesz, *Biochim. Biophys. Acta*, 24 (1957) 19.
[27] C. E. White, M. Ho and E. Q. Weimer, *Anal. Chem.*, 32 (1960) 438.
[28] R. H. Hughes, *Rev. Sci. Instr.*, 31 (1960) 1156.
[29] R. L. Bowman, P. A. Caulfield and S. Udenfriend, *Science*, 122 (1955) 32.
[30] B. Chance and V. Legallais, *Rev. Sci. Instr.*, 30 (1959) 732.
[30a] C. S. French, in F. H. Johnson (Ed.), *The Luminescence of Biological Systems*, Am. Assoc. Advancement of Science, Washington, 1955, pp. 51–74.
[31] F. W. J. Teale and G. Weber, *Biochem. J.*, 65 (1957) 476.
[32] C. E. White, *Anal. Chem.*, 30 (1958) 729.
[33] H. Theorell, *Biochem. Z.*, 290 (1937) 293.
[34] H. Theorell, A. Nygaard and R. Bonnichsen, *Acta Chem. Scand.*, 9 (1955) 1148.
[35] A. D. Winer and H. Theorell, *Acta Chem. Scand.*, 14 (1960) 1729.
[36] H. A. Barker, R. D. Smyth, H. Weissbach, A. Munch-Petersen, J. I. Tookey, J. N. Ladd, B. E. Volcani and R. M. Wilson. *J. Biol. Chem.*, 235 (1960) 181.
[37] O. Warburg, W. Christian and A. Griese, *Biochem. Z.*, 279 (1935) 143 and 282 (1935) 157.
[38] L. N. M. Duysens and G. H. M. Kronenberg, *Biochim. Biophys. Acta*, 26 (1957) 437.
[39] H. Theorell and A. D. Winer, *Arch. Biochem. and Biophys.*, 83 (1959) 291.
[40] H. Theorell and R. Bonnichsen, *Acta Chem. Scand.*, 5 (1951) 1105.
[41] S. Shifrin and N. O. Kaplan, *Proc. Natl. Acad. Sci. U.S.*, 44 (1958) 177.
[42] B. Chance and J. B. Neilands, *J. Biol. Chem.*, 192 (1952) 383.

[43] A. D. Winer, W. B. Novoa and G. W. Schwert, *J. Am. Chem. Soc.*, 79 (1957) 6571.
[44] G. Pfleiderer and B. Hohnholz, *Biochem. Z.*, 331 (1959) 245.
[45] H. Theorell and T. A. Langan, *Acta Chem. Scand.*, 14 (1960) 933.
[46] T. A. Langan, *Acta Chem. Scand.*, 14 (1960) 936.
[47] H. Theorell and J. S. McKinley McKee, *Acta Chem. Scand.*, in the press.

Chapter VII

Electronic Paramagnetic Resonance

S. I. WEISSMAN

Department of Chemistry, Washington University, St. Louis, Mo. (U.S.A.)

1. Principles of the method

Electronic paramagnetic resonance is exhibited by only a small fraction of the known chemical substances. Nevertheless, fifteen years after the discovery of the phenomenon by Zavoiski[1] its use in chemical investigations is thriving and appears to be continually increasing. The reasons for the flourishing state of activity in the field apparently lie in the importance as reaction intermediates of just those substances which may be studied by paramagnetic resonance, and the remarkably detailed information concerning structure, rates, and mechanisms which the method is capable of yielding.

The method consists of determination of the response of an appropriate sample of material to combined static and oscillating magnetic fields. The experimental arrangement usually used measures the absorption of energy from an oscillating magnetic field of fixed frequency as a function of the static magnetic field. The static magnetic field is varied so slowly that effects associated with its variation in time are negligible. Other methods, including determination of the index of refraction ("dispersion mode") and variation of frequency rather than field have been used, but since almost all of the useful chemical results may be obtained from the first method, we shall deal with it exclusively.

The behavior of a material system in a magnetic resonance experiment may be described either in terms of its macroscopic magnetization or of the molecular properties from which the macroscopic magnetization may be calculated. We adopt the latter procedure. A necessary condition for occurrence of magnetic resonance is the occupation of states which are degenerate in the absence of an external magnetic field. The static magnetic field splits the degenerate levels into sub-levels between which transitions are produced by the oscillating field. The sub-levels correspond to the various

References p. 208

permitted orientations of angular momentum relative to the static field. In gaseous atoms and ions as well as in certain ions in solids and liquids, both orbital and spin angular momenta are involved. However, in most polyatomic molecules the orbital degeneracy is removed by strong electrostatic interactions within the molecule and only spin degeneracy remains. Therefore we shall be mainly concerned with spin degeneracy.

(a) Hyperfine structure

We consider first a particularly simple system—a dilute gas of hydrogen atoms* in which many of the phenomena which concern us take place. We first disregard the effects of the magnetic moment of the nucleus. The lowest energy state of the hydrogen atom is doubly degenerate because of two possible orientations of the electron spin angular momentum. In the presence of a uniform magnetic field B the degenerate levels become separated, the energy of one level becoming $\sim + \mu_0 B$ and of the other $\sim - \mu_0 B$, relative to the energy in the absence of the field. μ_0 is the Bohr magneton:

$$\mu_0 = \frac{eh}{4\pi mc} = 0.92723 \cdot 10^{-20} \text{ ergs per oersted}$$

Application of the Bohr frequency condition to the two levels evoked by the field B leads to $h\nu \sim 2\mu_0 B$ or

$$\nu = \frac{2.0023\ \mu_0\ B}{h} = 2.800 \cdot 10^6 B \tag{1}$$

B being expressed in oersteds and ν in cycles per second.

The factor 2.0023 in eqn. (1) is frequently called the g value. 2.0023 is characteristic of the electron spin. Other values are found when orbital magnetism contributes.

Experiments reveal that (1) gives only an incomplete description of the phenomena. At fields greater than a few thousand oersteds the spectrum of ^1H atoms consists of two absorption lines of almost equal intensities symmetrically disposed about the position required by (1). The lines are separated in frequency by 1420 megacycles, in field by 507 oersteds. The spectrum of ^2H atoms consists of three lines of equal intensities, the central one at the position predicted by (1). The separation between adjacent lines is 210 megacycles or 77 oersteds.

---

* Despite the superficial resemblance of this system to the fictitious arrangements of weightless, frictionless pistons, ideal gases, etc., which are frequently used in text books, the dilute hydrogen atom gas is a real system which has been subjected to most careful investigations by the methods of magnetic resonance.

At high magnetic field (1) yields the position of the center of the resonance but fails to account for its structure. The level schemes indicated in Figs. 1a and 1b account for the high field spectra of ^1H and ^2H atoms respectively.

Both ^1H and ^2H possess nuclear magnetic moments whose contributions to the magnetic fields at the position of the electron must be included in the analysis of the phenomena. Eqn. (1) may still be used if $\mathbf{B}$ is an appropriate vector sum of external field and the internal field produced by the magnetic nuclei. The adjective "hyperfine" has been preempted for effects which are produced by magnetic fields of nuclei, and we shall use it in the following pages.

While the effects of nuclear magnetic moments on paramagnetic resonance absorption spectra may be treated by calculation of the fields at the positions of the electrons, it is more convenient to work directly with the energies of the appropriate quantum states. We note first that the energies of interactions of electrons with external or internal magnetic fields are usually very small compared with the energies of internal electrical interactions in molecules. The magnetic interactions therefore do not produce significant changes in electronic distribution.

The contributions to the energy of a molecular system by the magnetic effects are given by their Hamiltonian operator H_{op}.

$$H_{op} = \sum_i \left[\frac{e_i}{m_i C} p_i \cdot \mathbf{A}(r_i) - \mu_i \cdot \text{curl}\, \mathbf{A}(r_i) \right] \tag{2}$$

e_i, m_i, p_i and μ_i are the charge, mass, linear momentum operator, and spin magnetic moment operator of the ith particle. C is the velocity of light. $\mathbf{A}(r_i)$ is the vector potential at the position of the ith particle. Contributions to $\mathbf{A}$ from external fields and all particles other than the ith one must be included. The vector potential $\mathbf{A}$ is a proxy for the magnetic field. $\mathbf{B} = \text{curl}\, \mathbf{A}$. The summation is carried out over all particles. The term containing the momenta p_i represents the interactions of the motion of the charges with the magnetic field and the one containing μ_i the interaction of the spin magnetic moments with the magnetic field.

In the situations to which we devote primary attention the terms involving the momenta p_i produce only small modifications of the observed spectra. The spin interactions are the dominant ones. Calculation of their contribution to the energy leads to the expression

$$H'_{op} = \sum_i - \mu_i \mathbf{B} + \sum_{i,j} \left\{ \frac{\mu_i \mu_j - 3(\mu_i \hat{r}_{ij})\,(\mu_j \hat{r}_{ij})}{(r_{ij})^3} - \frac{8\pi}{3} \delta(r_i - r_j) \mu_i \mu_j \right\} \tag{3}$$

H'_{op} is the contribution to the Hamiltonian operator from interactions of spin

References p. 208

magnetic moments with the external field and with each other. B is the external field, r_{ij} is the distance between particles i and j, $\hat{r}_{ij}$ the corresponding unit vector, and $\delta(r_i - r_j)$ is the delta function operator. The second summation is carried out over all pairs of particles. The term which is proportional to the reciprocal of the cubes of the distance is the familiar "direct" dipole–dipole energy. The term which involves the delta function operator was discovered by Fermi[2]. It represents the part of the interaction which is associated with pairs of spins being in the same place. It may at first sight seem strange, but we can not avoid it, since it is responsible for most of the hyperfine structure which is observed from liquid solutions.

We now discuss how the interactions included in H'_{op} (eqn. 3) account for the spectra of ^{1}H and ^{2}H atoms. The main splitting of the levels is accounted for by the interaction with the external field. The direct dipole–dipole interaction between electron and nucleus vanishes in hydrogen atoms in

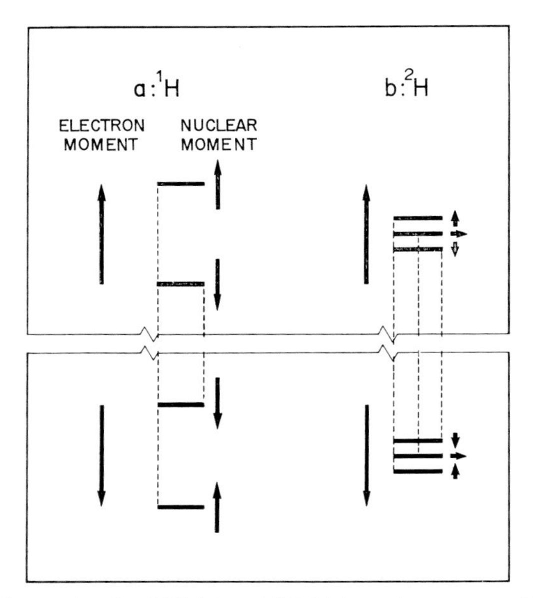

Fig. 1. Energy levels of ^{1}H (a) and ^{2}H (b) in a strong magnetic field.

their lowest states because of the spherical symmetry of the wave function. The Fermi term does not vanish and yields a splitting of each of the electronic levels which is proportional to the square of the electronic wave function at the nucleus and to the scalar product of the electronic and nuclear magnetic moments. The two arrows on each of the levels in Fig. 1

represent the orientation of electronic and nuclear moment respectively*.

The paramagnetic resonance lines arise from the transitions shown by the dotted lines, *i.e.*, transitions in which the orientation of the electron moment is changed, the nuclear orientation remaining fixed. In ^1H (nuclear spin $\frac{1}{2}$) the nuclear moment may assume two orientations, one augmenting the external field at the position of the electron, the other diminishing it. Correspondingly, there are two resonance fields. In deuterium (nuclear spin 1) three nuclear orientations are permitted, one augmenting the external field, one diminishing it, and the other not changing it.

Many features of the behavior of gaseous hydrogen atoms appear in the polyatomic free radicals in liquid solutions. The spin angular momentum and magnetic moment of the latter are almost equal to those of hydrogen atoms. Their hyperfine splittings arise almost solely from the Fermi interactions because of the spherical symmetry of the distribution of electrons about the nuclei. In hydrogen atoms the spherical distribution is intrinsic to the atom. In polyatomic molecules in liquid solution it is a consequence of rapid and random molecular tumbling[3,4].

(b) *Intensities*

In the preceding paragraphs we have discussed the field-frequency relations for the positions of magnetic resonance absorption lines. We now consider intensities and shapes of lines.

The intensity of magnetic resonance absorption is limited by factors associated with the close spacing of the levels. Even at the highest frequencies at which magnetic resonance spectroscopy has been carried out, the energy interval between magnetic levels is small compared with thermal energies at temperatures higher than a few degrees Kelvin. Consequently the number of molecules occupying the higher of a pair of levels between which transitions are observed is comparable to the number occupying the lower level. The radiation induces absorptive transitions from lower to upper level and simultaneously produces emissive transitions from upper to lower level. Because of the coherence of the two processes only the excess of absorptions over emissions is observed. At thermal equilibrium the fractional difference between the number of occupants in two levels separated by $h\nu$ is approximately $h\nu/kT$ when $h\nu/kT \ll 1$. At $\nu \sim 2.5 \cdot 10^{10}$ cycles per second and $T \sim 300°$ K, $h\nu/kT \sim 4 \cdot 10^{-3}$, only a few molecules per thousand

* Under certain conditions such as low magnetic fields or low symmetry the states are not the "pure" ones depicted in the diagram. They are instead mixtures of the pure states. At zero field a splitting associated with the various permitted mutual orientations of the two spins persists. The zero field splitting of 1420 megacycles accounts for radiation from hydrogen atoms in interstellar gases.

References p. 208

yield the excess of absorption over emission. Further, if the measurements are carried out under steady-state conditions the excess is diminished by the absorption process. The useful intensity of radiation is limited because in many instances thermal equilibrium is established slowly. If the characteristic time T_1 (spin lattice relaxation time) for establishment of the equilibrium population is long, the power which can be absorbed is small. On the other hand, if T_1 is short, the line becomes broad. The breadth of the line in frequency units $\Delta\omega$ (radians per unit time) is always greater than $1/T_1$. In optical and infrared spectroscopy neither the limitation associated with saturation nor with lifetime plays an important practical role. Fortunately, in magnetic resonance spectroscopy many chemically interesting cases are found in which the relaxation times lie in the intermediate region in which the limitations are not severe. Measurements are frequently carried out at concentrations lower than 10^{-6} moles per liter.

(c) Polyatomic radicals

In the opening paragraphs of this chapter general criteria for the occurrence of magnetic resonance were presented. We now discuss more specifically the substances which meet the criteria. Among monatomic gases in their lowest electronic states all those containing incomplete sub-shells of electrons possess the necessary degeneracy. Included among the gaseous atoms in which resonance absorption has been observed directly are hydrogen, nitrogen, oxygen, sodium, phosphorus, potassium, and iodine. Observation of resonance by the methods of molecular beams have been made for many more atomic species. Among gaseous diatomic molecules, oxygen and nitric oxide have been studied thoroughly by magnetic resonance.

Magnetic resonance absorption of polyatomic molecules has been observed for the most part in solids and liquids. Observation in gases would be most valuable, but not many paramagnetic polyatomic molecules may be obtained in sufficient concentration in the gaseous phase. Because of phenomena associated with the condensed phases, observation of resonance has been possible mainly with species containing odd numbers of electrons. Even electron paramagnetic molecules require special arrangements, to be described later, for observation of their resonance.

The marked differences between the magnetic behavior of gaseous atoms and polyatomic molecules result from their differences in symmetry. The spherical symmetry of gaseous atoms permits a high degree of spatial degeneracy. The lowest energy state in an atom associated with an incomplete sub-shell is one which has the maximum spin degeneracy ("Hund's rule"). In polyatomic molecules, on the other hand, the symmetry is rarely high enough to permit spatial degeneracy; each sub-shell consists of only one orbital. A theorem of Jahn and Teller demonstrates that polyatomic molecules with spatial electronic degeneracy are not stable[5]. Hence, even electron polyatomic molecules in their lowest energy states usually possess no electronic degeneracy.

Each of the lowest orbitals is occupied by a pair of electrons whose spins must be antiparallel because of the Pauli exclusion principle.

In molecules containing an odd number of electrons all states must be at least doubly degenerate[6]. The list of paramagnetic polyatomic molecules, exclusive of those containing transition element or rare earth atoms, consists almost exclusively of odd electron molecules. The classification "free radical" practically coincides with possession of an odd number of electrons and we shall use the terms "free radical" and "odd electron molecule" interchangeably.

We now take up the behavior of polyatomic free radicals in magnetic resonance. At high fields in liquid solution the center of the absorption is given by the field–frequency relation (1), to an accuracy of a few parts per thousand. The spectra of various molecules are distinguished from each other by the hyperfine splittings. Just as the two permitted orientations of the proton moment produce two resonant fields for ^{1}H, the array of possible orientations of all magnetic nuclei in a molecule are capable of producing spectra of many hyperfine components. Hyperfine splittings in polyatomic radicals by ^{1}H, ^{2}H, ^{6}Li, ^{7}Li, ^{10}B, ^{11}B, ^{13}C, ^{14}N, ^{15}N, ^{19}F, ^{23}Na, ^{31}P, ^{39}K, have been recorded. In addition, splittings by the nuclei of transition elements, rare earths and trans-uranic elements in compounds in which the magnetism is associated principally with a magnetic ion, have been observed.

The polyatomic free radicals and the hydrogen atom resemble each other because the spin of only one electron contributes to the magnetism. Both the free radical molecules and the hydrogen atom are in doublet states, *i.e.*, their wave functions are eigenfunctions of the spin angular momentum operator, with identical eigenvalues.

If ψ is the state function for the molecule

$$S_{op}^2\psi = (\tfrac{1}{2})\,(\tfrac{1}{2}+1)\left(\frac{h}{2\pi}\right)^2\psi \tag{4}$$

S_{op} is the spin angular momentum operator. $S_{op} = \sum_i s_i$ where the summation is carried out vectorially for all electrons. Eqn. (4) states that all spins but one are perfectly paired. In triphenylmethyl, for instance, with 129 electrons the magnetism and spin angular momentum are very close to those of the hydrogen atom. The orbital contributions, while not completely absent, are very small.

We now return to the Hamiltonian H'_{op} and consider the contributions of the various terms to the magnetic energy of a free radical molecule. The dominant term at high fields is $\sum \mu_i \mathbf{B}$. It yields only two energies, $\pm \mu_0 \mathbf{B}$ since the contributions from electrons with antiparallel spins cancel each other.

The contribution of the Fermi term at sufficiently high fields is

$$- \frac{8\pi}{3} \mu_0 \sum_N \delta(r_N) \mu_N \tag{5}$$

μ_0 is the Bohr magneton. $\delta(r_N)$ is the density per unit volume of electronic spin at r_N, the position of nucleus N; μ_N is the projection of the magnetic moment of nucleus N along the field $\mathbf{B}$. The summation is carried out over all nuclei. The number of possible projections for each nucleus is $2I + 1$, where I is the nuclear spin. The projections of magnetic moment of a nucleus of spin I and magnetic moment μ may have one of the $2I + 1$ values

$$\frac{\mu}{I}(-I), \frac{\mu}{I}(-I+1) \ldots \frac{\mu}{I}(I-1), \frac{\mu}{I}(I)$$

Because of the symmetrical distribution of projections of nuclear moments about zero, the hyperfine structure consists of a symmetrical distribution of lines about the center. Analysis of the hyperfine spectrum consists of finding the spin densities $\delta(r_N)$ at the positions of the nuclei.

Since the spin density $\delta(r)$ is a most useful concept for analysis of hyperfine splittings in polyatomic molecules we shall devote some space to it. $\delta(r)$ is a vector function of position which yields the mean density of a spin at a particular place r. It is calculated from the wave function by the standard recipe of quantum theory, *i.e.*, by finding an operator which corresponds to it and carrying out the appropriate integration. The operator for the density of charge in quantum theory is the delta function. If $\psi(r_1 \ldots r_k, s_1 \ldots s_k)$ is the space spin wave function of system of k particles, the charge density at R is given by

$$\int \psi^* (r_1 \ldots r_k, s_1 \ldots s_k) \sum_i \delta(r_i \ldots R) \psi (r_1 \ldots r_k, s_1 \ldots s_k) \, \mathrm{d}\tau$$

The spin density operator is obtained by multiplying each term of the particle density operator

$$\sum_i \delta(r_i - R)$$

by the operator for a component of spin:

$$\delta_{\mathbf{B}} (R) = \int \psi^* \sum_i \delta(r_i - R) \, \sigma_{\mathbf{B}_i} \psi \, \mathrm{d}\tau$$

For perfect pairing of spin $\delta(R)$ is everywhere zero. For a single electron in a pure spin state the spin density is everywhere proportional to charge density. In polyatomic molecules no simple numerical relation exists. The volume integral over the molecule of each component of spin density is easily shown to be equal to the average value of that component of spin for the molecule. In case the molecule is in a eigenstate of some component of spin, the integral of spin density is equal to the eigenvalue of spin. One special case should be mentioned: If all electrons but one are perfectly paired, the spin density at each position R in the molecule is simply the spin density of the single unpaired electron. Most of the cases of chemical interest are more complicated, but the electron distribution of a single unpaired electron serves as a convenient ideal case with which the experiments may be compared.

The expression for the Fermi term reveals that the isotropic part of the splitting, observable in liquid solutions, depends only on the spin density at the position of each nucleus. The spin density at points not occupied by the nucleus contributes to the anisotropic dipole–dipole hyperfine interaction. We shall discuss the latter following the discussion of liquid solutions.

We now present a few examples of the spectra which are observed in solution. The first example is an aqueous solution of sodium hydrosulfite $Na_2S_2O_4$. A single resonance less than one oersted in breadth is observed at the position of the free electron resonance predicted by (1). The species responsible is undoubtedly SO_2^- which is in equilibrium with $S_2O_4^=$. No hyperfine structure is observed because SO_2^- contains no nuclei with magnetic moments. Verification of the assignment could be made with a sample enriched in ^{33}S.

A more interesting example is the ion $(SO_3)_2NO^=$. The resonance of an aqueous solution of the potassium salt consists of three sharp equally spaced lines of equal intensities. The spacing is 13.0 oersteds, the breadth of each line about 0.4 oersteds. The three lines arise from hyperfine splitting by ^{14}N, a nucleus with spin $I = 1$. The rarer isotope of nitrogen ^{15}N with $I = \frac{1}{2}$ has magnetic moment 0.6943 as great as that of ^{14}N. Two additional lines with position and intensity corresponding to the magnetic moment and natural abundance of ^{15}N are found. The spectra are shown in Fig. 2. (The derivative of absorption is given as a function of yield. Most spectrometers present derivative of absorption rather than absorption.) The spin density may be calculated from the splitting by eqn. (5). A value of $7.62 \cdot 10^{23}$ cm^{-3} is obtained.

A somewhat more complex case of splitting by ^{14}N is observed in solutions of diphenylpicrylhydrazyl. Unless extreme precautions are taken, the spectrum consists of five evenly spaced lines with relative intensities 1:2:3:2:1, the spacing between lines being 9 oersteds. Isotopic substitu-

References p. 208

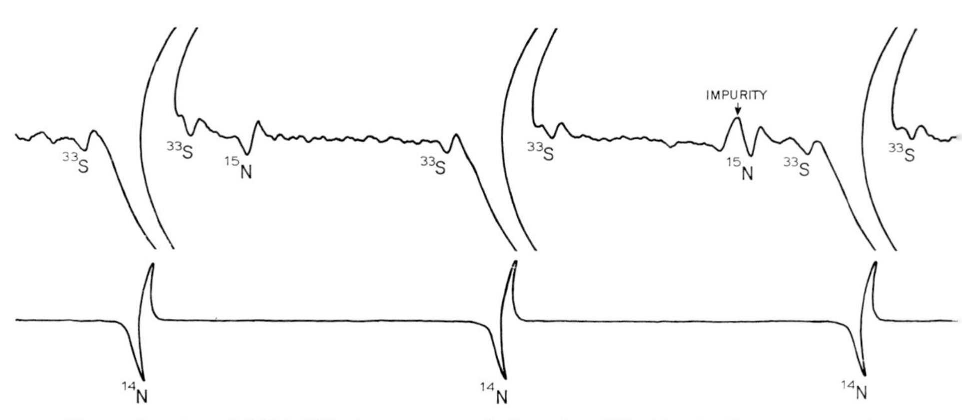

Fig. 2. Spectra of $(SO_3)_2NO^{=}$ in aqueous solution. Amplification in the upper spectrum is fifty times that of the lower one.

tions reveal that the splitting is produced by the hydrazine nitrogens. The splitting by two nitrogens with spin densities δ_1 and δ_2 would give a spectrum of nine lines corresponding to the scheme in Fig. 3.

The arrows give the orientation of the two nitrogen nuclei. When $\delta_1 = \delta_2$, coincidences occur and the spectrum becomes one of five lines.

More careful investigation of the spectrum of very dilute liquid solutions of diphenylpicrylhydrazyl in solvents from which the oxygen has been rigidly excluded has demonstrated further splitting by the protons. The spectrum of a dilute solution in tetrahydrofuran is shown in Fig. 4.

Generally with increasing complexity in the free radical molecules the spectra become more complex and the assignment of coupling constants becomes correspondingly more difficult. The symmetry of the molecule, when its structure is known, is helpful in the interpretation. For instance, the spectrum of the ion $C_6H_6^-$, found by reduction of benzene, consists of seven equally spaced lines with relative intensities 1:6:15:20:15:6:1. The spacing between adjacent lines is 3.6 oersteds. Splitting by six protons with equal coupling constants accounts for the spectrum. The intensity distribution corresponds to the numbers of ways in which the spins of six equivalent protons may be oriented. An arbitrary number N of equivalent protons yields a pattern with intensities varying according to the binomial coefficients

$$1, N, \frac{N(N-1)}{2!} \ldots \frac{N(N-1)\ldots(N-r)}{r!}$$

The spectrum of the negative ion of toluene consists of five groups of lines in intensity ratio 1:4:6:4:1 with splitting 5.5 oersteds (Fig. 5). Each group

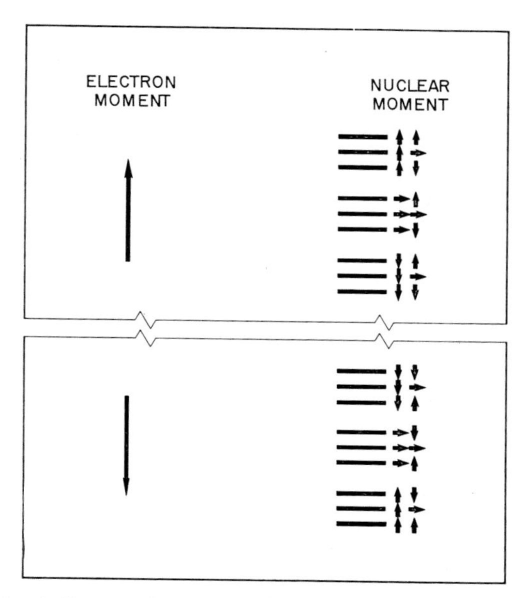

Fig. 3. Energy level diagram for two nuclei of spin 1 with different spin densities.

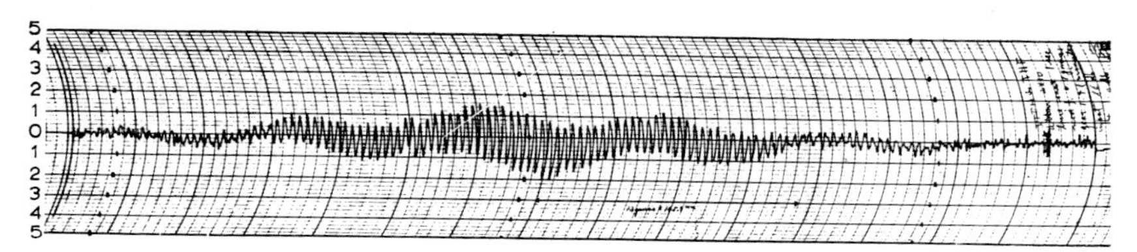

Fig. 4. Spectrum of dilute solution of diphenylpicrylhydrazyl in tetrahydrofuran.

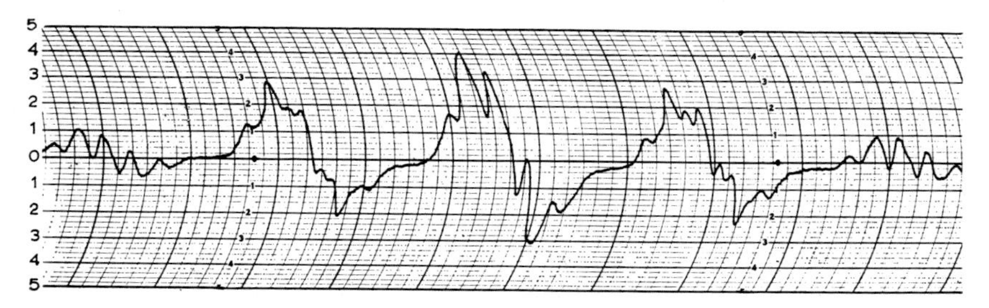

Fig. 5. Spectrum of toluene negative ion.

References p. 208

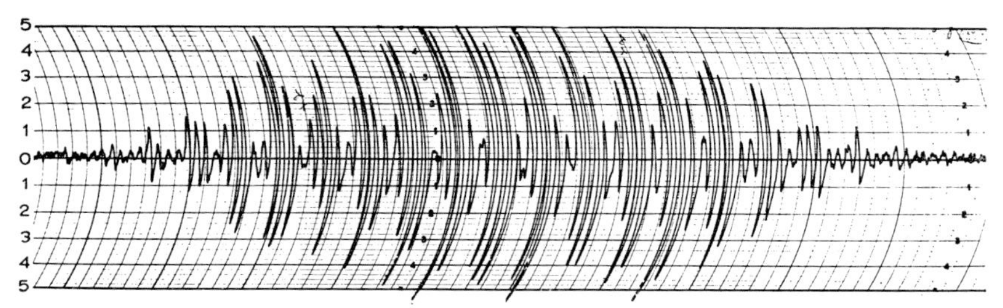

Fig. 6. Spectrum of triphenylmethyl.

is in turn split into several closely spaced components. The principal splitting arises from four equivalent protons. The symmetry of the molecule does not require fourfold equivalence. Experiments with deutero-toluenes show that *ortho* and *meta* protons are practically equivalent, each proton yielding a splitting of 5.5 oersteds. The methyl and *para* protons have very small coupling constants, 0.1 oersted.

Further examples of the kinds of spectra which may be observed are those of triphenylmethyl (Fig. 6), and of the sodium and potassium addition compounds of bis-*p*-nitrophenyl ether (Fig. 7)

O_2N ⟨ ⟩ —O— ⟨ ⟩ NO_2

The latter shows splitting by one nitrogen, by two pairs of equivalent protons, and by sodium or potassium.

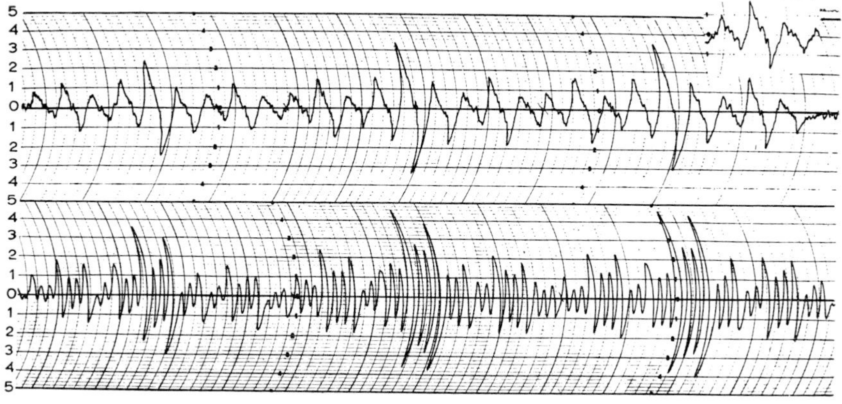

Fig. 7. Spectra of sodium and potassium addition compounds of bis-*p*-nitrophenyl ether. The sodium splitting (above) is larger than the smallest proton splitting. The potassium splitting is barely resolved.

2. Spin densities and electronic structure

(a) Aromatic radicals

From a sufficiently exact description of the structure of a molecule, *i.e.*, from a precise wave function, its magnetic resonance spectrum can be calculated. The converse is not true. The magnetic resonance spectrum imposes conditions on the wave function but does not determine it completely. Most of the wave functions of polyatomic molecules which had been used for interpretation of optical spectra, reactivity, thermodynamic stability, etc., have proved to be partially deficient for interpretation of magnetic resonance spectra. With appropriate modifications each of the two familiar theoretical approximations, valence bond theory and molecular orbital theory, has been found to be applicable to a certain class of substances.

Consider first aromatic free radicals. Their aromatic characteristics are ascribed to the π electrons. The unpaired electron is included in the π population. If no interaction between π and σ electrons were allowed for, the spin density would vanish in the plane of the molecule where all π orbitals vanish. Hence, no hyperfine coupling would be expected from nuclei which lie in the plane of the molecule. The experiments reveal coupling with nuclei (^{1}H, ^{13}C, ^{14}N) in the molecular plane. Neither static distortion from planarity nor out of plane vibrations are capable of producing splittings of the magnitude of the observed ones.

The difficulties are associated with the inaccuracy of the description which puts all the spin density in π orbitals and none in σ orbitals. An exchange interaction resulting from a combination of the requirements of the Pauli exclusion principle and electrostatic interaction produces a slight mixing of π and σ orbitals. Sufficient spin density is produced in the σ bonds to yield the observed splittings. The orbitals associated with the σ bonds do not vanish at the positions of the protons. Proximity of an unpaired electron in a π orbital results in a small pairing of a σ electron with the π electron and leaves a small unpairing in the σ bond. Moreover, the spin density at a proton in an aromatic C—H bond is proportional to the integrated spin density in the π orbitals on the adjacent carbon. The latter statement has good theoretical justification*, and is consistent with many experiments. The interaction is very small, amounting only to a few hundredths of one percent for the squares of the amplitudes of the admixed states with spin density in the σ bonds. It is large enough to yield observable effects, yet small enough so as not to require serious modification of the approximation which has been developed for treatment of phenomena other than magnetic resonance.

* See McLachlan, Dearman and Lefebvre[7] for a recent paper on this subject.

Thus the proton splittings, while not produced directly by spin density in π orbitals, are useful for determining the distribution of spin in the π orbitals. Ideally the connection between spin density in π orbitals and the measured proton splittings should be established by independent measurements of the two quantities. While such measurements seem to be possible, they are difficult in polyatomic systems and the connection is established in the hybrid fashion which has come to be known as "semi-empirical". Distribution of π density is calculated from a molecular theory, and a spectrum predicted from it. The procedure is successful in a large number of cases. Nevertheless, corroboration by independent measurements would be welcome.

Let us now return to consideration of the spectra of the molecules which were mentioned at the beginning of this section and to a few others. The spectrum of benzene negative ion arises from coupling of an electron spin to six equivalent protons. The total spread of the spectrum, 22 oersteds, yields a proportionality constant between π spin density and proton coupling constant. The splittings in toluene negative ion arise almost entirely from the *ortho* and *meta* proton with equal couplings and hence about one-quarter of the spin is on each of the corresponding carbon atoms.

Chemical experiments with this ion show that the predominant attack on toluene negative ion by protons occurs at the *ortho* and *meta* positions[8]. In a molecular orbital approximation, toluene negative ion could be described as having a single electron in an orbital which is antisymmetric in the symmetry plane which passes through the methyl group and the position para to it. All other orbitals are either filled or vacant.

Naphthalene negative ion exhibits a spectrum of twenty-five lines, which arise from couplings to two sets of four equivalent protons each. The coupling constant to each member of one set is 4.95 oersteds, the other 1.89 oersteds. Deuterium substitution reveals that the α protons have the larger coupling constant. The ratio of the coupling constants is, within a few percent, the ratio of the squares of the corresponding coefficients in the lowest vacant molecular orbital of naphthalene. The distribution of spin is well represented by molecular orbital theory with coefficients given by the procedure devised by Hückel[9]. The ions of a large number of even alternant aromatic hydrocarbons (hydrocarbons with an even number of carbon atoms in the conjugated system and with rings containing even numbers of carbons) have been investigated. With only a few exceptions, the distribution of spin (and presumably of charge) is given remarkably well by simple molecular orbital theory.

The situation in odd alternant radicals, on the other hand, is quite different. Triphenylmethyl, as an example, would by simple molecular orbital theory have zero spin on the *meta* carbons and equal amounts of spin on the *ortho* and *para* positions. Such a distribution of spin would yield ten lines with binomial intensity distribution. Simple valence bond theory predicts quite a different distribution of spin. The spin density at the *meta* positions is approximately minus one-half the density at the *ortho* and *para* positions. The complex spectrum of triphenylmethyl shown in Fig. 6 is accounted for remarkably well by the valence bond approximation. The assignments have been checked by isotopic substitution.

The assignment of spin densities with opposite signs to adjacent carbon atoms is a characteristic feature of the valence bond theory. It cannot be obtained from the simple versions of one configuration molecular orbital theory. More sophisticated versions of molecular orbital theory which include mixed configurations or which permit electrons of opposing spins to occupy different orbitals are capable of treating odd alternant radicals[10]. The situation may perhaps be summarized as follows: In aromatic radicals simple valence bond theory gives a fairly satisfactory representation of the odd-alternant ones, while simple molecular orbital theory is satisfactory for the even-alternant ones. The simple theories are not interchangeable.

In aromatic radicals which contain other atoms in addition to carbon and hydrogen (semiquinones, phenoxy radicals, hydrazuls, etc.) the connections between spin density on carbon and the splittings produced by adjacent protons appears to be the same as in the hydrocarbon radicals. Thus the splitting of only 2.37 oersteds by each of the four ring protons in semiquinone negative ion may be interpreted to mean that only 0.4 of an electron spin is on the carbon atom adjacent to protons; the remaining 0.6 is divided between oxygen atoms on the carbon atoms adjacent to them. Only a beginning has been made on the theoretical treatment of splittings by nitrogen and carbon thirteen. The connections between coupling constant and spin density given in eqn. (3) are valid but the further connections with overall spin distribution are not yet completely worked out.

(b) Aliphatic radicals

Many aliphatic radicals have been produced in glasses, plastics, and crystalline solids by ultraviolet light or X-rays. Account must be taken of the direct dipole–dipole interaction in the analysis of their spectra. The analysis is difficult unless the molecules are oriented at one or at most a few known directions relative to the field. The spectra from randomly oriented samples consist of superpositions of the spectra from molecules lying in all directions. Most of the interpretations of such spectra have been based on the assumption that the splittings are isotropic. Serious errors may result from such an interpretation since the angular dependences may be such that the superpositions resemble isotropic patterns of species quite different from those actually involved.

References p. 208

The following results may be questioned because they were obtained in polycrystalline materials. Nevertheless, their internal consistency indicates that they are probably correct. In the radical CH_3, the isotropic coupling constant with each proton is about 20 oersteds[11,12]. The radical is presumably planar, the spin density appearing on the protons by the mechanism of π–σ interaction which was described in the discussion of aromatic radicals. In the radical H_2CCH_3 the coupling to each of the 5 protons is also about 20 oersteds. The mechanism which produces the spin on the methyl groups is presumably hyperconjugation. The structure of the radical is mainly

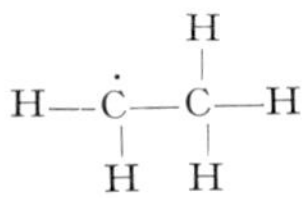

```
        H
        |
H—Ċ—C—H
   |    |
   H   H
```

Admixture of only 4% of each of the structures

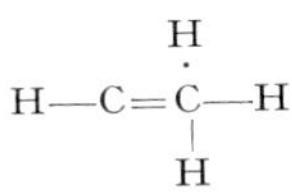

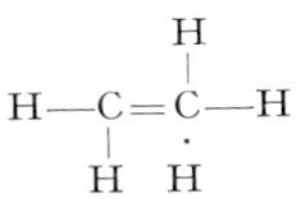

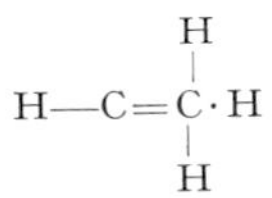

```
     H                    H                  H
     ·                    |                  |
H—C=C—H         H—C=C—H         H—C=C·H
     |               |   ·               |
     H               H  H                H
```

is capable of producing the observed spectra[13]. Thus in every radical R_2—CH—R_1 coupling to the protons on the "trivalent carbon" where the spin is predominantly localized is almost equal to the coupling to the protons on the adjacent carbons through the hyperconjugative mechanism.

Similarly in mixed aliphatic–aromatic radicals unusually large couplings to aliphatic protons are often found. Large couplings to methyl protons are found in Wurster's salts, methyl substituted semiquinones, etc.

(c) Anisotropic effects, triplet molecules

The anisotropic effects lead to displacement of levels from the schemes indicated in Fig. 1 (p. 192) and Fig. 2 (p. 198) and to mixing of the nuclear spin states. The effective magnetic field at each nucleus is not generally parallel to the external field; its direction is different in the two electrons spin states. The failure of the nuclei to be aligned along the direction in which electron spins are aligned leads to more lines than our previous simple scheme would allow for. Thus the hydrogen atom which has spherical symmetry has two lines in its spectrum, but the radical HO_2C—CH—CO_2H in which the electron interacts with only one proton has four lines at most orientations of the molecule. Only a few studies of single crystals with known orientation of radicals have been published[14–16] at the time at which this chapter was prepared. From such spectra not only are the spin densities at the positions of the nuclei obtainable, but also the five components of a tensor which describe the distribution of spin about each nucleus. A detailed picture of spin distribution, including six parameters for each nucleus, may thus be obtained from oriented free radical molecules.

Much of the early interest on the part of physical chemists in paramagnetic resonance lay in the possibility of using the method for triplet molecules. Despite the early interest and continuous work, almost a decade elapsed before a successful experiment was performed. Hutchison and Mangum[17] observed magnetic resonance absorption from the photoexcited state of naphthalene. The naphthalene was in solid solution in a single crystal of durene. The spectrum is highly anisotropic, the lines executing an excursion of 2100 oersteds as the crystal is turned in the magnetic field. This high degree of anisotropy prevents observation in randomly oriented solids or in liquids.

The anisotropy arises because a triplet state has two unpaired electrons. The magnetic field at a distance of one ångstrom from an electron is about ten thousand oersteds, a field comparable to the largest fields at which experiments are done. Large direct dipole splittings are expected in triplet molecules from the magnetic field of one electron at the position of the other (the Fermi term for electron–electron interaction vanishes in the triplet state). Observation of triplet molecules is possible but more difficult than observation of doublet molecules. However, analysis of the results leads to valuable data, not only about the distribution of the two unpaired electrons relative to the nuclei, but also about the correlations between them. The separation between electrons and the orientation of the vector between them relative to the molecular axes determines the magnitude of the electron–electron splitting and its directional properties.

3. Variations in g value

The splitting factor 2.0023 which appears in eqn. (1) applies to situations in which the resonance is associated with the spin magnetic moment exclusively. In aromatic radicals the relation (1) applies very accurately, because the coupling of spin to the molecular axes is very weak. Such coupling occurs through the spin–orbit interaction which arises from the magnetic field associated with the motion of the electronic charge through the electric fields within the molecule. In some circumstances, particularly in molecules containing heavy atoms, such coupling is not negligible and deviations from the splitting constant 2.0023 are found. Further, since the deviations are associated with electric fields which are tightly coupled to the molecular axes, the splitting factor may depend on the orientation of the molecules

References p. 208

relative to the external fields. This effect (g value anisotropy) is particularly useful for helping to locate molecular axes relative to crystal axes. It has been applied to haemoglobins[18].

4. Rates and mechanisms

The preceding discussion has been concerned for the most part with time average properties of free radical molecules. In our statements concerning the positions of electron spin resonance lines we frequently used the concept "average magnetic field". "Average" refers to a time average. The nature of the fluctuations about the average and the shapes of the absorption lines are related.

The variations in magnetic field may be produced by chemical processes. Hence it is possible to extract information concerning chemical processes from the shapes of the lines themselves. Theories of great generality concerning connections between variations in time of the relevant variables and shapes of spectral lines have been worked out[19,20]. We may use the results for the limiting cases of slow and rapid processes.

Consider an electron spin which may migrate among sites of different resonance frequencies. The slow limit corresponds to one in which the frequency of migration is small compared with the frequency differences between lines. The rapid limit is one in which the frequency of migration is large compared with the excursion in frequency over all sites. The behavior of naphthalene negative ion in appropriate environments is a good example. The spectrum consists of 25 lines each associated with one of the 25 distinct ways in which the protons magnetic moments may be arranged. The breadth of each line is about 10^5 cycles per second, splittings range between 10^6 and $15 \cdot 10^6$ cycles per second, and the entire spectrum is $80 \cdot 10^6$ cycles per second in breadth. In the presence of neutral naphthalene at low concentration the unpaired electron occasionally leaves a naphthalene negative ion and moves to a previously neutral naphthalene molecule. The position of the resonance line in the new site is usually not the same as in the old site. If the shifts in position of resonance lines are randomly distributed in time with mean life τ in each site, the migration process contributes $1/2\pi\tau$ to the breadth of each line. In the case just mentioned $1/\tau$ has been found to be proportional to the concentration of added naphthalene. $1/\tau$ measures a mean frequency of "turnover" for the naphthalene negative ion. Similar measurements have been made in other cases.

The limiting case corresponding to rapid processes occurs when the exchange frequency $1/t$ is large compared with the total excursion of frequencies in the various static configurations. A narrowing of the line whose total extent in the absence of the migration process is ΔV_0 to one with breadth $\tau(\Delta V_0)^2$ occurs.

In the naphthalene negative ion–naphthalene system the rapid exchange range may be reached at large concentrations of naphthalene. The entire spectrum collapses into a single line whose breadth diminishes as τ is shortened.

In certain cases intramolecular electronic motions may contribute to line breadths. Generally electrons move so rapidly in molecules that the residual line breadths associated with their motion is negligible. In the limit of very rapid fluctuation ($\tau \rightarrow 0$) the averaging of the fields becomes perfect. But in molecules in which various possible sites for an unpaired electron are well separated from each other, the migrations may become slow enough so that their contribution to line breadths are observable.

The use of line shapes for measurements of rates has not been exploited as fully as has been the determination of average distributions from positions and intensities of lines. But in view of its possibilities for studying kinetics in systems in equilibrium or in steady states, we may expect growing uses in that direction.

References p. 208

REFERENCES

[1] E. Zavoiski, *J. Phys. (U.S.S.R.)*, 9 (1945) 245.
[2] E. Fermi, *Z. Physik*, 60 (1930) 320.
[3] S. I. Weissman, *J. Chem. Phys.*, 22 (1954) 1378.
[4] N. Bloembergen and W. C. Dickinson, *Phys. Rev.*, 79 (1950) 179.
[5] H. A. Jahn and E. Teller, *Proc. Roy. Soc. (London)*, 161A (1937) 220.
[6] H. A. Kramers, *Koninkl. Ned. Akad. Wetenschap. Proc.*, 33 (1930) 959.
[7] A. D. McLachlan, H. H. Dearman and R. Lefebvre, *J. Chem. Phys.*, 33 (1960) 65.
[8] A. Krapcho and A. Bothner-By, *J. Am. Chem. Soc.*, 81 (1959) 3658.
[9] E. Hückel, *Z. Physik*, 70 (1931) 204.
[10] R. Lefebvre, H. H. Dearman and H. McConnell, *J. Chem. Phys.*, 32 (1960) 176.
[11] W. Gordy and C. G. McCormick, *J. Am. Chem. Soc.*, 78 (1956) 3293.
[12] B. Smaller and M. S. Matheson, *J. Chem. Phys.*, 28 (1958) 1169.
[13] D. Chestnut, *J. Chem. Phys.*, 29 (1958) 43.
[14] T. Cole, D. Heller and H. McConnell, *Proc. Natl. Acad. Sci., U.S.*, 45 (1959) 525.
[15] D. Whiffen and N. Atherton, *Molecular Physics*, 3 (1960) 1.
[16] I. Miyagawa and W. Gordy, *J. Chem. Phys.*, 32 (1960) 255.
[17] C. Hutchison and B. Mangum, *J. Chem. Phys.*, 29 (1958) 925.
[18] D. Ingram, *Arch. sci. (Geneva)*, 10 (1957) 109.
[19] P. W. Anderson, *J. Phys. Soc. Japan*, 9 (1954) 316.
[20] R. Kubo and K. Tomita, *J. Phys. Soc. Japan*, 9 (1954) 888.

Chapter VIII

Nuclear Magnetic Resonance

CHRISTINE D. JARDETZKY AND OLEG JARDETZKY

The Biological Laboratories, Harvard University, Cambridge, Mass. (U.S.A.)
and
Department of Pharmacology, Harvard Medical School, Boston, Mass. (U.S.A.)

1. Introduction

The absorption (and re-emission) of radiofrequency radiation by the atomic nuclei of molecules placed in a strong magnetic field, is referred to as nuclear magnetic resonance (NMR). This phenomenon was predicted by Gorter in 1936 from theoretical considerations, and was experimentally detected in 1945 by Purcell and Bloch on protons in water. The original observations were subsequently extended to the nuclei of other elements, providing information on their magnetic properties.

In 1949 Knight discovered that the nuclei of a series of elements (Li, Na, Al, Cu, Ga) absorbed radiation at a higher frequency, when the element was in the metallic state, than when it was in an ionic form as the dissolved chloride salt. It was thus found that large differences in the resonance frequency of a given element can arise from the presence of conductance electrons in the metallic but not in the ionic state of that element. This phenomenon is known as the *Knight shift*. Almost simultaneously a shift of much smaller magnitude, known as the *chemical shift*, was also discovered by Knight. The resonance frequency of a given element was found to depend on the type of chemical group(s) to which the element was bonded. This small but definite effect has since served as the basis for identifying distinct chemical groups and for establishing chemical structures from NMR spectra.

Additional structural information can be derived from the spectral changes which may be attributed to interactions between nuclei in the same molecule. Resolution of the resulting fine differences in resonance frequency requires the use of strong and exceedingly homogeneous magnetic fields. The emergence of high resolution NMR spectroscopy over the last ten years as a powerful method for the study of molecular structure as well as of chemical

References p. 264

processes and interactions between molecules is due in large measure to the development of suitable magnets.

In NMR spectroscopy one is confronted with two distinct theoretical problems. The first lies in establishing the mathematical relationships which describe the absorption of radiation in terms of the behavior of a given set of atomic nuclei in the presence of external magnetic fields. These relationships predict quantitatively such experimentally measurable parameters as positions, widths and intensities of absorption lines which characterize NMR spectra. The second consists of correlating observed differences in absorption lines which are due to nuclei of the same element in a given substance with the chemical structure of the substance. Insofar as such a correlation is possible, it provides a theoretical basis for inferences concerning chemical structures and processes.

The present chapter is primarily an introduction to those physical principles which are essential for an elementary understanding of the nuclear magnetic resonance phenomenon and its applications. A complete and detailed treatment of the methods developed for the analysis of NMR spectra requires this knowledge as well as a knowledge of quantum mechanics and is to be found elsewhere[1]. More detailed discussion of different aspects of the theory and applications of NMR can also be found in several other references[2-9].

A. PHYSICAL PRINCIPLES

2. Physical properties of atomic nuclei

Experiments on the scattering of subatomic particles by atomic nuclei have shown that the latter have radii of the order of 10^{-13} cm, *i.e.* 10^5 times smaller than the radii of whole atoms which consist of nuclei and electrons and have dimensions of about 10^{-8} cm (= 1 Å). Since the mass of each of the elementary particles which comprise the nucleus (*i.e.* protons and neutrons) is approximately 1836 times greater than the mass of an electron, the nuclei may be regarded as very dense, small particles bearing virtually the total mass of the corresponding atoms. Each nucleus has a charge equal to the number of protons, which it contains, times the elementary charge of the proton, *i.e.* $4.8 \cdot 10^{-10}$ electrostatic units (esu).

From the splitting of spectral lines (which represent discrete changes in the total electronic energy of the atom) Pauli concluded in 1924 that nuclei possess magnetic properties. This is readily understandable since the nuclei may be thought to consist of orbiting or spinning charges (Fig. 1), which are equivalent to an electric current. The existence of magnetic forces between two wire loops through which a current is passing has been known since their discovery by Ampère in 1820.

The magnetic properties of a circular wire loop may be measured by its magnetic dipole moment $\boldsymbol{\mu}$ which is defined as a vector pointing in a direction perpendicular to the plane of the loop*. Its magnitude μ is a function of the

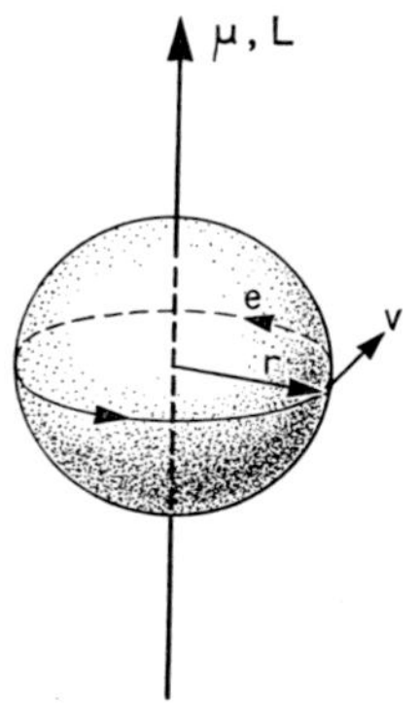

Fig. 1. Spherically symmetrical nucleus of radius r. A positive charge e orbiting with linear velocity $\boldsymbol{v}$ gives rise to two collinear vectors, the angular momentum $\boldsymbol{L}$, and the magnetic moment $\boldsymbol{\mu}$, both of which are perpendicular to the plane defined by the orbit of the charge. The direction of these vectors is found by the right-hand rule (it is the direction of the thumb when the rest of the fingers of the right hand are curved in the direction of the current due to the moving charge). In this case the current and the charge move in the same direction. A negative charge, however, would move in a direction opposite to that of the current.

current i flowing in the wire and of the area of the circle A,

$$\mu = \frac{iA}{c} \tag{1}$$

where c is by definition the ratio between the electrostatic and electromagnetic units of measurement and is numerically and dimensionally equal to the velocity of light ($3 \cdot 10^{10}$ cm/sec)**. In the case of a charge moving in a circular path the current is given by the product of the charge e by its velocity v, divided by the length of the path $2\pi r$, where r is the radius of the circle. Since the area of the circle is πr^2 we have

$$\mu = \frac{1}{c}\frac{\pi r^2}{2\pi r}ev = \frac{erv}{2c} = \frac{e}{2mc}L \tag{2}$$

* Vector quantities are shown in bold face letters and scalar quantities in italics.

** For a bar magnet the magnetic moment may be defined as the product of the strength of one of its poles m by its length l, *i.e.* $\boldsymbol{\mu} = ml$. Since the bar magnet corresponding to an orbiting or a spinning charge is fictitious, one may assume any values for its pole strength and its length as long as the product of the two remains constant.

References p. 264

where L is the angular momentum of the charge about the axis of rotation. In an isolated system the angular momentum (like charge and mass) remains constant with time. An atomic nucleus may for all practical purposes be regarded as an isolated system, and eqn. (2) therefore indicates that the magnetic moment may be taken as one of its characteristic constants.

Several systems of units are used in magnetic measurements, the one most directly related to the *cgs* system being referred to as the absolute electromagnetic *cgs* system (emu) (ref.[10]). It is based on Coulomb's law for magnetic poles just as the electrostatic system of units of charge, current, potential etc. is based on Coulomb's law for electric charges. The magnitude of the force, F, between two magnetic poles is thus given by

$$F = \frac{m_1 m_2}{r^2 \hat{\mu}_0} \tag{3}$$

Where m_1 and m_2 are the two isolated poles, r is the distance between them and $\hat{\mu}_0$ is a constant of proportionality (referred to as the magnetic permeability of free space), necessary to reconcile the dimensions on the two sides of the equal sign.

The unit magnetic pole is accordingly defined as that pole which *in vacuo* attracts or repels another equal pole placed at a distance of 1 cm with a force of 1 dyne. Unlike a charge, an isolated magnetic pole is never found in nature and so is always represented by either end of a very long narrow magnet. The unit of pole strength thus defined is known as the (absolute) *electromagnetic cgs unit.*

The region of space in which a magnetic force exists is known as a magnetic field. The strength or intensity of a magnetic field at a given point is defined as the force which acts on a pole of unit strength at this point. The unit of magnetic field intensity is commonly known as the *gauss* even though its name has been officially changed to *oerstedt* by the International Electrotechnical Commission in 1930. It is defined as the force on a unit magnetic pole exerted by a unit magnetic pole at a distance of 1 cm.

If a unit pole is placed inside a sample of matter, the force exerted on it by an external magnetic field will be different from what it would have been in the absence of the surrounding matter. The effective field intensity inside a medium is referred to as the magnetic induction, B, and its ratio to the magnetic field intensity *in vacuo*, H, is called the magnetic permeability of the medium, $\hat{\mu} = B/H$. In the newer nomenclature the term *gauss* is applied to the unit of magnetic induction.

The work required to bring a unit magnetic pole from infinity to a given point in the magnetic field is defined as the magnetic potential at that point. Its unit in the electromagnetic cgs system is the *gilbert*, defined as 1 erg per electromagnetic unit of magnetic pole strength. The total force acting on a unit pole across a given area is known as the magnetic flux and is measured in *maxwells*, 1 *maxwell* = 1 *gauss* $\times$ 1 cm^2. The magnetic flux across the total surface of a magnetic pole is equal to the pole strength.

3. An isolated atomic nucleus in a magnetic field

Measurements of nuclear magnetic moments, carried out by passing beams of nuclei across inhomogeneous magnetic fields have established the fact that these moments can have only one of a small number of discrete values. This finding has been interpreted to mean that the magnetic moment vector associated with the nucleus (Fig. 1) can only assume a finite number of orientations when placed in a magnetic field of intensity H_z (Fig. 2). Each

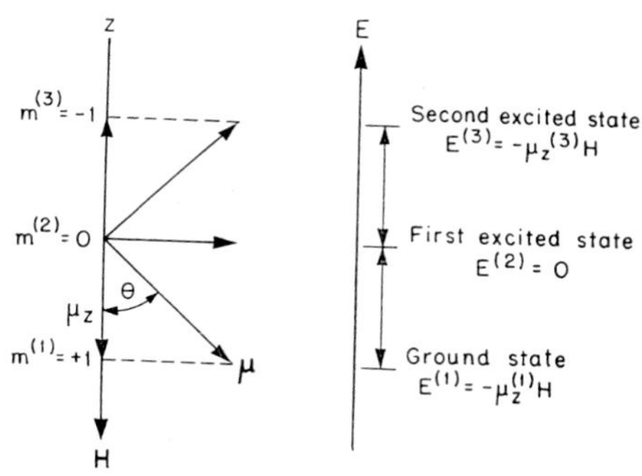

Fig. 2. Quantization of the magnetic moment $\boldsymbol{\mu}$ and the energy of interaction E in a magnetic field H. The nuclear spin I is equal to 1. Thus the magnetic quantum number m can have the values 1, 0 and — 1. The energy of interaction is increasing in a direction opposite to the magnetic field H and can have three values since the component of the magnetic moment along the z-axis, μ_z, is given by $m\gamma\, h/2\pi$. Transitions occur between adjacent energy levels for which $\Delta m = 1$ and the frequency of the radiation inducing these transitions is

$$\nu_{(\mathrm{sec}^{-1})} = \frac{\Delta E}{h} = \frac{E^{(2)} - E^{(1)}}{h} = \frac{E^{(3)} - E^{(2)}}{h}$$

of these measurable values of the nuclear magnetic moment corresponds accordingly to one of the possible projections of its magnetic moment vector $\boldsymbol{\mu}$ on the direction of the field H_z. The magnitude of this projection is

$$\mu_z = \mu \cos \theta \tag{4}$$

where θ is the angle between $\boldsymbol{\mu}$ and H_z (Fig. 2). As long as the angle θ is not subject to experimental observation, only values of μ_z but not of μ can be measured. It has therefore become customary to refer to the maximum measurable value of μ_z as the magnetic moment of a given nucleus rather than to the corresponding value of μ.

According to eqn. (2) a definite value of the angular momentum corresponds

References p. 264

to each value of the magnetic moment. The observed values of the magnetic moment for a given nucleus can be systematized in a simple manner if it is assumed that the projection of the angular momentum vector L on the direction of the magnetic field H_z must always be a half integral multiple of $h/2\pi$, where h is Planck's constant ($h = 6.62 \cdot 10^{-27}$ erg·sec). However, if this is done, the ratio of magnetic moments to angular momentum called the magnetogyric (more commonly gyromagnetic) ratio is no longer exactly equal to its value in the theoretical model, *i.e.* $e/2mc$. The relationship between the magnetic moment of a nucleus and its angular momentum is accordingly written

$$\mu_{z\,\max} = g \frac{e}{2mc} I \frac{h}{2\pi} = \gamma I \frac{h}{2\pi} \tag{5a}$$

where I is the maximum value of the nuclear angular momentum expressed in units of $h/2\pi$ and known as the nuclear spin; g is called the nuclear g factor and is a dimensionless constant characteristic of a given nuclear species*.

The other observed values of μ_z may then be found from the relationship

$$\mu_z = \frac{m}{I} \mu_{z\,\max} \tag{5b}$$

where m is called the nuclear magnetic quantum number and can have values equal to I, $I - 1$, $I - 2$, etc. to a minimum value of $-I$. Thus if a given nucleus (like the proton) has a spin $I = \frac{1}{2}$, m can have the values $+\frac{1}{2}$ and $-\frac{1}{2}$ and there will be two corresponding values of the magnetic moment, $\mu_z^{(1)} = \frac{1}{2}\gamma(h/2\pi)$ and $\mu_z^{(2)} = -\frac{1}{2}\gamma(h/2\pi)$ respectively. Numerical values of the spins and magnetic moments for several nuclei of interest in biological chemistry are given in Table I.

The following three empirical rules hold for the relationship between the spin, the mass number A and the charge number Z of a given atomic nucleus: (1) If the mass number A and the charge number Z are both even, the spin, and hence the magnetic moment of the nucleus, is equal to 0. (2) The spin of any nucleus which has an odd mass number A is half integral. (3) The spin of any nucleus whose mass number A is even and the charge number Z is odd, is integral.

* If e and m are taken to represent the charge and mass of the proton respectively, the quantity $e/2mc \cdot h/2\pi$ is used as a unit of nuclear magnetic moment called the nuclear magneton. The magnitude of the nuclear magneton is $5.0493 \cdot 10^{-24}$ erg/gauss. The units of γ accordingly are (gauss·sec)$^{-1}$ or radians per second per gauss.

TABLE I

SPIN RESONANCE DATA FOR SOME COMMON NUCLEI*

Isotope	*Spin, I, in multiples of h/2π*	*Magnetic moment, μ, in multiples of the nuclear magneton (eh/4πmc)*	*Electric quadrupole moment, Q, in multiples of $e \cdot 10^{-24}$ cm²*	*NMR frequency in megacycles/sec in a field of 10 kilogauss*	*Relative sensitivity for equal number of nuclei*		*Natural abundance in % by weight of the element*
					At constant field	*At constant frequency*	
^{1}H	1/2	2.79277	—	42.57	1.000	1.000	99.9844
^{2}H	1	0.85738	$2.77 \cdot 10^{-3}$	6.536	$9.64 \cdot 10^{-3}$	0.409	$1.56 \cdot 10^{-2}$
^{3}H**	1/2	2.9788	—	45.41	1.21	1.07	—
^{7}Li	3/2	3.257	$-4.2 \cdot 10^{-2}$	16.55	0.294	1.94	92.57
^{13}C	1/2	0.7022	—	10.71	$1.59 \cdot 10^{-2}$	0.251	1.108
^{14}N	1	0.4036	$2 \cdot 10^{-2}$	3.077	$1.01 \cdot 10^{-3}$	0.193	99.635
^{15}N	1/2	−0.2831	—	4.316	$1.04 \cdot 10^{-3}$	0.101	0.365
^{17}O	5/2	−1.893	$-4 \cdot 10^{-3}$	5.772	$2.91 \cdot 10^{-2}$	1.58	$3.7 \cdot 10^{-2}$
^{19}F	1/2	2.627	—	40.07	0.834	0.941	100.
^{23}Na	3/2	2.217	0.1	11.262	$9.27 \cdot 10^{-2}$	1.32	100.
^{25}Mg	5/2	−0.8547	—	2.606	$2.68 \cdot 10^{-2}$	0.714	10.05
^{31}P	1/2	1.131	—	17.24	$6.64 \cdot 10^{-2}$	0.405	100.
^{33}S	3/2	0.6429	$-6.4 \cdot 10^{-2}$	3.267	$2.26 \cdot 10^{-3}$	0.384	0.74
^{35}Cl	3/2	0.8209	$-7.97 \cdot 10^{-2}$	4.173	$4.71 \cdot 10^{-3}$	0.490	75.4
^{39}K	3/2	0.3910	—	1.987	$5.08 \cdot 10^{-4}$	0.233	93.08
^{43}Ca	7/2	−1.315	—	2.864	$6.39 \cdot 10^{-2}$	1.41	0.13
^{55}Mn	5/2	3.462	0.5	10.56	0.178	2.83	100.
^{57}Fe	—	$\leqslant$ 0.05	—	—	—	—	2.245
^{59}Co	7/2	4.639	0.5	10.103	0.281	4.83	100.
^{63}Cu	3/2	2.226	−0.15	11.285	$9.38 \cdot 10^{-2}$	1.33	69.09
^{65}Cu	3/2	2.379	−0.14	12.09	0.116	1.42	30.91
^{75}As	3/2	1.435	0.3	7.293	$2.51 \cdot 10^{-2}$	0.856	100.
^{79}Br	3/2	2.099	0.30	10.667	$7.86 \cdot 10^{-2}$	1.26	50.57
^{81}Br	3/2	2.263	0.25	11.498	$9.84 \cdot 10^{-2}$	1.35	49.43
^{85}Rb	5/2	1.349	—	4.111	$1.05 \cdot 10^{-2}$	1.13	72.8
^{127}I	5/2	2.794	−0.59	8.519	$9.35 \cdot 10^{-2}$	2.33	100.
^{133}Cs	7/2	2.564	$\leqslant$ 0.3	5.585	$4.74 \cdot 10^{-2}$	2.75	100.
^{137}Ba	3/2	0.936	—	4.76	$6.97 \cdot 10^{-3}$	0.59	11.32

*From the Varian Associates NMR table.
** Indicates radioactive isotope.

References p. 264

To each of the discrete orientations assumed by the nuclear magnetic moment vector in the external magnetic field of intensity H_z corresponds an energy* of interaction E

$$E = - \boldsymbol{\mu} \cdot \mathbf{H}_z \tag{6}$$

The potential energy of a nucleus in a magnetic field can thus have only one of a discrete set of values and one speaks of each value as defining an "energy state" or "energy level" of the nucleus in the field**. Any change in the orientation of the nuclear magnetic moment vector with respect to the external field must be associated with a discrete change in the potential energy, equal to the difference between the energy values defining two energy levels. This process is called a *transition* between energy levels, the transition energy ΔE being defined by

$$\Delta E = E^{(2)} - E^{(1)} = (\mu_z^{(1)} - \mu_z^{(2)})H_z \tag{7}$$

If the transition is to result from the absorption of electromagnetic radiation, the frequency ν ($\sec^{-1}$) of this radiation must be such that the transition energy for one nucleus can be expressed as the energy of one absorbed quantum, *i.e.*

$$\Delta E = h\nu \tag{8}$$

From eqns. (4), (7) and (8) one thus sees that the frequency of electromagnetic radiation causing the transition must be directly proportional to the strength of the magnetic field in which the transition occurs,

$$\nu = \frac{\Delta E}{h} = \frac{\mu_z^{(1)} - \mu_z^{(2)}}{h} H_z = \frac{\gamma}{2\pi} H_z \tag{8a}$$

Thus far we have considered only the static picture of the discrete orientations in space of the angular momentum and magnetic moment vectors in the presence of the external field $\mathbf{H}_z$. Although the relationship between frequency of absorbed radiation and the intensity of the external field can

---

* $\mathbf{A} \cdot \mathbf{B}$ denotes the scalar product which is given by $AB \cos \theta$, while $\mathbf{A} \times \mathbf{B}$ denotes the vectorial product of two vectors, $\mathbf{A}$ and $\mathbf{B}$, and is represented by a vector perpendicular to the plane formed by $\mathbf{A}$ and $\mathbf{B}$ with a magnitude given by $AB \sin \theta$, where θ is the angle between the vectors $\mathbf{A}$ and $\mathbf{B}$. The vector resulting from the above cross product points toward the observer facing the AB plane when he has to rotate $\mathbf{A}$ counterclockwise in this plane in order to superimpose it on $\mathbf{B}$.

** Because of the negative sign in eqn. (6) the orientation corresponding to $\mu_{z\,\max}$ and H_z defines the state of *lowest* potential energy, referred to as the *ground state*. All energy levels defined by *higher* values of the potential energy are called *excited states*.

be derived from it (eqn. 8a), in order to understand the process of magnetic resonance it is essential to consider the dynamic picture as well.

In the presence of the strong external field H_z the angular momentum and magnetic moment vectors experience a torque (= moment of the magnetic force) whose direction is perpendicular to both $\boldsymbol{\mu}$ and the field H_z. The magnitude of this torque

$$T = \mu H_z \sin\theta \tag{9}$$

measures the tendency of the magnetic moment vector to align itself along the direction of H_z. While a permanent magnet which does not possess angular momentum due to spinning becomes perfectly aligned along H_z, the effect on the spinning nucleus is one of rotation of L (and $\boldsymbol{\mu}$) and thus of the nucleus itself about the H_z axis at a fixed angle. This motion is referred to as precession* and is illustrated in Fig. 3. From the laws of

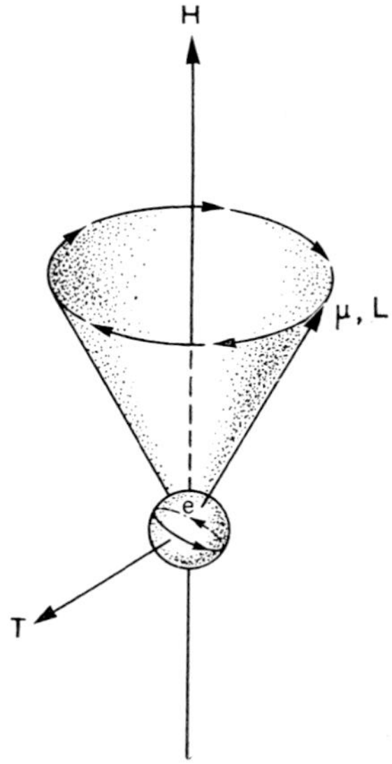

Fig. 3. Nuclear precession about the magnetic field axis H.

rotational motion the rate of change of the angular momentum vector with time is equal to and has a direction parallel to the torque

$$\frac{\mathrm{d}L}{\mathrm{d}t} = T \tag{10}$$

* Precession is defined as the rotation of an axis of rotation about another axis.

Thus
$$\frac{dL}{dt} = \boldsymbol{\mu} \times H_z \tag{10a}$$

and since $\boldsymbol{\mu} = \gamma L$
$$\frac{d\boldsymbol{\mu}}{dt} = \gamma(\boldsymbol{\mu} \times H_z) = -\gamma(H_z \times \boldsymbol{\mu}) \tag{11}$$

where $-\gamma H_z$ represents the angular frequency of precession of the magnetic vector, $\boldsymbol{\mu}$ about the external field H_z. It is called the Larmor precession frequency*,
$$\boldsymbol{\omega}_0 = -\gamma H_z \tag{12}$$

The magnitude of the angular frequency ω is given by γH_z and is measured in radians/sec. The frequency of the radiation ν in cycles/sec is related to it by $\omega = 2\pi\nu$, since 1 cycle $= 2\pi$ radians.

4. Magnetic resonance in the case of an isolated nucleus

In principle magnetic resonance may be understood by considering the precession of $\boldsymbol{\mu}$ about two mutually perpendicular external magnetic fields. Let us therefore consider the case where a second magnetic field H_1 is introduced perpendicular to H_z. Besides the torque tending to align $\boldsymbol{\mu}$ along the H_z axis there will be a torque $T_1 = \boldsymbol{\mu} \times H_1$ tending to tip $\boldsymbol{\mu}$ along the axis of H_1. However, if the intensity of H_1 is deliberately chosen to be much smaller than that of H_z, the torque due to H_1 will be much smaller than that due to H_z. Furthermore the magnitude of this torque will be changing constantly since $\boldsymbol{\mu}$ is changing its orientation with respect to H_1 in the course of its precession about H_z. Even if we allow the field H_1 to rotate in the plane perpendicular to H_z, the angle between H_1 and $\boldsymbol{\mu}$ and hence the torque will change with time depending on ω, the angular frequency of rotation of H_1 relative to the Larmor frequency ω_0, *except* when $\boldsymbol{\mu}$ and H_1 rotate at the same frequency about the H_z axis, *i.e.* when $\omega = \omega_0$. At that point the torque $T = \boldsymbol{\mu} \times H_1$ will be constant and will induce precession of $\boldsymbol{\mu}$ about the field H_1 at an angular frequency $\omega_1 = \gamma H_1 \ll \omega_0$ as indicated in Fig. 4. However, as discussed in the preceding section, $\boldsymbol{\mu}$ can assume only a finite number of orientations with respect to the stationary field H_z (the

* Any rotational motion can be represented by the angular frequency vector $\boldsymbol{\omega}$, whose length is proportional to the angular frequency. Its direction is chosen so that a rotation which appears *counterclockwise* to an observer facing the plane of rotation is represented by a vector which is perpendicular to this plane and points *toward* the observer; then the sign of $\boldsymbol{\omega}$ is defined as *positive*. Under the same conditions a *clockwise* rotation is represented by a vector pointing away from the observer and a *negative* sign of $\boldsymbol{\omega}$. Thus the sign in eqn. (12) indicates that the precession of a nucleus will appear clockwise to an observer toward whom the positive vector H_z is pointing.

same is true for its orientation with respect to H_1), so that it cannot precess simultaneously about both H_z and H_1. The effect of H_1 will then be to induce a transition from one of the possible orientations in the H_z field, to another, the transition of each nucleus being accompanied by the absorption of a quantum of energy $\Delta E = (h/2\pi)\omega_0$ from the field H_1. Since resonance is

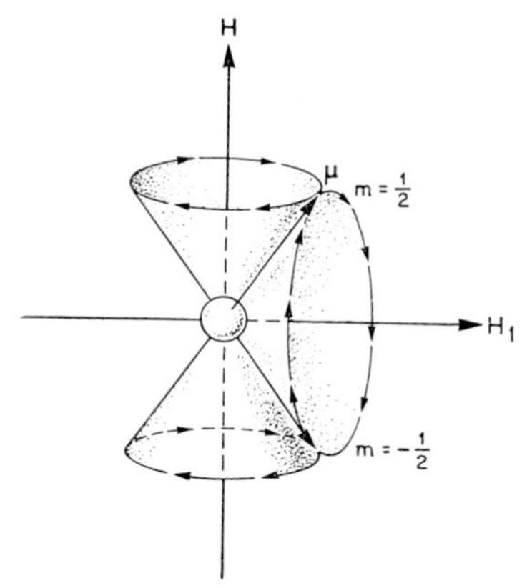

Fig. 4. Flipping of the magnetic moment vector from the ground ($m = + ½$) to the excited state ($m = — ½$) at resonance *i.e.* when the angular rotation frequency of the field H_1 is equal to the natural Larmor precession frequency of the isolated nucleus.

generally the term used to designate transfer of energy between two systems oscillating at the same frequency (in this case $\boldsymbol{\mu}$ and H_1), the phenomenon is appropriately referred to as nuclear magnetic resonance.

5. Magnetic properties of matter

The consideration of the behavior of an isolated nucleus in the presence of magnetic fields, has thus far allowed us to define in its essentials the physical process of magnetic resonance. However, in practice one does not observe magnetic resonance of an isolated nucleus, but of an assembly of nuclei embedded in and interacting with the surrounding matter. In order to gain further insight into the phenomenon of magnetic resonance as observed experimentally, we must now consider the magnetic interactions of nuclei with their surroundings and the behavior of an assembly of nuclei in external magnetic fields.

In general, if matter is placed between the two poles of a magnet, the magnetic field intensity in a region inside it is either greater than or less than the field intensity *in vacuo*, depending on the chemical nature of the material medium. The reasons for this divergent behavior of different materials are

References p. 264

clearly understood, when matter is thought to consist of particles, *i.e.* nuclei and electrons. In the presence of the external magnetic field the latter will undergo (in addition to their regular motion) a forced motion about the nuclei. This gives rise to an electronic magnetic moment induced by the external field and opposing its direction. Substances in which only such induced moments may occur tend to reduce the intensity of the applied magnetic field and are called *diamagnetic*. Alternatively substances containing large permanent moments, such as those of unpaired electrons are *paramagnetic*; in this case the permanent magnetic moments associated with the electron spin align themselves in the direction of an applied external magnetic field, yielding an effective field intensity greater than that observed *in vacuo*. A paramagnetic substance also has diamagnetic properties since magnetic moments can be induced by an external field, regardless of whether permanent moments are present. However, the reduction of the intensity of an external magnetic field due to the diamagnetism of the substance is much smaller than the increase in intensity due to the alignment of the paramagnetic moment associated with unpaired electrons. Nuclear magnetic resonance is most frequently observed in diamagnetic substances while electron spin resonance can occur only in paramagnetic materials (hence the term paramagnetic resonance).

The total induced magnetic moment in a unit volume of substance in the presence of an external magnetic field is called the magnetization vector **M**. It may be thought of as the vectorial sum of all individual magnetic moments, nuclear as well as electronic. Its magnitude is under most commonly used conditions directly proportional to the field intensity and its direction coincides with that of the external field. Thus

$$\mathbf{M} = \chi_v \mathbf{H} \tag{13}$$

where χ_v is the proportionality constant referred to as the *volume magnetic susceptibility*. If magnetic moments and field intensities are measured in electromagnetic units, χ_v is a dimensionless number of the order of -10^{-6} for most diamagnetic compounds and represents the magnetic moment/unit volume/unit field intensity. The *molar magnetic susceptibility* is the susceptibility/mole of substance or $\chi_{Mw} = M_w \chi_v / d$ where M_w and d are the molecular weight and density respectively.

If the components of magnetization ($M_x \neq M_y \neq M_z$) for a given substance are not the same in all directions in a homogeneous field H the susceptibilities are also different (*i.e.* $\chi_x \neq \chi_y \neq \chi_z$) and the substance is referred to as being magnetically anisotropic, in contrast to the magnetically isotropic substances for which $\chi_x = \chi_y = \chi_z$.

The effective field, or magnetic induction, **B**, experienced by a nucleus placed inside matter may also be written as

$$\mathbf{B} = \mathbf{H} + 4\pi \mathbf{M} \tag{14}$$

where $4\pi\boldsymbol{M}$ represents the field contributed by all the magnetic moments of the sample. The factor 4π arises because the net contribution at any nucleus is the vector sum of contributions from all directions of space and is obtained by integrating the magnetization over the surface of an imaginary sphere surrounding the nucleus. $\boldsymbol{M}$ and $\boldsymbol{H}$ have opposite signs for a diamagnetic substance and identical signs for a paramagnetic substance. From eqn. (14) and the definition of magnetic induction $\boldsymbol{B}$ given in Section 2 (p. 212) the following relationship is seen to exist between the magnetic permeability of the sample and its susceptibility.

$$\hat{\mu} = 1 + 4\pi\chi \tag{15}$$

6. Magnetic resonance in an assembly of nuclei

All of the nuclei in a given sample whose chemical environment is identical (and which consequently experience identical effective local fields when placed in an external magnetic field), may be thought of as an assembly, usually called a *magnetically equivalent set* (see also Section 9, p. 241). The characteristics of the absorption line which originates from a given set depend on the interactions of the nuclei within the set with their surroundings. The behavior of the set as a whole must therefore be understood, before an interpretation of the observed absorption patterns becomes possible.

When a given assembly is placed in an external magnetic field, the moments of its constituent nuclei will not all be aligned in the direction of the field, but as a result of interaction with their surroundings they will be found distributed among the orientations permitted by quantum rules. It can be shown from the statistical mechanical treatment of assemblies (ref. [11], pp. 100–105) that, given a set of energy levels (such as that defined by the possible orientations with respect to the external field), the population (in this case of nuclei) at each level is defined by the Boltzmann distribution, provided transitions between these levels can result from interactions which are affected by thermal motion.

According to this distribution, the ratio of the populations in the two energy levels for protons is given by

$$\frac{N_{(+\frac{1}{2})}}{N_{(-\frac{1}{2})}} = e^{-\frac{\Delta E}{kT}} \cong 1 - \frac{\Delta E}{kT} \tag{16}$$

where $N_{(+\frac{1}{2})}$ and $N_{(-\frac{1}{2})}$ indicate the number of nuclei with their magnetic moments aligned parallel and antiparallel to the external magnetic field respectively, and $\Delta E = E_{(+\frac{1}{2})} - E_{(-\frac{1}{2})} = 2\mu H_z$. Substituting the values of $\Delta E = 2.8 \cdot 10^{-19}$ erg (μ for a proton is about $2.8 \cdot 10^{-23}$ erg/gauss, $H_z =$ 10,000 gauss), and $kT = 4 \cdot 10^{-4}$ erg, one finds that for each million nuclei in the higher energy state there are one million and 7 nuclei in the ground state. Thus in a sample containing hydrogen nuclei there will be a net nuclear magnetization vector in the direction of the external magnetic field, representing the sum of the magnetic moments due to the excess number of nuclei in the ground state.

This magnetization vector $\mathbf{M}$ may in general be thought to consist of three components $\mathbf{M}_x$, $\mathbf{M}_y$ and $\mathbf{M}_z$ along the three mutually perpendicular axes x, y and z. If the z axis is taken as the axis of the external field H_z, and no other fields (such as the rotating field H_1) are introduced along the axes perpendicular to it, $\mathbf{M}_x = \mathbf{M}_y = 0$, because the distribution of nuclear moments with respect to the x and y axes will be random, as illustrated in Fig. 5.

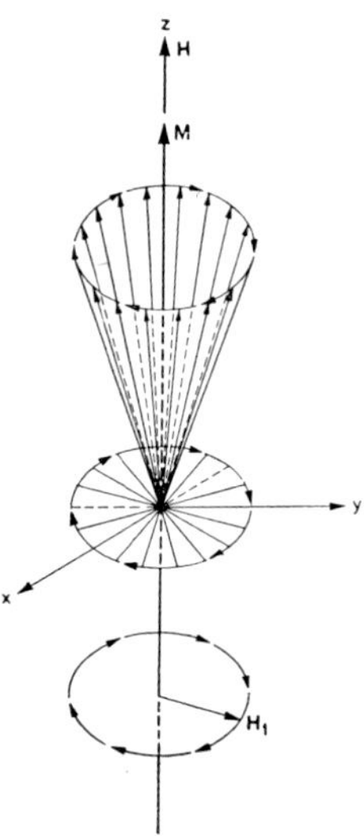

Fig. 5. Random distribution of the projections in the xy plane of the *excess* magnetic moment vectors that are aligned in the direction of the field H. The net magnetization vector M is directed along the H or z axis.

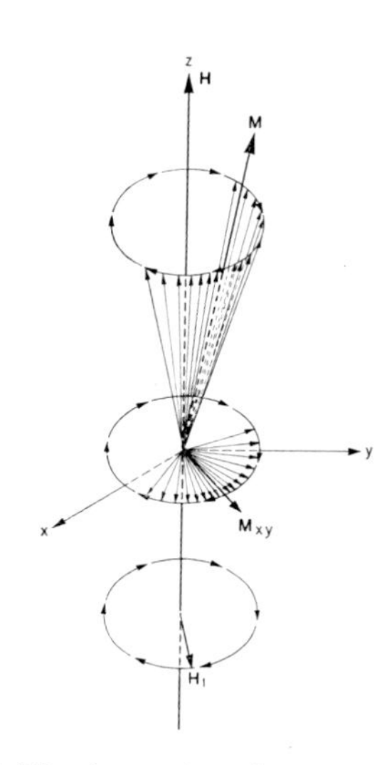

Fig. 6. The formation of a net magnetization vector in the xy plane, $\mathbf{M}_{xy}$, rotating at the Larmor frequency, under the influence of the field H_1 which is rotating with a frequency near the Larmor precession frequency. The net magnetization vector $\mathbf{M}$ due to the *excess* nuclei at the ground state is tipped away from the H or z axis. Its projection on the xy plane, $\mathbf{M}_{xy}$, is seen to lag behind the magnetic field vector $\mathbf{H}_1$.

However, in the presence of a field H_1, rotating with the Larmor precession frequency, the excess of nuclei in the ground state, made to precess in phase by this field will give rise to a component of the magnetization vector $\mathbf{M}$ in the plane perpendicular to H_z, and rotating with the Larmor frequency, as shown in Fig. 6.

The classical physical treatment of magnetic resonance in terms of the behavior of the nuclear magnetization vector $\mathbf{M}$ has been developed by Bloch[12]. The time rate of change of the components of the magnetization vector $\mathbf{M}$ along the x, y and z axes depends on (*a*) interaction of the set of nuclei, as represented by the net nuclear magnetization $\mathbf{M}$, with the magnetic field H_z, (*b*) interaction of $\mathbf{M}$ with the rotating field H_1 and (*c*) on interactions of the nuclei within the set with each other and with their surrounding environment.

(*a*) The equations of motion for the three components of the magnetization vector in the presence of the field H_z are as follows:

$$\frac{d\mathbf{M}}{dt} = \frac{dM_x}{dt} + \frac{dM_y}{dt} + \frac{dM_z}{dt}$$

However, according to eqn. (12)

$$\frac{d\mathbf{M}}{dt} = \gamma(\mathbf{M} \times \mathbf{H_z}) = \gamma(\mathbf{M_x} \times \mathbf{H_z} + \mathbf{M_y} \times \mathbf{H_z} + \mathbf{M_z} \times \mathbf{H_z}) \qquad (17)$$

$$\frac{d\mathbf{M}}{dt} = -\gamma M_x H_z \sin\theta + \gamma M_y H_z \sin\theta \text{ where } \sin\theta = 1 \text{ since } \theta = 90°$$

and $\mathbf{M_z} \times \mathbf{H_z} = 0$ since the $\mathbf{M_z}$ and $\mathbf{H_z}$ vectors are collinear. The vector resulting from the product $\mathbf{M_z} \times \mathbf{H_z}$ points along the negative y direction as defined in the footnote on p. 218 and consequently gives the variation of $\mathbf{M}$ with time along that axis.

Thus
$$\frac{dM_y}{dt} = -\gamma M_x H_z$$

$$\frac{dM_x}{dt} = \gamma M_y H_z \qquad (17a)$$

and
$$\frac{dM_z}{dt} = 0$$

As stated previously, however, the M_x and M_y components of the magnetization are equal to zero at equilibrium, when there is a random distribution of the magnetic moments about the field H_z. Therefore the time dependence of the magnetization under the influence of H_z is finite only in the absence of equilibrium.

(*b*) Similarly, the motion of the magnetization vector is affected by the presence of the field H_1. The components of the rotating field H_1 along the x and y axes will change with time according to eqn. (18).

$$H_x = H_1 \cos \omega t$$

and
$$H_y = -H_1 \sin \omega t \tag{18}$$

where ω is the angular frequency of rotation of the field H_1 about the z axis, so that the equation of motion for the magnetization vector under the influence of H_1 is given by

$$\frac{d\mathbf{M}}{dt} = \gamma(\mathbf{M} \times \mathbf{H}_x) + \gamma(\mathbf{M} \times \mathbf{H}_y) \tag{19}$$

Expanding and evaluating the vector products as in eqn. (17) the contribution to the time rate of change of the x, y and z components of $\mathbf{M}$ due to interaction with the field H_1 are found to be

$$\frac{dM_y}{dt} = \gamma M_z H_x$$

$$\frac{dM_x}{dt} = -\gamma M_z H_y \tag{19a}$$

$$\frac{dM_z}{dt} = -\gamma M_y H_x + \gamma M_x H_y$$

(*c*) Changes in the magnetization which are due to interaction of nuclei with the surrounding medium and with each other can be taken into account in the following manner. At resonance the excess nuclei of the ground state absorb energy from the field H_1 and align their magnetic moments in a direction opposite to that of the field H_z. In order that this process may be repeated, it is necessary that the energy absorbed be dissipated in some way so that the excess nuclei may return to the ground state. This dissipation of energy is accomplished by two mechanisms (*a*) re-emission of absorbed energy as electromagnetic radiation, a process exactly the reverse of absorption, which precludes the observation of resonance to the extent to which it occurs, and (*b*) conversion of energy into heat through the rotational and translational motion of the molecules in solution. The second mechanism may be understood by considering that Brownian motion leads to a fluctuation of the local magnetic fields produced by nuclei and electrons in the sample. This fluctuation is characterized by a range of frequencies, so that some of the x and y components of the local magnetic fields will oscillate with a frequency near the Larmor precession frequency of the nuclei. These oscillating components can therefore induce transitions and provide a mechanism by which the excited nuclei lose their excess energy as heat to the medium. This process is known as spin–lattice relaxation* and requires a finite characteristic time called the spin–lattice relaxation time T_1, which is operationally defined as the time required for the Boltzmann distribution to be established when the sample is placed in the magnetic field H_z. Thus

* The term has originated from considering the given set of nuclei as a "spin system" embedded in a "lattice" of other nuclei and electrons.

$$\frac{dM_z}{dt} = \frac{M^0 - M_z}{T_1} \quad (20)$$

where M^0 is the maximum magnetization along the z axis due to the excess nuclei of the ground state found at equilibrium and M_z is the value at some time before the equilibrium state is attained so that $M_z < M_0$.

It should be noted that this relaxation mechanism governs only the magnitude of the z-component of the magnetization in the sample and T_1 is therefore sometimes referred to as the longitudinal relaxation time.

There will be no resultant magnetization vector in the xy plane unless the magnetic moments due to the individual excess nuclei precess in phase with each other, *i.e.* unless the angles between their individual magnetic moment vectors are small and constant with time (Fig. 6), a situation realized only at resonance when the field H_1 is rotating with the Larmor frequency*. Thus the effect of H_1 at resonance is to cluster the excess nuclear moments of the ground state so that their vector sum, $\mathbf{M}$, is maximum and consequently its projection on the xy plane is also maximum. A constant induced precession of the magnetization vector $\mathbf{M}$ about H_1 will then tend to occur in much the same way as depicted in Fig. 4 for the case of a single nucleus.

However, even at resonance the nuclear moments can get out of phase through two mechanisms operating simultaneously. One is due to the slight field inhomogeneity over the sample volume which is responsible for having a narrow distribution of precession frequencies of identical nuclei instead of a perfectly sharp single precession frequency (Fig. 6). The second arises from the direct dipole–dipole interaction between nuclei precessing at exactly the same frequency. If one of the nuclei is in the excited state and the other in the ground state, the two may exchange their orientations with respect to the external field H_z. The ground state nucleus flips to the excited state under the influence of the xy component of the excited nuclear moment and *vice versa*. If the ground state nucleus is one of the excess nuclei pictured in Fig. 6, this exchange of states will bring about a spreading of the vectors in the xy plane. On the average, it will take a finite time, T_2, to bring a nuclear moment in phase with the rest of the vectors under the influence of H_1. The time T_2 is also referred to as the transverse relaxation time, since it is the characteristic time with which the dephasing of the nuclear moments in the xy plane occurs after passing through resonance. This dephasing is responsible for the decrease in magnitude of the x and y components of the magnetization with time. Taking this effect into account

$$\frac{dM_x}{dt} = -\frac{M_x}{T_2} \quad \text{and} \quad \frac{dM_y}{dt} = -\frac{M_y}{T_2}$$

the M_z component clearly remaining unaffected by changes in phase.

* In-phase rotation of the excess magnetic moment vectors may also be visualized as a maximum oscillation of their vector sum, $\mathbf{M}$, along any given axis since the oscillations of the individual magnetic moment vectors along that axis occur in phase, *i.e.* the oscillations attain a maximum amplitude simultaneously.

The Bloch equations, describing the total rate of change of the nuclear magnetization which results from the simultaneous operation of all the three effects discussed above, are obtained by adding eqns. (17a), (19a), (20) and (21). Thus

$$\begin{aligned}\frac{dM_x}{dt} &= \omega_0 M_y - \gamma M_z H_y - \frac{M_x}{T_2} \\ \frac{dM_y}{dt} &= \omega_0 M_x + \gamma M_z H_x - \frac{M_y}{T_2} \\ \frac{dM_z}{dt} &= \gamma M_x H_y - \gamma M_y H_x + \frac{M_0 - M_z}{T_1}\end{aligned} \tag{22}$$

If it is remembered that γH_1 is (in agreement with eqn. 12) the angular precession frequency of **M** about the rotating field H_1, it is apparent from these relations that the motion described by the nuclear magnetization vector at resonance is the same as that of the isolated moment pictured in Fig. 4 (p. 219).

The simplest solution of the Bloch equations is obtained in the case in which the magnetization at any instant is independent of time and a function only of the frequency difference $\omega_0 - \omega$ (that is, the difference between the Larmor precession frequency of the nuclei and the angular frequency of rotation of H_1). This *steady-state* solution is applicable to those experiments in which the change of magnetization with time at any given field setting is negligible. Most high-resolution experiments satisfy this condition. The component of the magnetization along the x axis is then given by

$$M_x = \tfrac{1}{2} M_0 \gamma T_2 \frac{T_2(\omega_0 - \omega) 2H_1 \cos \omega t + 2H_1 \sin \omega t}{1 + T_2^2(\omega_0 - \omega)^2 + \gamma^2 H_1^2 T_1 T_2} \tag{23}$$

It is clear that the Bloch equations have been derived on the basis of a nuclear magnetization induced by a rotating field H_1. However, in actual experiment a radio-frequency field oscillating along the x axis is used. This linearly polarized field may be thought to consist of two magnetic fields rotating with opposite sense about the field H_z, so that its total amplitude is $2H_1$. However, only one of these fields, rotating in the same sense as the nuclear moments, is capable of inducing transitions. Its components are given by eqn. (18). The field rotating in the opposite sense is alternately in-and-out of phase with the nuclear system and its effect may therefore be neglected. For a summary see Fig. 7.

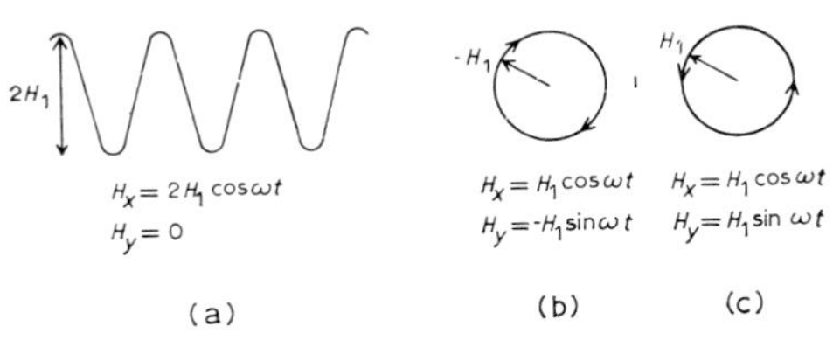

Fig. 7. (a) Linearly polarized field $2H_1$ along x axis. (b) H_1 field rotating in the same sense as nuclear moments. H_z points toward the reader. (c) H_1 field rotating in opposite sense.

As discussed in section 5, the magnetization may be generally expressed as a function of the field intensity, as $M = \chi H$, where χ is the magnetic susceptibility or magnetic moment/unit volume/unit field intensity. In the case where the magnetic field is not constant, the magnetization, M_x or M_y, induced by the field rotating in the same sense as the nuclear moments, is always equal to the magnetization induced by the linearly polarized field. In the latter case the magnetization induced along a fixed axis (*e.g.* the x axis) can be represented by the sum of two terms, one of which changes in-phase ($\cos \omega t$) and the other 90° out-of-phase ($\sin \omega t$) with the oscillation of the field along that axis.

$$M_x = \chi'(2H_1 \cos \omega t) + \chi''(2H_1 \sin \omega t) \tag{24}$$

$$M_y = \chi''(2H_1 \cos \omega t) - \chi'(2H_1 \sin \omega t)$$

Comparison between the two eqns. (23) and (24) for M_x immediately defines the two susceptibilities χ' and χ'' for the steady state as

$$\chi' = \tfrac{1}{2}\chi_0\omega_0 \frac{T_2{}^2(\omega_0 - \omega)}{1 + T_2{}^2(\omega_0 - \omega)^2 + \gamma^2 H_1{}^2 T_1 T_2} \tag{25}$$

$$\chi'' = \tfrac{1}{2}\chi_0\omega_0 \frac{T_2}{1 + T_2{}^2(\omega_0 - \omega)^2 + \gamma^2 H_1{}^2 T_1 T_2}$$

respectively, where γ_0 is the static susceptibility in the absence of the field H_1.

The average energy absorbed by the nuclear system in a single period (the time required for H_1 to rotate once about H_z, $2\pi/\omega$), in the steady state, *i.e.* when $d\mathbf{M}/dt = 0$, is given by integrating the expression $-M_x(dH_x/dt)$, (where $H_x = 2H_1 \cos \omega t$ and M_x is shown in eqn. 24) since this is the differential of the expression for energy given by eqn. (6). Thus by carrying out the integration one finds that

$$E_{\text{absorbed/period}} = -\int_0^{2\pi/\omega} M_x \frac{dH_x}{dt}\, dt = 2H_1{}^2 \omega \varkappa'' \tag{26}$$

It may be noted that the absorption of energy is proportional only to the out-of-phase susceptibility χ''. Consequently χ'' plotted as function of $(\omega_0 - \omega)$, represents the shape of the absorption line while χ' plotted in a similar fashion represents the shape of the dispersion line* (Fig. 8).

---

* Dispersion of a physical quantity, in this case of χ', is given by the dependence of that quantity on the frequency of the radiation which is absorbed during a transition, in this case, a nuclear magnetic moment transition.

References p. 264

If, as is the case in high resolution experiments, H_1 is very small ($\sim 10^{-4}$ gauss), then the expression $\gamma^2 H_1{}^2 T_1 T_2$ becomes much smaller than 1 and may be omitted from the denominator of the equation for the susceptibility (eqn. 25). If, on the other hand, either H_1 or T_1 and T_2 are large, so that the factor $\gamma^2 H_1{}^2 T_1 T_2$ is not negligible compared to unity, the magnitude of χ'' and hence

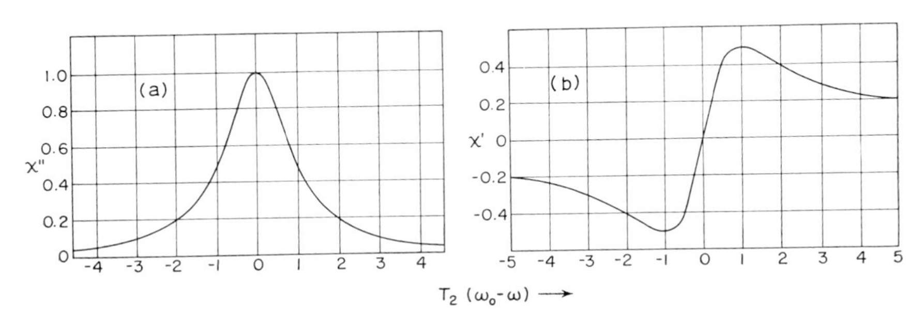

Fig. 8. (a). Shape of absorption signal when the saturation factor $\gamma_2 H_1^2 T_1 T_2$ is much less than 1 and is omitted from the denominator of eqn. (25). At resonance the frequency of rotation of H_1, ω, is equal to the frequency of precession of the nuclear magnetization ω_0, *i.e.* $\Delta\omega = 0$. Then $\chi''_{\max} = \frac{1}{2}\chi_0\omega_0 T_2$. The curve is obtained by plotting $\chi''/\frac{1}{2}\chi_0\omega_0 T_2$ (when $\frac{1}{2}\chi_0\omega_0 T_2$ is taken equal to unity) *versus* $T_2\,(\omega_0 - \omega)$. (*b*) Shape of dispersion signal obtained by plotting χ' in units of $\frac{1}{2}\chi_0\omega_0 T_2$ *versus* $T_2(\omega_0 - \omega)$ as in the case of the absorption signal.

the intensity of the observed signal are decreased. The signal is said to be saturated under these conditions and the product $\gamma^2 H_1{}^2 T_1 T_2$ which measures the extent of saturation is known as the *saturation factor*.

Assuming a steady state and the absence of saturation, it is noted that at resonance the intensity of the absorption line, described by χ'', is maximum, and that at half-maximum intensity,

$$\tfrac{1}{2}\chi''_{\max} = \tfrac{1}{2}\chi_0 \omega_0 \frac{T_2}{2} \tag{27}$$

By comparing eqn. (27) with eqn. (25) for χ'' when $\gamma^2 H_1{}^2 T_1 T_2$ can be neglected, it is seen that $T_2{}^2(\omega_0 - \omega_{\frac{1}{2}})^2$ must be equal to unity for eqn. (27) to hold. Thus T_2 is given by the inverse of the line width at half maximum intensity $1/(\omega_0 - \omega_{\frac{1}{2}})$.

It is thus seen that a consideration of the induced magnetization along the fixed x, y and z axes has led to explicit expressions for the susceptibilities and the shapes of the absorption and dispersion lines. Further physical insight into the resonance phenomenon may be obtained by considering also the relationship between the field H_1, which rotates with angular velocity $-\,\omega$ about the z axis, and the magnetization in the xy plane, $\mathbf{M}_{xy}$, which is rotating with angular velocity $-\,\omega_0$. Since both are rotating it is useful to consider only the projections of $\mathbf{M}_{xy}$ on H_1 and on the axis 90° behind H_1 (this axis is taken by convention to be negative) at all possible values of $(\omega_0 - \omega)$. These projections are often referred to as the in-phase or u and the out-of-phase or v components of $\mathbf{M}_{xy}$, respectively. They can be expressed in terms of the in-phase and out-of-phase susceptibilities as follows:

$$u = 2H_1\chi'$$

and

$$-v = 2H_1\chi''$$

In Fig. 9 one may clearly observe the variation of the angle Ψ between the field H_1 and the magnetization vector $\mathbf{M}_{xy}$, as one goes through resonance by varying the frequency, keeping in mind the dependence of χ' and χ'' on $(\omega_0 - \omega)$ as shown in Fig. 8a and b.

$$\cos\psi = \frac{u}{M_{xy}} = \frac{1}{\sqrt{u^2 + v^2}}$$

Then

$$\cos\psi = \frac{\chi'}{\sqrt{\chi'^2 + \chi''^2}}$$

where the z axis and H_z point out of the paper toward the reader and the vectors shown in the xy plane are rotating clockwise about the z axis. Substituting the values for χ' and χ'' from Fig. 8a and b in the expression for $\cos\psi$ one finds that $1 > \cos\psi > 0$ and therefore $90° > \psi > 0°$, when $\omega < \omega_0$ before resonance. At

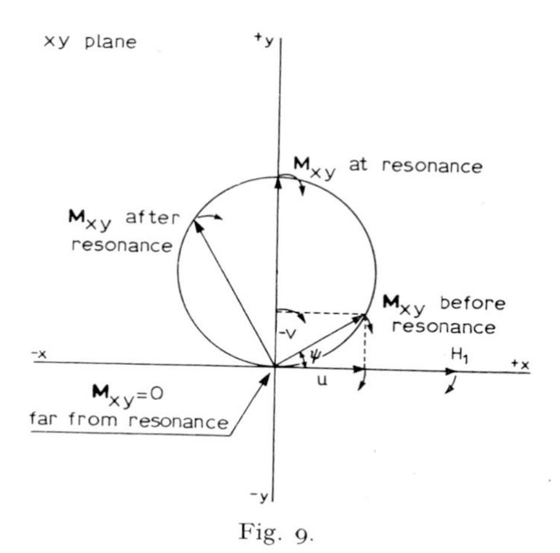

Fig. 9.

resonance, $\omega_0 = \omega$, and $\cos\psi = 0$ or $\psi = 90°$. After having passed resonance, when $\omega > \omega_0$, $0 > \cos\psi > -1$ and $180° > \psi > 90°$. It is also seen that the magnetization in the xy plane is zero when one is far from resonance corresponding to the situation shown in Fig. 5 (p. 222), that it reaches a maximum value at resonance and that near resonance it assumes intermediate values. A complete circle is then defined by the magnitude of the M_{xy} vector as one goes through resonance once. The circumference of the circle goes through the origin of the coordinate system, and the whole circle is rotating about the z axis in the same sense as H_1.

7. The experimental arrangement for the observation of nuclear resonance

The experimental observation of nuclear magnetic resonance requires three basic component systems. (1) A large magnet with a power supply to produce the stationary field H_z in which the nuclear moments assume discrete orientation and energy levels. (2) An oscillator and a transmitter, generating electromagnetic radiation of a frequency corresponding to the Larmor precession frequency. (3) A receiver and a detector which pick up the resonance signal and permit it to be amplified and recorded.

The magnet (A) (Fig. 10), usually consists of two cylindrical coils, each wound around an iron core having a pole diameter of 10–12″. When these are placed in series $1\frac{1}{2}$–2″ apart, magnetic fields up to 15,000 gauss can be

Fig. 10. The 60-mc high resolution NMR spectrometer. A – 12″ magnet, B – Power supply to the magnet, C – Super-stabilizer, D – Sample tube held in probe, E – Probe assembly containing the transmitter and the receiver coils as well as a preamplifier, F – Console containing the crystal oscillator that generates the fixed frequency H_1 field and further amplification stages of the signal coming from the probe, G – Oscilloscope exhibiting absorption or dispersion signal, H – Wide-range oscillator often used for measuring relative positions of resonance lines, I – Counter for measuring accurately frequencies of H, and J – Recorder.

produced in the resulting gap by the flow of current from a high-voltage power supply (B). Since for accurate measurements it is of utmost importance that the field be very stable, a separate feedback control mechanism (C) is used to compensate for small current fluctuations.

The sample (D) is held in the gap of the magnet by a probe (E), which also contains the coils used for transmitting the radiation and receiving the signal. Although a single coil can be made to serve both purposes, systems employing separate coils, connected to the transmitter and the receiver respectively, are in more widespread use. In this arrangement, the nuclear magnet induces a signal in the receiver coil in the process of re-orienting itself with respect to the stationary field H_z.

The geometrical arrangement of the magnetic field H_z, the transmitter and the receiver coils with respect to one another and to the sample, is of considerable importance. Ordinarily the two coils are placed with their axes at right angles to each other and to the axis of the magnetic field defining a Cartesian coordinate system as seen in Fig. 11.

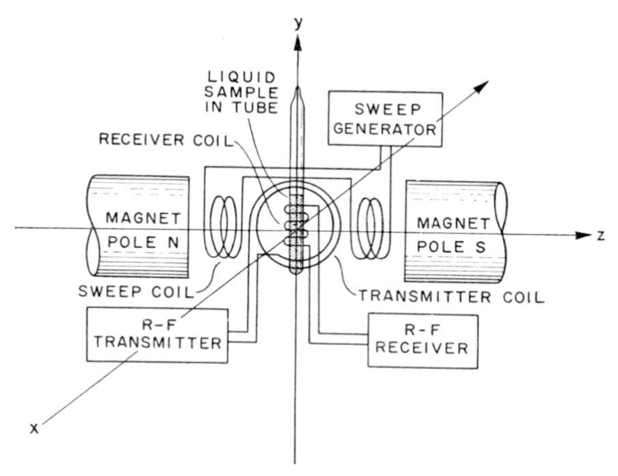

Fig. 11. Block diagram of the spectrometer shown in Fig. 10, indicating the essentia components and the directions of the coordinate axes. (After Varian Associates.)

As may be seen from eqns. (8) and (12) resonance may be observed either by scanning the frequency of the rotating magnetic field H_1, at constant field strength of H_z, until it coincides with the nuclear precession frequency, or, alternatively, by varying the magnitude of H_z, at constant frequency of H_1, scanning, in effect, a range of nuclear precession frequencies. From the point of view of stability and performance of the instrument, the latter arrangement is preferable. Thus the transmitter coil is part of an oscillating circuit controlled by a crystal oscillator (F) whose frequency is fixed at such a value as to allow resonance to be observed at field strengths which can readily be produced in the magnet gap. The oscillating circuit generates electromagnetic radiation of fixed frequency corresponding to the Larmor precession frequency. The fixed frequency usually selected for observation of proton resonance is either 40 or 60 mc/sec, and the field H_z is varied over a range $\pm$ 500 milligauss about the average values of 9,400 or 14,000 gauss respectively. Frequencies at which resonance of other nuclei may be observed, can be calculated from eqn. (8) using the data in Table I (p. 215).

The receiver coil is part of an oscillating circuit tuned to the same frequency as the transmitter and connected through a series of amplifiers to either or both a recorder and an oscilloscope on which the resonance signal can be directly visualized.

According to Faraday's law, the voltage induced in the receiver coil, along the y axis, is proportional to the time rate of change of the nuclear magnetization along this axis, that is to $\mathrm{d}M_y/\mathrm{d}t$. Since the magnitude of M_y is given by $\chi''(2H_1 \cos \omega t) - \chi'(2H_1 \sin \omega t)$, the induced electromotive force, ε, in the receiver is

$$\varepsilon = -k\frac{\mathrm{d}M_y}{\mathrm{d}t} = k2H_1\omega(\chi' \cos \omega t + \chi'' \sin \omega t) \tag{28}$$

where k is the proportionality constant which depends on the coil geometry and on the effective coil area occupied by the nuclear system. In order to observe resonance absorption, however, only the out-of-phase component of the induced voltage is desired, as is evident from eqn. (25) and Fig. 8. This is accomplished experimentally by providing a carrier voltage, usually referred to as leakage which varies in phase with χ'' at the receiver coil, upon which the small voltage of the absorption signal is superimposed.

B. CHEMICAL CORRELATIONS

8. The chemical origin of magnetic effects

(a) The chemical shift

As discussed in section 5, the intensity of the magnetic field at which a given nucleus will come into resonance, will not be identical to that of the applied field H_z, but will generally be somewhat lower because of the predominant diamagnetic shielding by surrounding electrons. For purposes of chemical analysis, it is informative to distinguish between the *intra*- and the *inter*molecular diamagnetic contributions.

(1) The *intramolecular* diamagnetic shielding reduces the intensity of the field H_z to an extent which is proportional to the electron density around the nucleus (as well as to the field intensity H_z) and is therefore different for chemically different nuclei in the same molecule. Thus chemically distinct protons in a compound give rise to resonance absorption at somewhat different magnetic field intensities and can serve as fingerprints of its structure.

The effective field intensity at a nucleus H^{eff}, is less than the intensity of the external applied field at which resonance is observed, H^r, by a factor given in eqn. (29)

$$H^{eff} = H^r (1 - \sigma) \tag{29}$$

where σ is called the *intramolecular shielding factor*. σ is directly measurable only for molecules in the gaseous state (see footnote on p. 237).

The difference of magnetic field strength between the resonance line of a substance and that of a reference compound is referred to as the *chemical shift*, Δ.

$$\Delta = H^r_s - H^r_{ref} = H^r_s \sigma_s - H^r_{ref}\sigma_{ref} \tag{30}$$

This relationship can be easily derived from eqn. (29), keeping in mind that the difference between the effective fields at the protons of the substance and the reference compound must be equal to zero at resonance when the oscillator frequency is fixed, *i.e.* $(H^{eff}_s - H^{eff}_{ref}) = 0$. The quantity Δ can be expressed in frequency units, cycles/sec, or in magnetic field units, milligauss (1 milligauss $= 10^{-3}$ gauss $= 4.26$ cycles/sec as defined by the equation $\nu = (\gamma/2\pi)H$).

Most commonly, however, the chemical shift is expressed as a dimensionless number, δ, by dividing both sides of eqn. (30) by H^{eff}. The value of H^{eff} at resonance is 9,400 or 14,000 gauss corresponding to $40 \cdot 10^6$ and $60 \cdot 10^6$ cycles/sec respectively. Approximating then both H^r and H^r_{ref} by H^{eff} one obtains the chemical shift as the difference between the intramolecular shielding factors of the substance and the reference compound,

$$\delta = \frac{(H^r_s - H^r_{ref}) \text{ (in cps)}}{40 \cdot 10^{-6}} = \sigma_s - \sigma_{ref} \tag{31}$$

In order to avoid expressing δ in very small numbers, eqn. (31) is multiplied by the factor 10^6. Thus the chemical shift δ is most often expressed in parts per million being equivalent to $(\sigma_s - \sigma_{ref})\ 10^6$.

In an isolated atom, the shielding constant σ reflects solely the electronic charge density about the nucleus. For an atom in a given position in a

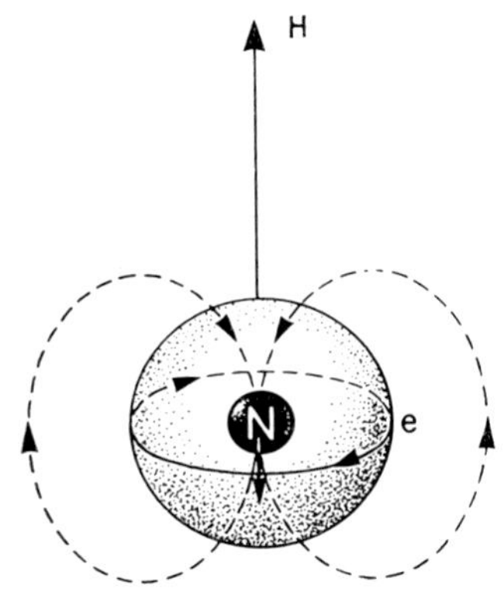

Fig. 12. Induced *diamagnetic* moment in isolated atom depicted by the arrow pointing in the direction opposite to that of the external field H. This moment is due to the current which arises from the induced orbital motion of the electronic charge e. The induced orbital motion of the electron is in turn a consequence of the precession of the electronic orbital angular momentum about the field axis in the presence of the external magnetic field H. The arrows along the circle around the nucleus indicate the direction of the induced current and the dotted lines show the lines of force due to the induced magnetic moment.

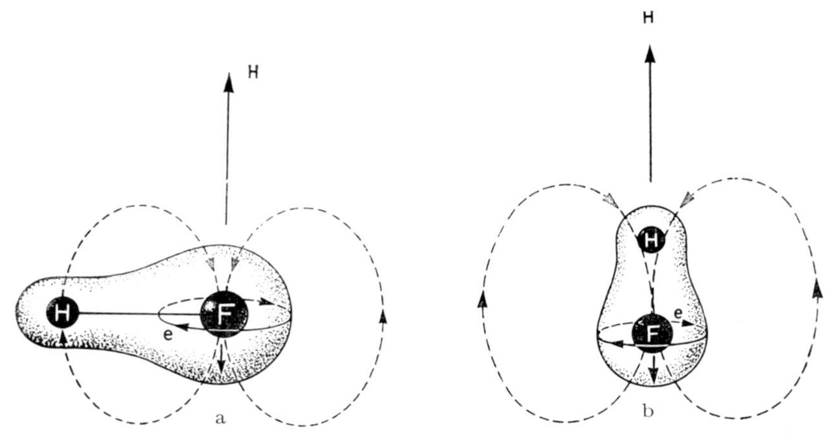

Fig. 13. Neighbor diamagnetic anisotropy effect. (a) HF molecule with the molecular axis perpendicular to the field H. The induced *diamagnetic* moment at the fluorine atom causes a decrease in the shielding of the proton, since the lines of force at the proton are directed along the field axis. (b) HF molecular axis parallel to the field H_1. In this case the induced moment at the fluorine increases the shielding of the proton since the latter experiences lines of force opposing the direction of the external field. In both instances the arrows along the circles around the fluorine nuclei indicate the direction of the induced current. As the molecule changes orientation in solution, the net effect at the proton will depend on the relative magnitude of the moments induced along the different directions. For fluorine the *diamagnetic* anisotropy is small and its average effect at the proton is close to zero. However, in the case of other hydrogen halides diamagnetic anisotropy may account for proton shielding of the order of 0.2–0.4 p.p.m.

molecule, however, the symmetry of the charge distribution accounts for additional effects. Generally, it is possible to distinguish the following intramolecular contributions to the magnitude of σ.

(i) The diamagnetic contribution from the atom itself, related only to the charge density (Fig. 12).

(ii) The paramagnetic contribution from the atom itself (1st order paramagnetic effect), which opposes the diamagnetic effect and arises from the asymmetry of its electronic charge distribution. This effect does not exist

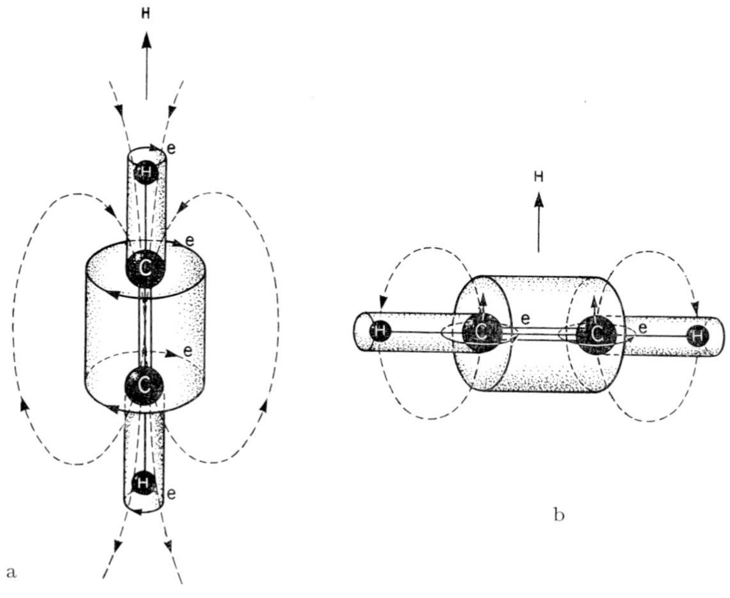

Fig. 14. Neighbor paramagnetic anisotropy effect. (a) Acetylene with its molecular axis parallel to the field H_1. Induced electronic motion gives rise to a *diamagnetic* moment at the carbon atoms (arrows along circles around the atoms indicate the direction of the current). This moment causes shielding of the protons, as shown by the dotted lines of force. No paramagnetic effect is encountered in this orientation since the charge distribution about the field axis is totally symmetrical. (b) Acetylene with its molecular axis perpendicular to the field H. In this orientation, the magnetic field causes mixing among ground and excited electronic states of the carbon atoms and induces an asymmetric electronic charge distribution in the molecule about the field axis which results in a *paramagnetic* moment at the carbon atoms. This moment is oriented in the direction of the field H and its lines of force can be seen to shield the protons. The arrows along the circles around the carbon atoms indicate the induced current's direction, which is opposite to that giving rise to a diamagnetic moment. The induced *diamagnetic* moment (not shown here) is present in this orientation also and it unshields the protons as in Fig. 13(a). Thus, the net effect of the induced *diamagnetic* moment (averaged over all molecular orientations) is negligible as in the case of HF. The paramagnetic effect, on the other hand, does not average to zero when considered over all orientations. Its existence explains the abnormally high shielding of the protons in acetylene.

References p. 264

in the case of a proton nucleus since its electronic charge distribution is represented by the 1s orbital which is perfectly symmetrical.

(iii) Contributions, both diamagnetic and paramagnetic, from other atoms and bonds in the molecule (Figs. 13a, 13b, 14a, 14b).

(iv) Contribution from interatomic electronic currents, such as may occur in aromatic or heterocyclic ring systems containing conjugated double bonds (Fig. 15).

(2) The *intermolecular* shielding due to neighboring diamagnetic molecules in solution is averaged to a constant effect for all molecules in a given solution as a result of their Brownian motion. It accounts for a slight reduction of the intensity of the field at which resonance is observed, and depends on the diamagnetic properties of the solution and on the shape of the sample.

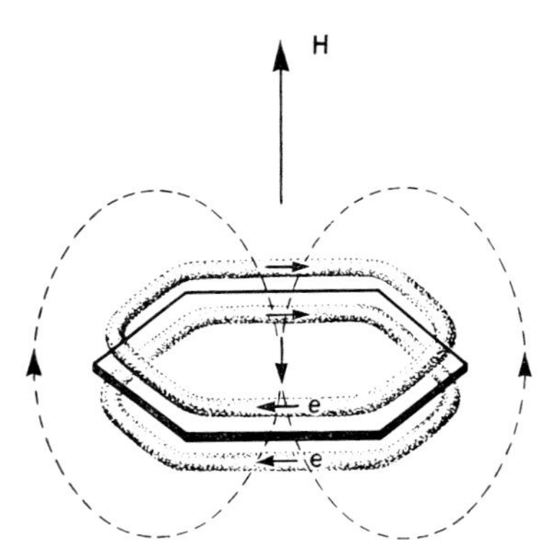

Fig. 15. Diamagnetic moment in benzene, arising from induced motion of the π-electrons above and below the plane of the ring, when the external field H_z is perpendicular to the plane of the molecule. The induced lines of force cause a shielding of the protons located at the periphery of the ring. When the plane of the molecule is parallel to the field, the motion of the π-electrons is not affected, and no additional shielding of the protons results. (Arrows above and below the ring indicate the direction of the current due to the motion of the π-electrons.)

Thus the applied field at which resonance should be observed, H^r, is somewhat less than the field at which resonance is observed, H^{obs}, and is given for cylindrical samples of small diameter by eqn. (32)

$$H^r = H^{obs}(1 - \tfrac{2}{3}\pi\chi_v) \tag{32}$$

where χ_v is the volume susceptibility of the sample. The last term in parentheses is the bulk diamagnetic susceptibility correction which must be applied for proper determination of absolute chemical shifts, (*i.e.* shifts representing intramolecular effects only) whenever the sample and the reference compounds are in separate compartments (*external reference*) and their volume susceptibilities are not the same. In this case the chemical shift in cycles/sec, corrected for bulk diamagnetic differences between sample and reference compound is given by

$$\Delta_{\text{corr}} = H_s^r - H_{\text{ref}}^r = H_s^{\text{obs}}(1 - \tfrac{2}{3}\pi\chi_{v_s}) - H_{\text{ref}}^{\text{obs}}(1 - \tfrac{2}{3}\pi\chi_{v_{\text{ref}}}) =$$

$$\Delta_{\text{obs}} + \tfrac{2}{3}\pi(\chi_{v_{\text{ref}}} - \chi_{v_s})\,H^{\text{eff}} \qquad (33)$$

where the approximation that H^{eff} does not differ much from either H^{obs} or $H_{\text{ref}}^{\text{obs}}$ is made again.

The corrected shift in parts per million is obtained by dividing by H^{eff} and multiplying both terms on the right-hand side of eqn. (33) by 10^6. If the reference compound is introduced directly into the sample with which it is completely miscible (*internal reference*), the volume susceptibility is the same for both and the correction terms cancel. However, in using an internal reference there is always the danger of association with the solvent, the solute, or both, leading to a change of the magnetic field at which resonance is observed, and hence to incorrect values of δ. On the other hand, the use of an external reference has the disadvantage that the volume susceptibility of the sample is usually not known, but for most compounds must be approximated from atomic susceptibilities*.

(3) *Specific intermolecular* contributions arise from chemical association and chemical exchange. It is important that these be not confused with those contributions to the apparent magnitude of σ, which result from differences in the bulk susceptibilities of sample and reference (see under section 2, p. 210) when no correction for the latter is applied. These intermolecular association effects contributing to the magnitude of σ may be considered intramolecular in the sense that they reflect the formation of new chemical entities. They are distinct from bulk diamagnetic shielding, in that they will not affect all nuclei in a given molecule to the same extent, but will selectively change the electron density in the groups directly participating in the association, more so than in others.

A special case of an apparent shift results from chemical exchange, *i.e.* the transfer of a nucleus between two or more chemically non-equivalent

---

* A more complete definition of σ for substances in the liquid state has been given recently[13]. The intramolecular contribution to σ is identified with the shielding factor measured when the molecules are in the gaseous state. Thus in liquids $\sigma_{\text{measured}} = \sigma_{\text{gas}} + \sigma_{\text{solvent}}$; σ_{solvent} is made up of four terms; σ_b, the contribution due to the bulk susceptibility of the solution; σ_w, the contribution due to weak Van der Waals forces between solute and solvent molecules; σ_A, the contribution from the magnetic anisotropy of the solute, the solvent, or both; and σ_E, the contribution from the electric field on the intramolecular electronic distribution due to the presence of polar molecules.

positions. If this is sufficiently rapid, the nucleus will in effect precess about a field which is an average of the fields characteristic of each of the chemical environments between which it is exchanging, weighted by the duration of its stay in each environment. Examples of this important effect and a simplified treatment from which activation energies may be obtained are mentioned in a later section.

(b) Intramolecular spin–spin coupling

Coupling between the magnetic moments of two or more protons of a molecule alters the effective magnetic field experienced by them and leads to a splitting of their resonance lines into two or more components. This effect may be clearly understood by considering two protons on adjacent carbon atoms as in the case of acetylene $H—C_1{\equiv}C_2—H$. The proton on C_1 will experience a slightly different external field depending on whether the magnetic moment of the proton on C_2 is oriented with or against the field H_z. In a sample there is at any given time a statistical distribution of the magnetic moments of C_2 protons between the two states, so that the resonance peak of the proton on C_1 will be a doublet. This effect is thought to arise through the polarization of the electron magnetic moments in the bonds $H—C_1$, $C_1{\equiv}$ and $C_2—H$, under the influence of the two spin orientations of H on C_2, and is therefore referred to as *electron-coupled spin–spin interaction*. Similarly, the resonance of the C_2 proton is also a doublet as a result of the two possible orientations of the C_1 proton. However, since the molecule is symmetrical and the two protons are chemically equivalent to each other, the doublets are exactly superimposed. Thus the spectrum of acetylene consists of two resonance lines of equal intensity spaced at 9.1 ± 2.0 cycles/sec apart. In general, the maximum number of lines into which a given group of nuclei can split the absorption peak of a neighboring group, is given by the number of possible orientations of its total spin I with respect to the external field H_z, *i.e.* $(2I + 1)$. Thus as a rule, a single proton will split the absorption line of a proton on an adjacent carbon into a doublet, a methylene group will split into a triplet, a methyl group into a quadruplet, etc.

The energy of the coupling between two nuclei i and j is given by

$$E = hJ_{ij}\, \mathbf{I}_i \cdot \mathbf{I}_j \tag{34}$$

where h is Planck's constant and $\mathbf{I}_i$ and $\mathbf{I}_j$ are the spin vectors of the nuclei i and j respectively. The proportionality constant J_{ij} is referred to as the *spin–spin coupling constant* and is measured in cycles/sec from the spacing between adjacent lines of a given multiplet. However, this simple measurement is valid only when the chemical shift between the nuclei i and j is large compared to the spin coupling constant (see also section 9). Important characteristics of the spin coupling constant are: (*a*) Unlike the chemical shift, it is independent of the magnitude of the external field H_z, (*b*) it is dependent on the electron density of the bonds, and (*c*) it is dependent also on the relative orientation of chemical bonds with respect to each other, *i.e.* on the angle formed by the planes containing the bonds H—C_1—C_2 and C_1—C_2—H respectively, (called the dihedral angle) which is 180° in the case of the planar molecule of acetylene. Coupling between protons not located on neighboring carbons has been observed, but in general the magnitude of the spin coupling constant decreases rapidly as the number of carbon atoms between the two protons increases.

(*c*) *Relaxation*

The magnitude of the relaxation times of nuclei can be affected by any of several factors characteristic of the surrounding environment.

(1) T_1. Fundamentally, spin–lattice relaxation is accomplished by oscillating local magnetic fields which induce transitions in much the same way as the field H_1. The shortening of the relaxation time T_1 or, in other words, the efficiency of spin–lattice relaxation, is proportional to the intensity of the local magnetic fields which may be oscillating at the Larmor precession frequency in the sample. The origin of these fields may be largely attributed to the magnetic moments of all nuclei in the sample. The broad spectrum of the oscillation frequencies of these magnetic moments is a reflection of the rotational and translational motion of the molecules in which the nuclei are located.

An additional source of local fields are the magnetic moments arising from the motion of electronic charges in the vicinity of the nucleus. These may originate from two sources: (*a*) molecular motion, such as rotation or vibration and (*b*) the precession of electrons induced by the external magnetic field (the same effect as that responsible for diamagnetic shielding). The first of these is of importance mostly in gases, where the magnetic moments resulting from molecular rotation may become large enough. The second is ordinarily of little importance, because the x and y components of the induced moments are small and average out to zero. A special situation arises in the case of highly asymmetric molecules in which the magnetic moment induced by an external magnetic field may be anisotropic, *i.e.* differ in magnitude along different axes through the molecule. If the molecules change orientation with respect to the external field through Brownian motion at the right frequency, the magnetic fields produced by them at nearby nuclei will vary in magnitude and may cause transitions and shortening of T_1. In this case, unlike the preceding ones, the effect is dependent on the magnitude of the field H_z.

References p. 264

Large oscillating local magnetic fields arise in materials containing free electrons of radicals or paramagnetic ions. The magnetic moment of an unpaired electron is about 1836 times that of the proton and fields created by the motion of these electrons or by the motion of molecules past them can cause a reduction in T_1 to values as low as 10^{-4} sec.

In the case of those nuclei with spin $I > \frac{1}{2}$, which possess an electric quadrupole moment, spin–lattice relaxation may be accomplished by a mechanism not involving magnetic interactions*.

The interaction of a nuclear electric quadrupole moment with fluctuating electric field gradients, such as are found in asymmetric chemical bonds, causes a reorientation of the quadrupole in the electric field. Since the quadrupole moment possesses a fixed orientation with respect to the spin axis and hence with respect to the magnetic moment, its reorientation will always be accompanied by a reorientation of the magnetic moment with respect to the external magnetic field. For example in the case of ^{14}N ($I = 1$) in N-acetyl amino acids and glycyl peptides, the reorientation of the ^{14}N nuclear quadrupole is very rapid under the influence of the rapidly fluctuating asymmetric electric fields around the nucleus. The reorientation of the nuclear magnetic moments among the three energy levels is consequently also quite fast and T_1 is therefore shortened.

In liquids, where thermal motion is intense, T_1 is comparatively short, of the order of 1 sec. In solids, however, where molecular motion is restricted, T_1 can be very long, up to 10^4 sec. Theoretical treatment makes it possible to distinguish intra- and intermolecular contributions to T_1. Both are found to be inversely proportional to the viscosity of the medium.

(2) T_2. The transverse relaxation time, T_2, is shortened by any process which will bring the precession of a certain fraction of nuclei out of phase with the rotating field H_1 in the xy plane, either (*a*) directly, by causing them to precess about an oscillating component of the local magnetic field or (*b*) indirectly by changing their precession frequency as a consequence of a change in the homogeneity of the local field. Into the first category falls the spin–spin dephasing discussed earlier, as well as the dephasing produced

* An electric quadrupole may be considered to consist of two coupled electric dipoles. Possible quadrupoles arise from different mutual orientations of the dipoles, two of which are depicted here:

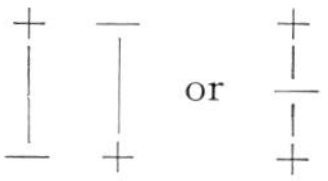

$$\begin{matrix} + & - \\ | & | \\ - & + \end{matrix} \quad \text{or} \quad \begin{matrix} + \\ | \\ - \\ | \\ + \end{matrix}$$

The charge distribution in nuclei with spin $I > 1/2$ is asymmetric and is characterized by an electric quadrupole, the magnitude of which is given by $e \cdot A$ where e is the total charge and the area A is in cm^2. The direction of the quadrupole moment is along a line perpendicular to the surface. In the case of nuclei with spin $I > 1/2$ (ellipsoidal surfaces), the quadruople moment is collinear with the magnetic moment and angular momentum vectors of the nucleus.

by all of the processes causing spin–lattice transitions (such as the motion of other nuclei, paramagnetic ions, and electric fields). Because any nucleus forced to undergo a transition by any field other than H_1 necessarily gets out of phase with the latter, it is clear that T_2 can never be longer than T_1, although it may be shorter. A shortening of T_1 can therefore manifest itself as the broadening of the absorption line (eqn. 27), whenever $T_1 = T_2$, as is the case in liquids and gases. Generally in liquids and gases the line width at half-maximum intensity $\Delta\omega$ may be approximated by the sum of two terms almost equally contributing to $1/T_2$,

$$\Delta\omega = \frac{1}{T_2} = \frac{1}{T'_2} + \frac{1}{T''_2} \tag{35}$$

where $1/T'_2$, defines the contribution to the line width due to processes discussed under (*a*) and $1/T''_2$ the contribution from the local field inhomogeneity which includes the inhomogeneity of the magnet, *i.e.* the spread of magnetic field intensities about the mean value of H_z. In more rigid systems, however, such as viscous liquids and solids, the second term predominates and T_2 may be as short as 10^{-6} sec.

9. The interpretation of spectra

It is necessary to consider the general features of NMR spectra as well as some of the theory essential for the interpretation of complicated spectra before discussing the types of chemical information obtainable from them. Under the experimental conditions of slow passage through resonance to which the steady-state solutions of the Bloch equations apply, the shape of the absorption signal is determined by eqn. (25). The signal can be characterized by:

(1) its position (*i.e.* the chemical shift),
(2) total intensity (*i.e.* the area under the absorption curve*), and
(3) width (*e.g.* the half-width at half-height, which is related to the relaxation time by eqn. 34).

Each spectrum is in turn characterized by groups of such resonance lines.

In many cases, such as that of ethanol (Figs. 16a and 16b) one can readily distinguish first and second order multiplicity of lines in the spectrum. The former reflects the chemical shift between individual chemical groups, and

* When the shape function of the line is known (*e.g.* eqn. 25), the line is completely characterized by either two of the following three parameters: (*a*) area (*b*) width and (*c*) height. As in all branches of spectroscopy, the area under the curve is proportional to the number of transitions occurring; the height of two lines can be used as a measure of the relative number of transitions only when the lines are known to have identical width.

References p. 264

the latter the coupling of nuclear spins. In the spectrum of 70% ethanol (Fig. 16a), three groups of protons are immediately recognized. The water protons and in this case the hydroxyl proton of ethanol give rise to a single peak at low field since they are the least shielded. The intermediate peak, a quadruplet, arises from the two protons of the CH_2 group and the triplet peak at the extreme right is due to the most shielded methyl protons of

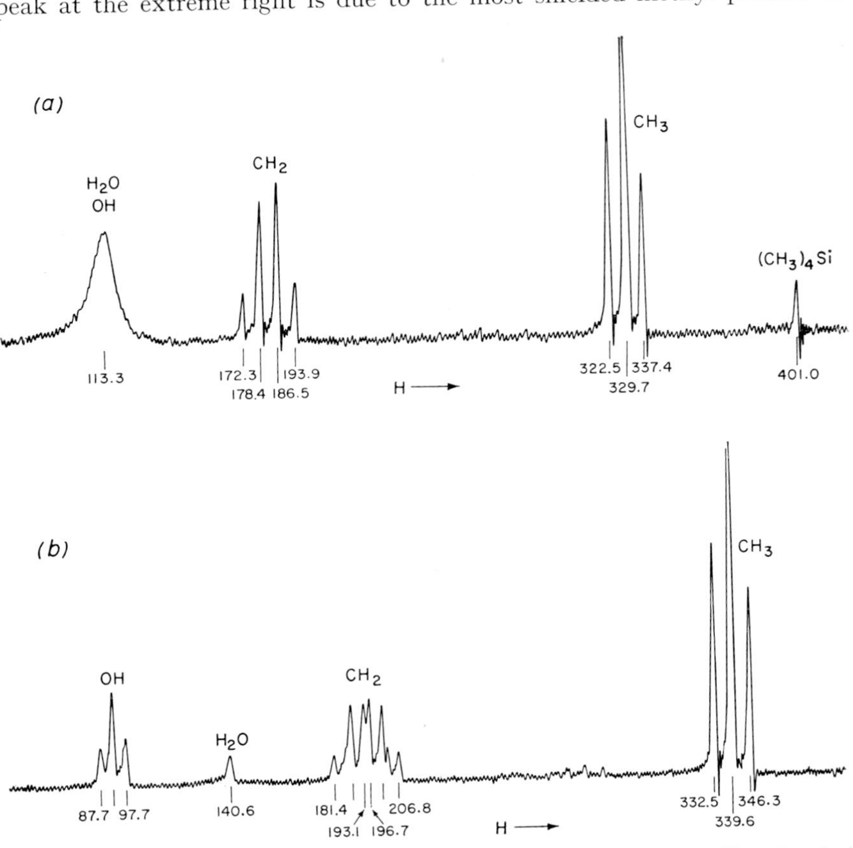

Fig. 16. (a) The NMR spectrum of 70% ethanol–30% water at 60 mc. The chemical shifts in cps for the various peaks are shown with reference to benzene, the external standard. The peak due to the internal standard, tetramethylsilane is seen at 401.0 cps. The magnetic field intensity H is increasing from left to right. (b) The NMR spectrum of 97% ethanol–3% water at 60 mc. The peak due to the internal standard, not shown here, occurs at 410.1 cps relative to benzene, the external standard. Thus the 9 cps difference noted also for the peaks due to CH_3 and for the center of the CH_2 peak in comparing the spectra in (a) and (b) may be attributed to the difference in the bulk diamagnetic susceptibility of the two solutions. Note that at 3% water the OH peaks due to water and ethanol are separate, reflecting a slow proton exchange between them. The increased splitting of the CH_2 peak arises from coupling with the ethanol -OH.

ethanol. The splitting or fine structure in these peaks is due to spin–spin coupling between the CH_2 and CH_3 protons. The peak due to the methyl protons is a triplet since the total spin of the CH_2 group can have the values +1, 0, —1 as the magnetic moments of the individual protons are oriented both in the direction of the external magnetic field ($I = 1$), one in the same and the other in the opposite direction ($I = 0$), and finally both opposite to the field ($I = -1$). It is noted furthermore, that the peak at the center of the triplet corresponding to $I = 0$ has an intensity twice that of either of the adjacent peaks. This is clear from the fact that there are two ways in which the spins of two protons can give rise to a total spin of 0, since each proton can have a spin of $+\frac{1}{2}$ or $-\frac{1}{2}$. Therefore, the methyl protons will be experiencing a local field of this magnitude twice as often as the other two. Due to rapid rotation about the C—C bond, the methyl protons are coupled equally to the CH_2 protons with an average coupling constant of about 6 cps. The chemical shift for the CH_3 protons from the reference peak of the tetramethylsilane is calculated with respect to the central peak of the triplet corresponding to the position of the line in the absence of splitting.

In a similar way, the quadruplet structure for the CH_2 peak may be seen to arise from the coupling of the CH_2 protons spins with the total spin due to the CH_3 protons which can have the values $\pm\frac{3}{2}$, $+\frac{1}{2}$, $-\frac{1}{2}$, and $-\frac{3}{2}$. In this case, the intensity of the two inner peaks is three times that of either outer peak since there are three ways in which three proton spins can be arranged to give a resultant spin of $+\frac{1}{2}$ or $-\frac{1}{2}$.

The new features observed in the spectrum of 99% ethanol–1% water (Fig. 16b) are the two separate peaks for the water and hydroxyl protons respectively and the quintet of the CH_2 peak. These arise from the fact that the hydroxyl proton is exchanging more slowly with the water protons than in the preceding case so that its chemical environment corresponds more closely to that present when it is associated with an ethanol molecule than with a water molecule. Therefore, the non-hydrogen bonded hydroxyl proton of ethanol gives rise to a separate peak and is somewhat less shielded than the water protons. Its life-time on an ethanol molecule before it exchanges with a water proton is also long enough to allow for spin coupling with the CH_2 group, giving rise to a triplet for the hydroxyl peak and to a quintet for the CH_2 group. In principle one could expect to observe 8 lines for the CH_2 group, since spin coupling with the hydroxyl proton would double each line of the quadruplet. In fact, the spectrum of ethyl alcohol at very high resolution appears much more complicated, exhibiting more than 8 lines for the CH_2 group. These extra lines arise when the shift between the CH_2 and CH_3 groups and the spin coupling constant are of a comparable order of magnitude. They are more distinguishable in spectra taken at low external magnetic field strength, since the difference in shifts between the

References p. 264

peaks due to CH_2 and CH_3 becomes smaller as the external field is decreased (ref. [3], p. 56). In other cases in which shifts (Δ) and the multiplet separation (J) are of the same order of magnitude when both are expressed in cycles/sec, a number of extra lines are present that cannot be accounted for by the first order analysis as outlined for ethanol. In such cases (an example of which is shown in Fig. 17) the magnitudes of Δ and J can not be obtained directly from the spectra, but (ref. [1], Chapter 6) only from the solution of the complete quantum mechanical problem.

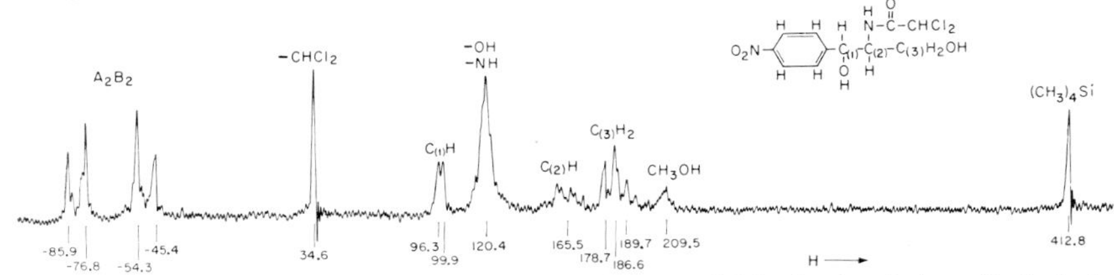

Fig. 17. The NMR spectrum of chloramphenicol, 0.75*M* in deuterated methyl alcohol (CD_3OD) at 60 mc. The chemical shifts are shown with reference to benzene, the external standard. The internal standard is tetramethylsilane. The peaks at lower field than the aromatic protons of benzene are due to the four protons on the nitrobenzene part of the molecule. The two A protons giving rise to the first two peaks from the left correspond to the two hydrogens *ortho* to the nitro-group and the B protons to the two *meta*-hydrogens. The peak due to $C_{(1)}H$ is a doublet because of spin coupling with $C_{(2)}H$. The spectrum due to the $C_{(2)}$ and $C_{(3)}$ protons is like an AB_2 type spectrum which is further complicated by the splitting of the A or $C_{(2)}$ proton peaks due to spin coupling with the $C_{(1)}$ proton. Rapid exchange between the OH and NH protons causes their peaks to merge at 120.4 cps. The peak labeled CH_3OH arises from the methyl protons of the solvent which is about 98% isotopically pure.

Generally NMR spectra can be classified according to whether they are represented by one, two or all three types of proton sets; (*a*) protons among which the chemical shift is zero while their spin coupling J may be finite, $J \gg \Delta$, where J and Δ are both in cycles/sec. These constitute an equivalent set and give rise to a single resonance line; (*b*) proton sets which are separated by large chemical shifts as compared with their spin coupling, $J \ll \Delta$; and (*c*) proton sets separated by chemical shifts comparable in magnitude with their spin coupling, $J \cong \Delta$.

On this basis, a systematic notation has been developed by Pople, Schneider and Bernstein[1], which allows one to distinguish a large number of spectral classes. In any given spectrum symbols A, B, C . . . are used to denote those sets of magnetically equivalent nuclei whose resonance lines are separated by small shifts, and the symbols X, Y, Z . . . to denote sets with lines separated by large shifts. Subscripts $_1$, $_2$, $_3$ are used to denote the number of equivalent nuclei per set, per molecule. In this notation, the spectrum of ethanol (Fig. 16a) is clearly an XY_2Z_3 spectrum, while that of chloramphenicol in Fig. 17 consists of a side chain which is of the type

AB_2XY and of an aromatic nucleus whose protons are of the type A_2B_2. This description is appropriate for chloramphenicol, since the two parts of the molecule interact very little with each other. As may have been noted already, it is customary to assign the letter nearest the beginning of the alphabet to the set with the least number of protons.

Although a rigorous explanation for the differences in the spectra between classes (*b*) and (*c*) is inappropriate here, an intuitive approach to the physical principles underlying these differences appears profitable.

At constant external field the shift Δ between two lines is a measure of the difference between the effective fields seen by the two corresponding sets of nuclei. On the other hand, the coupling constant J is a measure of the local magnetic field which results at a nucleus in one of the sets from the time average magnetic moment induced in the surrounding electron cloud by the nuclear spins of both sets. In the case of $\Delta \gg J$, the effective local field seen by a given nucleus (*i.e.* the resultant of the shielding and the coupling fields) and hence the precession frequency, will be very different, depending on whether the particular nucleus belongs to one set or the other. Thus, the interaction energy due to spin coupling will not suffice for nuclei of one set to affect the distribution of the nuclei in the other set between their energy states. Transitions occur separately in each set of nuclei, and the spectra can be predicted from a simple first order analysis as in the case of ethanol or in the case of the AX_2 spectrum seen in Fig. 18a.

If, however, the spin coupling between the two sets of nuclei is of the same order of magnitude as the chemical shift, $J \cong \Delta$, the effective fields seen by a fraction of nuclei in each of the two sets may be nearly identical. Hence nuclei belonging to different sets will precess at almost the same frequency, and transitions induced by H_1 can then occur simultaneously in both sets, changing the distribution of nuclei among energy levels in both sets. Such redistribution of nuclei, which can occur only when the energy levels for different sets of nuclei are very closely spaced together, is referred to as the "mixing of states", which is entirely analogous to the redistribution of electronic charge in atomic orbitals in the process of hybridization (also known as the mixing of states). Two points are apparent from the illustration which depicts the case of three nuclei, two of which are equivalent (Fig. 18b). One is that the energy of certain states (the ground state, with total spin equal to $+\frac{3}{2}$, the excited state with total spin equal to $-\frac{3}{2}$) are always sufficiently different from all other states, so that they will never be mixed with any other. Generally, mixing can occur only between states for which the total spin of the system (which is a measure of the total induced nuclear magnetization, eqn. (4), p. 213) remains unchanged. The second point is that in a given system, consisting of a given number of sets of different nuclei, the total number of allowed transitions remains unchanged by mixing.

References p. 264

However, the energy of the transitions may change upon mixing (AB_2 case) with the result that previously coinciding transitions become separated and the total number of observed spectral lines is larger than it is in the case in

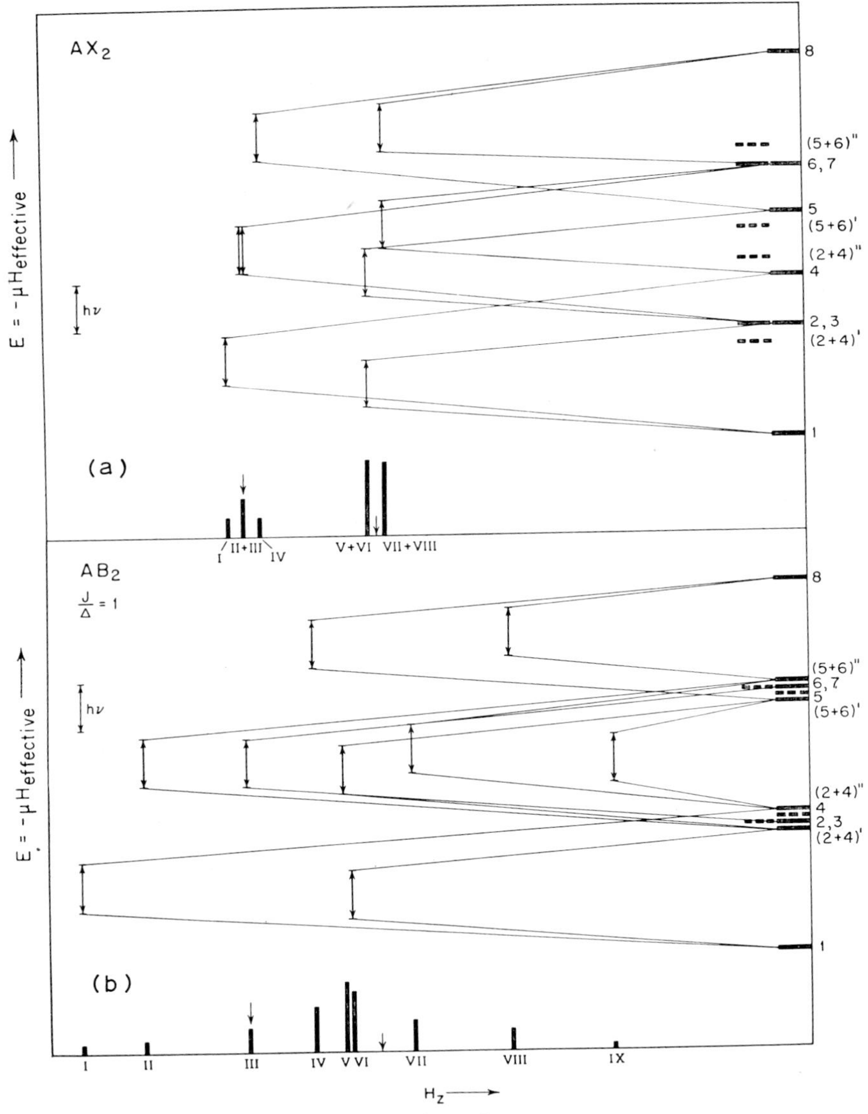

Fig. 18. For legend see p. 247.

which $J \ll \Delta$ (AX_2 case). Furthermore, the intensities of the observed lines are no longer related in any simple manner to the number of nuclei in any given set. Nevertheless the mathematical problem has been solved in some simple systems containing up to five nuclei and the exact spectra (position and intensities) have been predicted for different values of J and Δ when $J \cong \Delta$. Thus by comparing the spectrum of a given type with the predicted one, the values of Δ and J can be obtained. A detailed discussion of the methods used in this type of spectral analysis is beyond the scope of this chapter, but can be found in Chapter 6 of ref. [1].

Fig. 18. Spectrum and energy level diagram for a system of three nuclei, two of which are equivalent. The abscissa denotes the energy of interaction of the magnetic dipole of moment μ with the effective field H_{eff} (where H_{eff} is constant, for example 14,000 g). The ordinate shows the magnitude of the external magnetic field at which resonance is observed when a fixed r.f. oscillator frequency is employed. (a) For large shifts, AX_2 taking $\sigma_x > \sigma_A$. (b) For small shifts AB_2, in the case where $J/\Delta = 1$, $\sigma_B = 2\sigma_A$ and $J_{BB} = 1$.

If α_A and α_B denote the orientation of nucleus A or B respectively *parallel* to the field, and β_A and $\beta_B = \beta_X$ the respective orientations *antiparallel* to it, the possible values of the energy levels and total spin associated with each energy level are as follows:

Energy level	*Total spin*
1. $\alpha_A\alpha_B\alpha_B$	$(\frac{3}{2})$
2. $\alpha_A\beta_B\alpha_B$	$(\frac{1}{2})$
3. $\alpha_A\alpha_B\beta_B$	$(\frac{1}{2})$
4. $\alpha_A\alpha_B\alpha_B$	$(\frac{1}{2})$
5. $\alpha_A\beta_B\beta_B$	$(-\frac{1}{2})$
6. $\beta_A\beta_B\alpha_B$	$(-\frac{1}{2})$
7. $\beta_A\alpha_B\beta_B$	$(-\frac{1}{2})$
8. $\beta_A\beta_B\beta_B$	$(-\frac{3}{2})$

In the case of a large shift (AX_2) the energy differences between levels of the same total spin are large and transitions occur between the individual levels. On the other hand, in the case of a small shift (AB_2) these levels have comparable energies, so that the formation of new states, referred to as "mixed states" can occur.

As a result of mixing, levels 2 and 4 give rise to two new levels denoted $(2 + 4)'$ and $(2 + 4)''$ respectively and levels 5 and 6 to levels $(5 + 6)'$ and $(5 + 6)''$ respectively. The levels between which transitions actually occur are indicated by solid bars. The hypothetical mixed levels in (*a*) are indicated by dashed lines, while the dotted lines in (*b*) give the position of the original "unmixed" levels. Transitions between energy levels are indicated by vertical arrows. The transition between $(2 + 4)''$ and $(5 + 6)'$ in the AB_2 case, is a forbidden one and is characterized by a very low intensity. The resulting spectrum is shown at the bottom of each diagram, with the intensity of the lines plotted in arbitrary units.

References p. 264

10. Applications of nuclear magnetic resonance spectroscopy

(a) Proton magnetic resonance

(i) Chemical shifts in relation to molecular structure

Intramolecular electronic currents. Owing both to the relative ease of detection of proton signals, and to the fact that the shielding constant σ is a sensitive indicator of small differences in the distribution of electronic charge around the nucleus, extensive information on the proton shifts characterizing different chemical groups has been accumulated, and used in the study of chemical structure.

The measurement of the chemical shift, however, is not always carried out in the proper manner so that it is often impossible to compare the results of different investigators. The reference compound, with respect to which the shift is measured, is either present as a separate phase in a capillary tube inserted in the sample (external reference standard) or is mixed with the solution (internal reference standard). If the external standard technique is employed, it is imperative to correct for bulk diamagnetic susceptibility differences between the solution and the standard, before meaningful comparisons of the electronic shielding of protons in different molecules can be made. In order to apply the correction as given in eqn. (33), the volume diamagnetic susceptibilities for the solution and the reference may have to be computed from atomic susceptibilities (Pascal constants)[14] although a number of molecular volume susceptibilities are available[15]. These corrections are especially important when the pure liquid compounds are used, as is often the case with hydrocarbons, alcohols, etc. If the

TABLE II

NMR EXTERNAL REFERENCE SEPARATIONS AT 40 Mcps*

Compound		*$\Delta\nu$ in cps (at 30°C)*	*$d(\Delta\nu)/dt$ in cps/°C*
Benzaldehyde	aldehyde H	— 107.0	< 0.01
	ring H	multiplet	
Chloroform		— 34.2	— 0.079
Benzene		0	0.00
Toluene	ring H	3.1	+ 0.010
Water		68.6	+ 0.384
1,4-Dioxane		125.7	+ 0.039
Dimethyl sulfoxide		161.9	+ 0.040
Toluene	methyl H	199.7	< 0.01
Acetone		202.6	+ 0.042
Cyclohexane		212.1	+ 0.029
Tetramethyl silane		278.2	+ 0.055

* To convert to p.p.m. divide $\Delta\nu$ by 40 (see ref. [20]).

sample consists of an inert solvent to which the solute is added to give final concentrations of about 1–20% (by weight for solids or by volume for liquids) the susceptibility of the sample will have to be computed on the basis of its composition. An equally proper practice in this case would be to obtain the shift at infinite dilution by extrapolation from at least two measurements carried out at different concentrations. Then differences in the shifts for various compounds could be taken to represent faithfully differences in the intramolecular electronic

TABLE III

PROTONS CHEMICAL SHIFTS IN HYDROCARBONS*

Compound		Shifts from benzene		
		CH	*CH_2*	*CH_3*
Saturated hydrocarbons				
Methane, gas				6.5
liquid				6.5
Propane			5.4	5.8
Isobutane		5.2		5.8
n-Hexane			5.4	5.8
Cyclopropane			6.2	
Cyclopentane			5.0	
Cyclohexane			5.1	
Unsaturated hydrocarbons				
Propylene	$H_{(2)}(CH_3)C{=}CH_{(3)}H_{(4)}$	(2) 0.9	(3) 1.5 (4) 1.6	5.0
Styrene	$H_{(2)}(\varphi)C{=}CH_{(3)}H_{(4)}$	(2) 0.3 φ — 0.2	(3) 1.6 (4) 1.3	
α-Methylstyrene		φ — 0.3	(3) 1.5 (4) 1.6	5.0
2,4,4 Trimethyl-pentene-1	$\overset{(2)}{CH_3}((CH_3)_3C{-}CH_2)C{=}CH_{(3)}H_{(4)}$		(3) 1.7 (4) 1.9 4.6	(2) 4.8 5.8
Acetylene	H—C≡C—H	3.9		
Hexyne-1	$HC{\equiv}C{-}\underset{\alpha}{CH_2}{-}CH_2{-}CH_2{-}CH_3$	4.8	(α) 4.6 5.2	5.7

* The saturated and unsaturated hydrocarbons were used as the pure liquids. The chemical shifts were measured in parts per million from water, the external standard. They were then corrected for diamagnetic susceptibility differences between the pure liquids and water[21]. The shifts were then referred to benzene as external standard by adding 1.71 p.p.m. (68.6/40), the separation between water and the external reference, benzene, as seen from Table II.

References p. 264

shielding at the protons. However, this would be true only for shifts at infinite dilution using the same solvent and external standard. In this case the correction for bulk diamagnetic susceptibility would be constant and proportional to the difference $\chi_{v,\,ref} - \chi_{v,\,solvent}$ and could therefore be neglected. It is possible, however, to avoid both bulk susceptibility corrections, which are approximate, and extrapolation to infinite dilution, by using an internal standard, since the bulk susceptibility is then the same for the sample and the reference. The criteria for a proper internal standard are that it be (*a*) soluble to the extent of about 1 % in the solvents used for NMR studies (*b*) chemically inert, so that it does not associate with other molecules and its presence does not cause changes in the shifts (*c*) magnetically isotropic and (*d*) that it gives rise preferably to a single resonance peak in a convenient part of the spectrum. All four criteria are fulfilled in the case of tetramethylsilane, $(CH_3)_4Si$, its only disadvantage being that it is not soluble enough in polar solvents such as water and D_2O. Its use is therefore confined to organic solvents. Internal standards that have been used in aqueous solutions are acetone and (trimethylsilyl) carbinol[16,17].

Another way of expressing chemical shift is to calculate δ in p.p.m., with reference to tetramethylsilane (internal standard), eqn. (31), and to add 10.000 p.p.m., in order to avoid using a negative scale for δ. This defines a new scale, referred to as the τ-scale, where τ p.p.m. $= 10.000 + \delta$ p.p.m. The chemical shifts of protons of a number of organic compounds dissolved in CCl_4 have been established according to the τ-scale[18,19] and have been converted to benzene as external reference (Table V) for convenient approximate comparisons with data

TABLE IV

METHYL GROUP SHIFTS FROM BENZENE AS EXTERNAL STANDARD

External standard*: H_2O in a capillary tube.
Internal standard** in solution: $(CH_3)_4Si$

Compound	*Pure liquid*	*Infinite dilution in CCl_4**	*Electronegativity of atom next to CH_3****	*Solvent CCl_4***	*Concentration vol. %*
$C(CH_3)_4$	6.06	5.46	2.5		
$(CH_3)_2CO$	5.04	4.41	2.5	4.41	3
CH_3I	3.71	4.31	2.5	4.28	2
CH_3Br	3.73	3.81	2.8		
CH_3Cl	3.81	3.45	3.0		
CH_3OH	3.56	3.10	3.5	3.09	1
CH_3F	3.81	2.24	4.0		

* The shifts were measured from water as external standard [22] and then converted to benzene as external standard by adding 1.71 p.p.m. These shifts are not comparable to those of Table III unless they are corrected for susceptibility differences between benzene and water in one case and benzene and CCl_4 in the other.

** Chemical shifts were converted from the τ-scale to benzene as reference by adding 5.24 p.p.m. (separation of pure water from $(CH_3)_4Si$ $\frac{278.2 - 68.6}{40}$, Table II) and subtracting 1.71 p.p.m.

*** Ref.[23].

in Tables III and IV. It has been recently suggested that the shifts be measured with respect to both an internal as well as an external standard. If both standards are the same substance, for example $(CH_3)_4Si$, the difference between their resonance peaks is a measure of the bulk susceptibility difference between the solution and the external standard[20]. As noted from Table II, water is not a good external standard, because of the large temperature dependence of its resonance position. Benzene on the other hand is a favored external standard, the peaks of protons occurring at magnetic fields higher than that where the benzene resonance is observed, being characterized by positive shifts, while those seen at lower fields are characterized by negative shifts.

The chemical shifts of open chain hydrocarbons depend generally on the number and character of the carbon–carbon bonds (Table III). The most shielded protons attached to tetrahedral carbon atoms are the CH, CH_2 and CH_3 protons of the saturated hydrocarbons observed at about 5.2, 5.4 and 5.8 p.p.m. respectively from the benzene peak. On the other hand the CH

TABLE V

SOME SHIFTS FOR HYDROGEN BONDED TO CARBON WITH RESPECT TO THE τ-SCALE AND TO BENZENE AS EXTERNAL REFERENCE*

Solvent: CCl_4, Internal standard: $(CH_3)_4Si$

Compound	*Chemical shifts in CCl_4*	
	τ-Scale $(CH_3)_4Si$	*Benzene = 0*
φ—CHO	0.1	—3.4
R—CHO	0.4	—3.1
C = C—CHO	0.5	—3.0
Pyridine —CH = N	1.5	—2.0
HCO_2R, $HCONR_2$	2.0	—1.0
Furan = CH —O (α)	2.6	—0.9
Benzene	2.7	—0.8
Benzoic and CH = C—COOH	2.1	—1.4
Aniline	3.4	—0.1
Pyrrole CH = CH —CH (β)	3.9	0.4
$RCHCl_2$, dihalomethanes	4.2	0.7
R_2C = CHR	4.9	1.4
$R_2C = CH_2$	5.3	1.8
RCHCl, C = C— CH_2Cl	6.0	2.5
CH_3O— (ester)	6.4	2.9
CH_3OR (ether)	6.7	3.2
CH_3N (amide)	7.1	3.6
CH_3—φ, RC = CH	7.7	4.2
RCH_2C = C, CH_2C = O	8.0	4.5
CH_2 saturated 5-, 6-, 7- ring	8.5	5.0
CH_3 saturated chains and rings	9.1	5.6
$(CH_3)_4Si$	10.0	6.5

* The concentration in CCl_4 varied between 1 and 20% by volume for liquids or by weight for solids. Tetramethylsilane was added in concentration of 1% by volume[19].

References p. 264

and CH_2 protons of ethylenic hydrocarbons give rise to peaks at about —0.5 and 1.4 p.p.m. respectively. The decrease in shielding in this case may be associated with an increase in the s character of the planar sp^2 carbon bonds or a decrease in electron density around the protons, as compared with the tetrahedral sp^3 carbon bonds. By carrying this reasoning further to the triply conjugated compounds having linear sp carbon bonds, such as acetylene, one would expect to find their CH peaks at even lower fields. However, this is not the case. The signal due to liquid acetylene is observed at about +3.88 p.p.m. with respect to benzene as external standard. This unexpected shift to high field is attributable to the large paramagnetic effect induced when the external magnetic field is perpendicular to the axis of the molecule. In this case there is induced electronic motion about the two carbon atoms with a resultant magnetic moment *in* the direction of the applied field. The lines of force of the induced magnetic moment which pass through the proton nuclei have a direction opposing the external field and as a result the protons are more shielded (Fig. 14b). Generally, the shielding of side chain alkyl groups, CH_2 and CH_3 in ethylenic or acetylenic compounds is not affected by the anisotropy of the double or triple carbon–carbon bonds, if these groups are sufficiently far from these bonds. It is worth mentioning, however, that the α-CH_2 groups adjacent to single, double and triple bonds are seen at 5.4, 4.6 and 4.6 p.p.m. respectively. It is thus evident that the large neighbor anisotropy effect in the alkynes is responsible also for the shielding of the α-CH_2 group. The CH_2 resonance of cyclic hydrocarbons, cyclo-pentane and -hexane is seen at about 5.2 p.p.m. and that of cyclo-propane at 6.2 p.p.m. No obvious explanation has been offered to account for the magnitude of the latter shielding effect.

In the case of aromatic hydrocarbons, the ring protons of benzene, naphthalene, phenanthrene, etc. give rise to resonance peaks at lower fields than those for ethylenic protons, although the carbon hybridization is sp^2 in both cases. The lowering in shielding for aromatic protons may be understood in terms of the induced electronic currents around the ring whose lines of force going through the proton nuclei point in the same direction as the applied field (Fig. 15).

Electronegativity and resonance effects. Besides bond character and intramolecular electronic currents, the electronegativity or electron withdrawing ability of substituents attached to a given parent compound also affects chemical shifts. For example the CH_3 peak in the series of compounds CH_3X where X is I, Br, Cl and F, moves to lower field as the electronegativity of the halogen increases (Table IV).

A large decrease in the shielding of the CH resonance is noted, if the carbon bears a hetero atom such as N, in alkaloids and amino acids, or O, in sugar acetates. A further decrease in shielding is observed for the CH of the aldehydes and amides with peaks at about —3.1 and —1.0 p.p.m. with reference to benzene as external standard (Table V).

In heterocyclic saturated or unsaturated compounds the CN and CH_2 groups adjacent to the hetero atom N or O are also shifted to lower fields as compared with the corresponding cyclic compounds in which the hetero atom is substituted by a carbon atom. The groups further away from the electronegative atom are little or not at all affected.

It is interesting that electron withdrawing groups, such as OH, NH_2 and C = O, shift the resonance peaks to lower field when they are substituents of open chain compounds but have the opposite effect when they are substituents of aromatic compounds. The reason for the latter effect lies in their participation in resonance structures which contribute to the stabilization of the particular compound. The shielding of CH protons due to substituents has been observed in substituted benzene and its derivatives, as well as in substituted unsaturated heterocyclic compounds, such as the purines and pyrimidines. In the case of adenine, for example, one of the resonance structures contributing to the shielding of the C-2 and C-8 protons would be

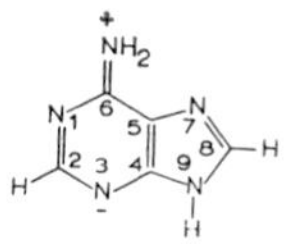

Consequently the C-2 and C-8 protons of adenine are more shielded than the corresponding protons of unsubstituted purine[16].

The pure liquid compounds bearing OH, NH, NH_2 and SH groups show characteristic peaks due to these protons. Generally, when they are substituents of aromatic nuclei their resonances occur at fields lower than those observed in the case of their corresponding alkyl derivatives. The NH_2 and NH peaks of alkylamines are found in the range of from 4.8 to 6.2 p.p.m. while the corresponding protons in aromatic amines are seen at about 2.9 to 3.7 p.p.m. with respect to benzene as external reference. On the other hand the NH and NH_2 protons of molecules containing more than one nitrogen group attached to the same carbon atom such as urea, citrulline, guanidine and arginine, give rise to distinct peaks[24] between —1.1 and 0.7 p.p.m. at pH's between 2 and 7. At pH's above 7 and below 2, base and acid catalysis of the proton exchange process probably cause the merging of these peaks with that of the solvent. The position of the NH_3^+ protons in amino acids varies from —0.5 to —1.6 p.p.m. in H_2SO_4. Titration of the amino and carboxyl groups of amino acids causes a shift in the resonance peak of the α-hydrogens; the effect on the β- and γ-hydrogens is much smaller. Thus, a plot of the chemical shift against hydrogen ion concentration results in a

References p. 264

titration curve. Similar titration curves are obtained for the amino but not for the oxy groups of water-soluble purine and pyrimidine derivatives. However, in this case large shifts may be observed in the resonance peaks of the stable protons of the heterocyclic ring far from the amino group, suggesting that the locus of proton attachment may be a ring nitrogen rather than the amino group[16].

Exchange, intra- and inter-molecular association effects. In aqueous solutions the protons attached on O, N or S atoms usually exchange rapidly with the solvent protons and do not give rise to resonance peaks distinct from the solvent line. However, if the exchange process is slowed down sufficiently, separate peaks may arise, as in the case of 99% ethanol–1% H_2O mixture. The rate of the exchange process is generally lower (*a*) in concentrated acids, (*b*) in mixtures with another liquid, which does not furnish exchangeable protons, (*c*) at low temperatures and finally (*d*) in the presence of strong intra- or inter-molecular hydrogen bonds.

For the sake of clarity the simple case of a proton of compound A exchanging with a proton of compound B will be considered (compounds A and B may be ethanol and water for example). Three situations are immediately recognized. (*a*) In the absence of exchange separate resonance peaks for each type of proton H_A and H_B appear in the spectra. The chemical shift between these protons, Δ, is then given by the difference in the field strengths at which the resonance peaks are observed. (*b*) In the case of very fast exchange only one peak is observed whose position is weighted by the life-time of the proton on molecule A (τ_A) and its life-time on molecule B (τ_B). In this case $1/\tau \gg 2\pi\Delta\nu$ where τ is the average life-time of the proton on either A or B

$$\tau = \frac{\tau_A \tau_B}{\tau_A + \tau_B}$$

$1/\tau$ is the average rate of exchange and $\Delta\nu$ is the separation in cps between the two proton peaks in the absence of exchange. (*c*) For intermediate exchange rates ($\tau \cong \Delta\nu$) either one broad line or two separate peaks are observed depending on the magnitude of $2\pi\Delta\nu$. Making the simplifying assumptions that $\tau_A = \tau_B$ and that the concentration of A is equal to that of B, a theoretical plot of the spectra for various values of $2\pi\tau\Delta\nu$ has been obtained[25,1]. It is thus possible to calculate the value of τ by comparing the observed with the theoretical spectra for which $2\pi\tau\Delta\nu$ is known and by substituting into this expression the observed value of $\Delta\nu$. This is of course an approximation which is subject to the assumptions made above. Since in this case

$$\frac{1}{\tau_A} = k_A = \frac{1}{2\tau}$$

where k_A is the rate constant for the reaction in which the proton goes from molecule A to molecule B, it is also possible to obtain the energy of activation for the exchange in the following manner:

The dependence of the rate constant on the energy of activation and on the temperature is given by the expression

$$k_A = k_A^0 \, e^{-E_a/RT}$$

where k_A^0 is the probability constant for the reaction and R is the gas constant. Then both sides of the equation are divided by $\pi \Delta \nu$ and the equation can be written in the form

$$\ln \frac{1}{2\pi\tau\Delta\nu} = \ln \frac{k_A^0}{\pi\Delta\nu} - \frac{E_a}{RT}$$

A plot of $\ln(1/2\pi\tau\Delta\nu)$ *versus* $1/T$ should give a straight line with a slope equal to $-E_a/RT$). Since both τ and $\Delta\nu$ can be obtained experimentally from the spectra as a function of temperature, an estimate of the activation energy can be obtained.

This simplified mathematical treatment is also useful in determining the energy barrier to internal rotation. For example the spectrum of dimethyl formamide at room temperature shows two peaks, one for each of the methyl groups. However, at higher temperature these merge into one line. The reason for the existence of the two peaks is that one methyl group is *cis* while the other is *trans* with respect to the carbonyl group and consequently the electronic shielding factor is different for the two orientations. The molecule is held rigidly at room temperature because of the distribution of double bond character as depicted below

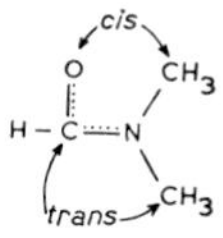

As the temperature is increased, however, the barrier to rotation about the C⋯N bond is overcome and when the rate of rotation $1/2\tau$ is greater than or equal to $2\pi\Delta\nu$ the two lines become merged (τ is the average life-time of the methyl group in either the *cis* or *trans* configuration and $\Delta\nu$ is the frequency separation between the methyl peaks).

The resonance peak for the hydrogen-bonded proton appears at lower field since the electrostatic interaction lowers the electron density at the proton. The existence of hydrogen bonds may be further established from a study of the concentration dependence of the shifts. A plot of the chemical shift against concentration and extrapolation to infinite dilution shows that the

References p. 264

resonance peak due to the proton of an intermolecular hydrogen bond appears at higher field than that of the intramolecularly bonded proton. As is expected also in the latter case, the position of the resonance peak is independent of concentration in the low concentration range. Estimates of hydrogen bond strength may be made from the temperature dependence of the shift of the hydrogen-bonded proton.

Interesting effects on chemical shifts arise when aromatic molecules are used as solutes or solvents. These effects cannot always be accounted for by a simple bulk diamagnetic susceptibility correction. For example, in the case of benzene in *n*-hexane the peak due to the benzene protons moves progressively to lower field as the concentration of benzene is decreased. A rational explanation for the dependence of the shift on concentration is based on the shielding of benzene molecules by the diamagnetic moment of neighboring benzene molecules at high concentration and a decrease of the shielding when the concentration is lowered. This would imply that the flat benzene rings are stacked above each other in solution so that the shielding due to neighbors becomes effective.

Another interesting example is the chloroform–1,2-dichlorobenzene system. As the concentration of chloroform is decreased its peak moves to higher field. The reason for this lies in the fact that at high dilution the chloroform molecule associates with the aromatic solvent more effectively, *i.e.* its proton is attracted by the π-electrons to the face of the benzene ring where the shielding by the ring diamagnetic moment is high.

(ii) Spin–spin coupling in relation to molecular structure

All the factors governing the magnitude of the spin–spin coupling constant are not yet thoroughly established. However, it has been shown theoretically that the coupling constant between two protons on adjacent carbon atoms depends on (*a*) the hybridization of the carbon orbitals, that is on whether the carbon is bonded to two, three or four atoms and (*b*) on the dihedral angle formed between the H_1—C—C— and the —C—C—H_2 planes[26] (Fig. 19a). In the case of ethylene and acetylene this angle is 180° while in ethane it has the value of 109°29′; in saturated five-and-lower-membered ring compounds it is often considerably smaller.

An explicit dependence of the coupling constant between the *gem*-protons of the same carbon atom ($C\!<^{H_1}_{H_2}$) on the angle between these protons has also been shown both theoretically and experimentally[27] (Fig. 19b).

This type of correlation between the magnitude of the coupling constant and the geometrical parameters characterizing the molecule is of great value in the study of structure and conformation.

A number of experimental findings, some of which will be mentioned, agree satisfactorily with these theoretical predictions.

In many compounds of the general structure

where R may be any of the following substituents: methyl, ethyl, saturated or unsaturated hydrocarbons, phenyl groups or halogen atoms, the coupling

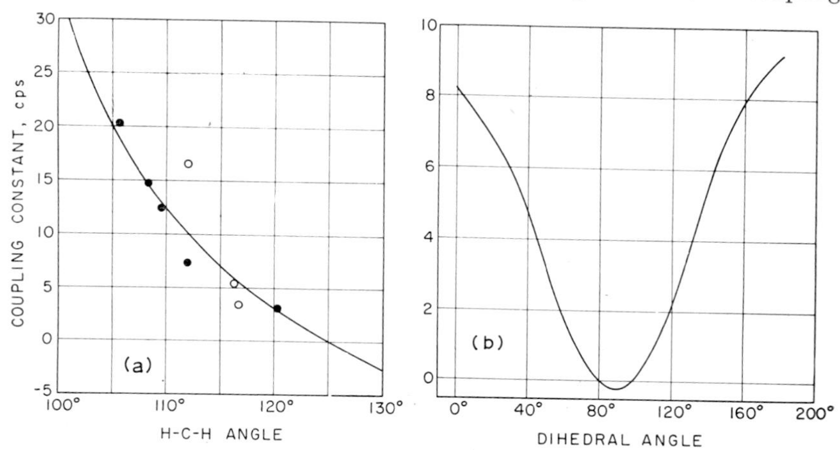

Fig. 19. (a) Theoretical curve showing the dependence of the coupling constant $J_{H_1H_2}$ on the H_1—C—H_2 angle. The points represent the measured coupling constants for a number of different compounds in which the H_1—C—H_2 angles are known experimentally (from Gutowsky, Karplus and Grant[27]. (b) Dependence of the coupling constant $J_{H_1H_2}$ on the dihedral angle formed by the intersecting planes H_1—C—C and C—C—H_2 in compounds having a H_1—C—C—H_2 configuration. The exact mathematical function describing this dependence is the following: $(8.5 \cos^2 \varphi - 0.28)$ cps for the range of angles $0° \leqslant \varphi \leqslant 90°$ and $(9.5 \cos^2 \varphi - 0.28)$ cps for the range of angles $90° \leqslant \varphi \leqslant 180°$ (after Karplus[26]).

constant between the two *cis*-protons H_1 and H_2 is of the order of 7 to 11 cps while that between the *trans*-protons H_1 and H_3 is of the order of 14 to 17 cps. Furthermore, the coupling constant between the *gem*-protons H_2 and H_3 is about 1.2 to 1.5 cps. The same generalizations hold for the hydrogen in disubstituted ethylenes, suggesting a larger dependence of the coupling constants on the relative orientation of the protons than on the number and nature of the substituents.

A similar situation is encountered in ethane and in the various substituted ethanes. There is, however, in this case an additional variable, that is, free rotation about the C—C single bonds which alters the relative orientation

References p. 264

of the protons on adjacent carbon atoms. The three most possible conformations of ethane and substituted ethanes are depicted below.

In this representation the methyl group in dark lines is situated above the plane of the paper while the other carbon which bears H_4, H_5 and R is found by the dashed circle right below the methyl carbon. Thus, each conformation differs from either of the other two by a rotation of 120° about the C—C bond, and two hydrogen atoms each on the adjacent carbon atoms can be twice *gauche* (60° apart) and once *trans* (180° apart) if all three conformations are equally possible. Clearly then the spectra of these compounds will fall into three classes depending on the rotation about the C—C bond: (*a*) rapid rotation, as in ethyl alcohol, causes averaging of the chemical shifts and coupling constants between the CH_3 and CH_2 groups. The average coupling constant calculated from considering all three conformations equally possible is $\frac{1}{3}$ $(9_{180°} + 3_{60°} + 3_{60°}) = 5$ cps while that observed is about 6 to 7 cps, (*b*) rapid interconversion between two isomers with longer time spent in the third isomer may give rise to a complicated spectrum having

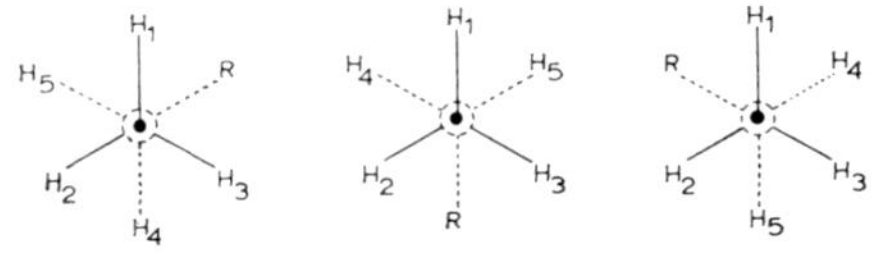

I II III

many similarities with the spectrum of the pure isomer and (*c*) hindered rotation about the C—C bond implies that the molecules may prefer one conformation or may be distributed between two or all three conformations giving rise to spectra representing one or a mixture of conformations respectively. In the latter case (*c*) the appearance of the spectra would be dependent on temperature, since at high temperatures an average spectrum would result from rapid internal rotation.

The dependence of the spin coupling constant between protons on adjacent carbon atoms on their relative orientation becomes evident also from the studies of 6-membered rings[28]. In this case, the dependence of the spin coupling constant and the proton shift on the orientation with respect to the plane of the ring, have formed the foundations for conformational analysis of these rings. It is well known that a 6-membered ring can assume two conformations referred to as the "chair" and the "boat" form, the former being the most stable one. In these conformations the tetrahedral carbon bonds not involved in the formation of the ring assume definite orientations with respect to the plane defined by four ring carbon atoms. The most interesting chair conformation can exist in the two chair forms (in rapid equilibrium as shown below), where *e* and *a* denote equatorial and axial, or more exactly that the substituent is located at about 0° and 90° respectively from the plane formed by carbon atoms 2, 3, 5 and 6.

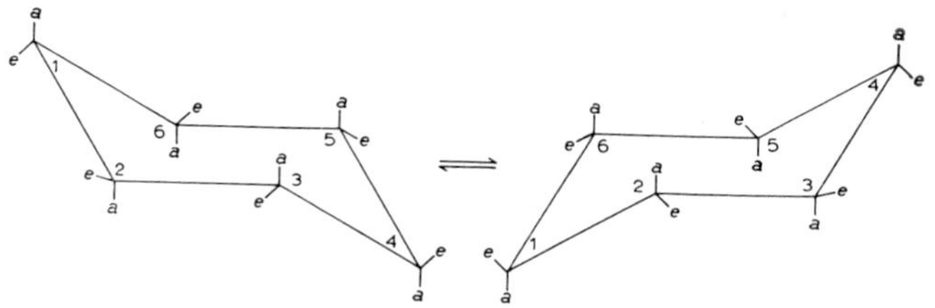

From studies on various substituted cyclohexanes and on the acetylated 6-membered sugar rings, it has been established (although with a few exceptions) that J_{aa} (the coupling constant between two axially oriented protons) is of the order of 5 to 9 cps while $J_{ae} \cong J_{ee} \cong 2$ to 3 cps (J_{ae} and J_{ee} denoting the axial–equatorial and the equatorial–equatorial coupling constants respectively). In addition, the axially oriented protons are generally seen at higher field than the equatorial ones, unless a rapid interconversion of the two chair forms gives rise to an average sharp line for both types of protons. Usually substituents on these rings tend to assume the equatorial orientations, thus preferentially stabilizing one of the chair conformations.

Recent NMR results on the saturated 5-membered rings of D-ribose in nucleosides and nucleotides suggest that the ribose ring is not planar and that either the second or the third or both carbon atoms may be out of the plane of the other three or four ring atoms. Tentative possible conformations for ribose have been based on the difference in the coupling constant between the *trans* protons on the first and second carbon atoms of ribose[29]. The preference for a specific conformation has been shown to depend on the number and kind of substituents on the ribose ring[30].

It is apparent that the proton chemical shifts and coupling constants can be interpreted in terms of the structure and conformation of small molecules in solution. Proton resonance is thus proving to complement the information from X-ray crystallography and to provide additional information on the stability of a particular molecular shape in a particular solution.

(iii) Shifts and line width in relation to molecular organization

Proton magnetic resonance of polymers. As has been mentioned previously the width of a resonance line is affected mainly by three factors: (*a*) the inhomogeneity of the externally applied magnetic field H_z, (*b*) the process of spin-dephasing in the *xy* plane characterized by the relaxation time T_2, which is required for the exchange of spin states between two nuclei precessing at the same frequency, one of which is in the ground and the other

References p. 264

in the excited state and (*c*) the local internal magnetic fields arising from the magnetic moments of the nuclei in the sample, whose contribution to the magnetic field inhomogeneity averages to zero in liquids, due to thermal motion.

The inhomogeneity of the applied magnetic field can be reduced to about 1 part per 10^8 at 40 mc, *i.e.* to 10^{-3} gauss = 4.26 cps. In polymer solutions it is the third factor that dominates the line width since the motion of protons relative to each other may be markedly retarded and the local inhomogeneity may rise to about ± 5 gauss or 21,300 cps as is the case with solids.

Freedom of motion of a polymer molecule as a whole or only of its segments is governed by the intra- and intermolecular organization of the polymer. For instance, while the spectra of native proteins in D_2O are generally characterized by two to five broad peaks[31], a larger number of sharper peaks make up the spectra of proteins dissolved in trifluoro-acetic acid or 8M deuterated urea in which both the tertiary or intermolecular structure and the secondary intramolecular helical structure are not present[32]. Such a breakdown of the molecular organization allows for a greater freedom of motion of segments in the protein molecules and therefore a decrease in the local field inhomogeneity in the sample. The spectra of several proteins such as ribonuclease, lysozyme, albumin, hemoglobin, etc. have been observed under different conditions and the ribonuclease spectrum has been quantitatively predicted from the spectra of the individual amino acids and its composition. Two points of interest in the case of polymer spectra are noted: (*a*) the molecular weight of the polymer is not limiting in getting well-defined spectra as noted for polystyrene of molecular weight $1.5 \cdot 10^6$ whose spectrum does not differ from that of polystyrene containing only 10 residues and (*b*) abnormal shifts of specific proton groups may be observed and are indicative of the internal organization of the whole molecule. An example of this is seen in the spectrum of polystyrene, which is characterized by a single peak due to the phenyl protons when the molecule is made up of less than 10 residues and two peaks in the ratio of 2 to 3 when the molecule is made up of more than 10 residues. These peaks in the latter case refer to the two *ortho*- and the three *meta*- and *para*-protons of the aromatic nucleus which are shielded to a different extent, suggesting a difference in intramolecular organization depending on the molecular weight[32].

Thus from the observation of line widths and shifts of polymer spectra it is possible in some cases to obtain information on the internal organization of the solution as well as of the polymer.

(*b*) *Nuclei other than protons*

Resonance spectra of many nuclei other than protons have been observed (for a more complete listing see ref. [1]). However, they have not been as extensively investigated as the proton spectra, owing largely to the greater difficulty of detection. This difficulty stems from several factors. First, the magnetic moments of all nuclei (except for tritium) are considerably smaller than the proton moment, so that the excess population in the ground state (which depends on $e^{\mu H/KT}$, and, therefore, the signal intensity (compared on a mole/mole basis) is lower. Second, the signal intensity may be further reduced in the case of many elements because the naturally abundant isotopes (*e.g.* ^{12}C, ^{16}O, ^{32}S) have no magnetic moments, so that the signals are due exclusively to the less abundant isotopes, (*e.g.* ^{13}C, ^{17}O, ^{33}S). Third, in the case of nuclei with a spin $I > \frac{1}{2}$ (*e.g.* ^{14}N, ^{23}Na, ^{35}Cl), the signal may be broadened due to quadrupolar relaxation effects.

Besides the proton, the nucleus by far most widely studied by resonance methods is ^{19}F, whose resonance is observed at 40 mc in a field of 10,000 gauss (as compared to the 42.6 mc for protons). From these investigations information has been obtained on the structure of many organic fluoro-compounds, the symmetry of halogen fluorides and other fluorine-containing molecules, electron distribution in fluoro-benzene and the types of bonds in fluorinated compounds.

Of greater interest for problems of biological chemistry is the observation of resonance in ^{13}C, ^{14}N, ^{17}O and ^{31}P. Although the natural abundance of ^{13}C is 1.1%, the resonance due to this small fraction of nuclei can be detected in many compounds in their pure liquid state. As yet the available information is largely limited to a survey of structural effects on the chemical shift, which indicates, however, that the position and splitting of the ^{13}C resonance lines have considerable promise as sensitive indicators of structural differences. Also, the splitting of proton lines by the ^{13}C nucleus (in ^{13}C enriched compounds) has allowed inferences concerning the effect of bond hybridization (electron density and shape of the charge distribution) on the ^{13}—CH coupling constants. In the case of ^{14}N, studies have been limited largely to comparatively simple and relatively symmetrical derivatives, because considerable line broadening results from the interaction of the ^{14}N nuclear quadrupole moment with the field gradients of asymmetrical charge distributions. Thus in a series of quaternary ammonium compounds the ^{14}N signal is very much broader in compounds of the types NH_3R, NH_2R_2, NHR_3 etc. (R being an organic substituent) than it is in the case of the ammonium ion itself, or of its symmetrical derivatives. ^{17}O resonance has been observed in only a few instances. The equivalence of oxygens in compounds like HNO_3, HCOOH etc. is quite apparent from these observations as is the fact that they become non-equivalent by esterification.

Absorption spectra of the ^{31}P nucleus ($I = \frac{1}{2}$) have proved very useful in the structure identification of phosphorus containing compounds, as the

References p. 264

lines are widely separated by large shifts not being subject to sharp quadrupole broadening, and split in a characteristic manner by the neighboring atoms. Phosphorus atoms occupying non-equivalent positions in molecules, as is the case in polyphosphates, are thus readily distinguished, an example being the ^{31}P spectrum of adenosine triphosphate whose three different phosphorus atoms give rise to three lines which are further split by spin–spin coupling[33].

The broadening which results from quadrupolar interactions has been used to detect very weak complexes of the ^{23}Na ion[34]. Comparatively narrow lines are observed for the free ions, as their charge distribution is spherically symmetrical, while in the case of strong binding (*e.g.* to ion exchange resins) the resonance absorption is broadened beyond detection. Line broadening observed in the presence of anions like citrate or polyphosphates reflects a relatively small deviation from spherical symmetry of the charge distribution and can be interpreted as being due to the formation of a weak bond. Similar inferences are possible from the spectra of other alkali metal and halide ions and a systematic exploration of spectral changes produced under different conditions can yield information on the chemical environment of the nucleus, which is not readily obtainable by other means.

11. Summary

The phenomenon of nuclear magnetic resonance (NMR) occurs only in the case of atomic nuclei possessing angular momentum and therefore a magnetic moment. Both of these are vector quantities and assume definite quantized directions with respect to a stationary external magnetic field. Each orientation with respect to the external field is characterized by a potential energy. Transitions between adjacent orientations or potential energy levels can occur by absorption of circularly polarized electromagnetic radiation which arises from a second weak magnetic field rotating in a plane perpendicular to the axis of the stationary magnetic field.

Unlike electron spin resonance (EPR), which depends on the presence of a free electron magnetic moment, as in paramagnetic compounds and free radicals (the Bohr magneton for an electron is $(e/2m_ec)\,(h/2\pi) = 9.273 \cdot 10^{-21}$ erg/gauss), NMR is based on the presence of a nuclear magnetic moment in atoms of diamagnetic compounds (the Bohr magneton for a proton is $(e/2m_pc)\,(h/2\pi) = 5.0493 \cdot 10^{-24}$ erg/gauss). Thus at comparable external magnetic field strengths the frequencies of electromagnetic radiation necessary to observe electron spin and nuclear spin resonance are very different, of the order of kilomegacycles/sec or $10^3 \times$ megacycles/sec and megacycles/sec respectively.

The nucleus most extensively studied by NMR is the proton with spin

$I = \frac{1}{2}$. Various protons of an organic compound experience slightly different local magnetic fields due to different electronic shielding depending on bond hybridization and electronegativity of neighboring atoms. Consequently, they will give rise to a number of resonance lines serving as a fingerprint of the structure of the compound and as a means of characterizing chemical processes in which it may be involved.

References p. 264

REFERENCES

1 J. A. Pople, W. G. Schneider and H. J. Bernstein, *High-Resolution Nuclear Magnetic Resonance*, McGraw-Hill, New York, 1959.

2 O. Jardetzky and C. D. Jardetzky, *Biochemical Applications of Magnetic Resonance Spectroscopy*, in D. Glick (Ed.), *Methods of Biochemical Analysis*, Vol. IX, Interscience, New York, 1961.

3 J. D. Roberts, *Nuclear Magnetic Resonance*, McGraw-Hill, New York, 1959.

4 L. M. Jackman, *Applications of Nuclear Magnetic Resonance Spectroscopy in Organic Chemistry*, Pergamon, London, 1959.

5 E. R. Andrew, *Nuclear Magnetic Resonance*, Cambridge University Press, New York, 1955.

6 N. F. Ramsey, *Nuclear Moments*, John Wiley and Sons, New York, 1953.

7 *Nuclear Magnetic Resonance*, *Ann. N.Y. Acad. Sci.*, 70 (1957) 673.

8 J. E. Wertz, *Chem. Revs.*, 55 (1955) 829.

9 G. E. Pake, *Am. J. Phys.*, 18 (1950) 438, 473.

10 G. P. Harnwell, *Principles of Electricity and Magnetism*, McGraw-Hill, Cambridge 1938.

11 K. S. Pitzer, *Quantum Chemistry*, Prentice-Hall, New York, 1953.

12 F. Bloch, *Phys. Rev.*, 70 (1946) 460.

13 A. D. Buckingham, T. Schaefer and W. G. Schneider, *J. Chem. Phys.*, 32 (1960) 1227.

14 *International Critical Tables*, Vol. VI, McGraw-Hill, New York, 1929.

15 J. A. Pople, W. G. Schneider and H. J. Bernstein, *High-Resolution Nuclear Magnetic Resonance*, McGraw-Hill, New York, 1959, Appendix C, p. 488.

16 C. D. Jardetzky and O. Jardetzky, *J. Am. Chem. Soc.*, 82 (1960) 222.

17 A. Kowalsky and P. D. Boyer, *Federation Proc.*, 19 (1960) 337.

18 G. V. D. Tiers, *J. Phys. Chem.*, 62 (1958) 1151.

19 G. V. D. Tiers, *Tables of τ-Values for a Variety of Organic Compounds*, Minnesota Mining and Manufacturing Company, St. Paul, Minn., 1958.

20 W. A. Anderson, N. F. Chamberlain, J. C. Guffy and C. A. Reilly, *Proposals for the Publication of NMR Spectral Data* (personal communication).

21 J. A. Pople, W. G. Schneider and H. J. Bernstein, *High-Resolution Nuclear Magnetic Resonance*, McGraw-Hill, New York, 1959, pp. 236, 245, and 247.

22 A. L. Allred and E. G. Rochow, *J. Am. Chem. Soc.*, 79 (1957) 5361.

23 L. Pauling, *Nature of the Chemical Bond*, 3rd ed., Cornell University Press, Ithaca, N.Y., 1960.

24 O. Jardetzky and C. D. Jardetzky, *J. Biol. Chem.*, 233 (1958) 383.

25 L. H. Meyer, A. Saika and H. S. Gutowsky, *J. Am. Chem Soc.*, 75 (1953) 4567.

26 M. Karplus, *J. Chem. Phys.*, 30 (1959) 11.

27 H. S. Gutowsky, M. Karplus and D. M. Grant, *J. Chem. Phys.*, 31 (1959) 1278.

28 R. V. Lemieux, R. K. Kullnig, H. J. Bernstein and W. G. Schneider, *J. Am. Chem. Soc.*, 80 (1958) 6098.

29 C. D. Jardetzky, *J. Am. Chem. Soc.*, 82 (1960) 229.

30 C. D. Jardetzky, unpublished results.

31 M. Saunders and A. Wishnia, *Ann. N.Y. Acad. Sci.*, 70 (1958) 870.

32 F. A. Bovey, G. V. D. Tiers and G. Filipovitch, *J. Polymer Sci.*, 38 (1959) 73.

33 M. Cohn, *J. Cellular Comp. Physiol.*, 54 (1959) 17, Suppl. 1.

34 O. Jardetzky and J. E. Wertz, *J. Am. Chem. Soc.*, 82 (1960) 318.

Chapter IX

Determination of Mass, Form and Dimensions of Large Particles in Solution

CHARLES SADRON AND MICHEL DAUNE

Centre for Research on Macromolecules, Strasbourg (France)

1. Introduction

During the last twenty years there has been a considerable intensification of research destined to give us a better knowledge of submicroscopic particles dispersed in the liquid phase. This is, it seems, attributable to two principal causes: in the first place to a rapid development of the high-polymer industry (plastic substances, artificial textiles, etc.) and in the second to the progress accomplished by biologists. The latter, since the beginning of the century, have indeed succeeded in isolating molecular species of high mass (nucleic acids, proteins, nucleoproteins, etc.) which constitute the essential materials of living organisms. In this field they have shown that not only chemical composition does play its part but they have also shown the role of the disposition of the functional groups with respect to one another. Hence it is no longer sufficient to know the simple chemical analysis of these elementary particles, but it is necessary to examine, with the greatest care, qualities other than their internal structure, *e.g.* their shapes and dimensions, as well as certain electrical, optical and mechanical properties. When it is realized that the essential biological mechanisms operate precisely in this region, the importance of this new branch of physical chemistry to biologists will become immediately apparent.

It is reasonable to hope that a detailed study of the morphology of biological macromolecules, made by the methods to be described, will help to elucidate the relations between specific biological phenomena and physical structure, and will conversely, enable us to bring about specific changes which promote desired alterations of structure.

References p. 310

(a) The macromolecular domain

Before entering into the subject fully it will be useful to state some very general considerations about macromolecules.

First, the order of macromolecular dimensions extends from about 10 Å to several thousand Å, which roughly corresponds to molecular weights of a few hundred to several millions. These limits are evidently very wide. In addition, there exist certain macromolecules composed of thousands of atoms which are visible to the naked eye, *e.g.* the diamond crystal. These cases are, however, exceptional and the largest of the macromolecules are still small enough to be involved in an intense Brownian movement. This will be a factor of great importance in all that follows.

The lower limit of the macromolecular domain is still less precise. It is estimated to be in the neighbourhood of some 10 Å for, in general, below this limit the molecules are sufficiently simple for their structures to be determined completely by the usual physical molecular methods (X-ray diffraction, infra-red and Raman spectra).

Although rather vaguely defined in this way, the macromolecular domain has its own definite physical properties.

The spectral methods (from X-rays to the infra-red) which have such power for studying small molecules, lose much of their efficacy in the case under consideration; they give in fact information concerning detail, but not assembly. They indicate how the atoms or certain groups of atoms are located, but they give only very vague indications of the whole assembly which they constitute. The molecular physics of small molecules is powerless to give us the outline, dimensions, shape and internal arrangement of the general structure. If the molecule is no longer a rigid structure, but is flexible and of varying configuration, it is still further powerless. For the study of macromolecules, especially in solution it is imperative to use specialised techniques and theories, which now constitute a well defined chapter of molecular physics.

(b) The two extreme types of macromolecules

In the first place, a direct distinction between two extreme types of macromolecules is evident, namely *rigid molecules* and *flexible chain molecules.*

Rigid macromolecules consist of an assembly of atoms in which the nuclei are situated in perfectly defined positions with respect to each other, from which the vibrations responsible for the infra-red and Raman spectra arise. Such a macromolecule is a small solid of well-defined shape, *e.g.* a microcrystal.

On the other hand, chain molecules, *e.g.* the linear high polymers, consist of successions of atoms, or groups of atoms, united one after the other by the valency links which give a certain number of degrees of freedom. In these conditions, in general, the macromolecule no longer has definite shape, but presents an infinite number of configurations and, in fact the idea of shape must be replaced by that of a statistical configuration.

It is obvious that a whole series of continuous transitions exists between the extreme possibilities of rigid and chain molecules.

In particular certain macromolecules of biological origin, such as the globular proteins, give us striking examples of these transitions. As a matter of fact we know that these substances are made up of chains of peptides with the general formula (primary structure)

$$\ldots CH_2-\underset{\displaystyle R}{\underset{|}{CH}}-CO-NH-CH_2-\underset{\displaystyle R'}{\underset{|}{CH}}-CO-NH\ldots$$

where R, R′ . . . represent the corresponding amino acid residues. These chains are coiled in a more or less regular manner on themselves to form a helix (secondary structure)[1], and the structure of the synthetic polypeptides (α-helix)[2] has been especially well studied.

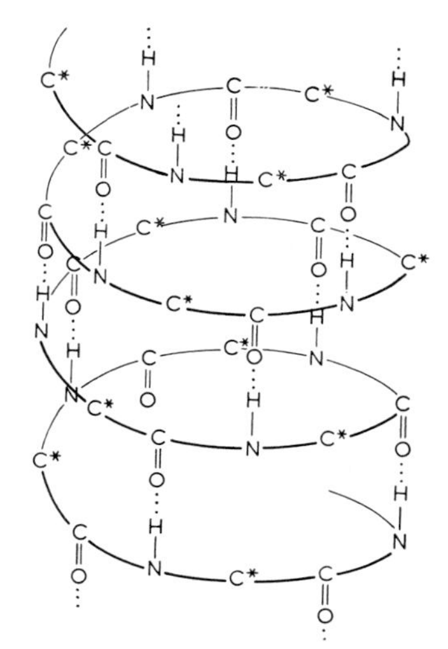

Fig. 1. Schematic diagram of an α-helix.

Finally this helix itself is curved (tertiary structure), in configurations that are still imperfectly understood, in such a manner that a kind of coil is formed, which is kept stable by internal bonds (hydrogen bonds, sulphide bonds), which give the macromolecule its globular appearance[3].

References p. 310

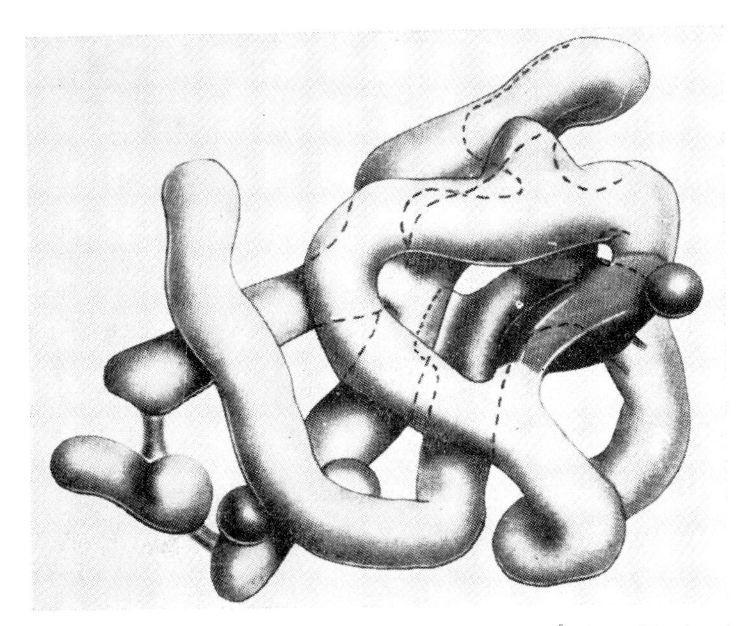

Fig. 2. Structure of myoglobin with a resolution of 6 Å (from Kendrew).

By careful chemical or physical actions the internal bonds can be progressively ruptured and finally the denatured protein becomes a long, flexible filament, which can take an infinity of different configurations. The protein molecule, originally thought to be a rigid molecule and to which one can assign, at any rate roughly, a form and dimensions, loses its specific properties and becomes a flexible chain, the configuration of which will be described below.

In what follows and to facilitate the explanation, we will examine successively the case of rigid macromolecules and that of coiled macromolecules.

(c) Statement of the problem

Suppose then, for the moment, that we are dealing with a solution of rigid particles whose dimensions and masses are within the region described above. It is proposed to determine the dimensions of these particles and also their mass. It generally happens in practice that one ignores initially whether or not the solution contains particles which are all identical (in this case the solution is said to be monodisperse). The problem to be considered consists of sorting the particles into different categories, so that all the particles of each group possess the same shapes, dimensions and masses.

Consider a solution containing ν particles per unit volume. It is required to determine the number $\nu_1, \nu_2 \ldots \nu_i$ of particles per unit volume in each of the groups 1, 2 . . . i . . . or more directly the percentages in weight $\gamma_1, \gamma_2 \ldots \gamma_i$ of these particles contained in any volume of the solution. We characterize this mixture by the mean of a weight distribution function $f(\lambda)$ which for $\lambda = \lambda_i$ takes the value

$$f(\lambda_i) = \gamma_i \delta(\lambda - \lambda_i) \tag{1.1}$$

where δ corresponds to the Dirac function.

The solution is said to be multidisperse relative to λ when there exists a small number of discrete values of λ. In this case, generally, it is possible to separate by appropriate techniques the different molecular species and to obtain successive fractions 1, 2 . . . , each of which is monodisperse relative to λ. If the number of discrete values of λ increases it is better to consider a continuous variation of λ and to define $f(\lambda)$ as the weight percentage $d\gamma$ of particles for which the parameter is situated between λ and $\lambda + d\lambda$, that is:

$$d\gamma = f(\lambda)\, d\lambda \tag{1.2}$$

Finally, one introduces the quantity $\langle \lambda_\alpha \rangle$ as the αth moment of the distribution function $f(\lambda)$ defined by the equation:

$$\langle \lambda_\alpha \rangle = \int_0^\infty \lambda_\alpha f(\lambda)\, d\lambda \tag{1.3}$$

In the course of this paper we shall see that all mean experimental values of λ may be expressed in terms of the different moments of $f(\lambda)$.

The main problem of polydispersity is to determine the distribution function. In simple cases one parameter only is necessary to characterize the molecule, for example the molecular weight in the case of a mixture of homogeneous rods with constant diameter, or spheres with equal density. We shall not consider here the superposition of two types of polydispersity (for example simultaneous mass and configuration heterogeneity).

(d) The electron microscope

Before pursuing the study of the methods used in the solution of the problem, it is necessary to devote a paragraph to the electron microscope. This instrument reveals, after suitable preparation, particles whose dimensions are largely below 1,000 Å. As is well known, the resolving power of electron microscopes descends, at least theoretically, and in practice for the best instruments, to a limit of about 20 Å. In these conditions the macromolecular domain will be almost entirely within the working limits of the electron microscope, and the problem described above will be resolved automatically. As a result of this, an immediate observation of the shapes of the particles studied is often possible, frequently by means of the shadow method. Further examination of a sufficient number of photographs of particles allows the deduction of the law of distribution $f(\lambda)$ in groups of homogeneous shape and size[4].

Certainly the electron microscope affords an excellent method for studying the morphology of particles. Without underestimating its importance, however, it should be emphasized that this method is, as with all experimental methods, open to criticism, and suffers limitations which make other methods necessary. The criticisms may be stated briefly.

(1) It frequently happens that, while one of the dimensions of the particles may be quite adequate for the limit of resolution of the electron microscope, the others are too small. For this category of particles the electron microscope is useless.

(2) In the favourable cases, where the particles are plainly visible, an extremely important question arises. Do the shapes and dimensions of the photographed particles correspond exactly to the shapes and dimensions of the particles in solution? It is known in fact that in many cases the particles are deposited on the preparation frame after desiccation of a small drop of the solution, after which they can be silhouetted by thin metallic films as in the shadow method, or rendered opaque by impregnation with a metallic salt. This treatment may modify the particle and change its dimensions, an effect which has been pointed out for virus particles such as TMV (tobacco mosaic virus) for example. Though the question is still controversial, it appears that in this case the dimensions as measured from the electron microscope picture are smaller than those obtained by "methods in solution"[5].

(3) Finally the use of the electron microscope is practically impossible in the study of the morphological changes of the particles in solution (swelling, denaturation, degradation, etc.) produced by different agents such as changes in the pH or the ionic strength of the solution.

From this brief analysis it will be concluded that the use of the electron microscope, although of wide application for the study of particles in solution, does not eliminate in any way the necessity of the use of methods in which the particles are studied in the liquid medium.

For the sake of clarity the case of the rigid particles, for which the general principles can be more clearly exposed, will be treated first, followed by the case of the flexible chains.

2. Rigid particles

(a) General principles

Contrary to the electron microscope method, where measurements are made on individual particles, the methods now to be discussed are concerned with a mean property of a macroscopic quantity of the solution, and therefore relate to a large number of particles. Having measured the mean property it is necessary to establish:

(*i*) The relation between the mean observed macroscopic observation and the size of each elementary microscopic phenomenon, relative to each of the particles contained in the mass of the solution.

(*ii*) The relation between the magnitude of the microscopic phenomenon and the dimensions of the particle.

These two relations, established by means of a suitable theory, permit the required sizes to be calculated from the results of observation, but when thoroughly applied impose serious handicaps.

Practically the calculation is possible only when the elementary property relative to each particle which produces the measured effect is independent of the presence of other particles. For example, the energy dissipated by viscosity when a particle moves relative to its "solvent" can easily be calculated for a single particle in the fluid. Otherwise the calculation is extremely difficult and can only lead to a result in very simple cases.

As before let ν be the number of particles per unit volume, φ the magnitude of the elementary phenomenon for which each particle is responsible (energy dissipated by viscous flow, intensity of diffracted light, etc.), and Φ the overall phenomenon observed in the assembly of the particles. In general φ depends on ν and we can write:

$$\varphi = \varphi_0 + a\nu + b\nu^2 + \ldots$$

where φ_0 represents the magnitude of the elementary phenomena at zero concentration—*i.e.* when the particle is alone in the fluid. Further we have:

$$\Phi = \nu\varphi_0 + a'\nu^2 + b'\nu^3 + \ldots$$

Hence by measuring Φ for decreasing values of ν, the limiting value of Φ/ν for $\nu = 0$ gives φ_0 *i.e.* the magnitude of the elementary phenomenon, of which the theory permits calculation from the dimensions of the particle. A suitable extrapolation thus gives φ_0 from Φ.

The methods used must therefore be designed to find Φ/ν for such small concentrations that the extrapolation towards $\nu = 0$ can be made with

References p. 310

sufficient accuracy. This justifies the study of macromolecular solutions at very high dilutions. It is evident that at large dilutions the magnitude of the overall phenomenon is very small, so that it is necessary to use very sensitive techniques.

Having thus determined the magnitude of the elementary phenomenon (φ_0) it can be expressed as a function of the characteristics of the particle, *e.g.* its dimensions.

Whether the phenomenon φ_0 is the hydrodynamic friction coefficient, or the dispersion of an incident electromagnetic field, it is clear that the calculation will only lead to a result when each elementary particle has a simple geometrical shape. In fact, at present these calculations are only possible if the particle is close to a sphere, a very elongated or flattened cylinder of revolution, an ellipsoid of revolution, or strictly a scalene ellipsoid.

It follows that the methods in solution cannot pretend to furnish an exact description of the shape of the particles and that they will only give the dimensions of the shape of revolution which approaches the real shape. This is undoubtedly a drawback of this type of method, but the real shape of macromolecules in solution is in fact so far from clear that the primary consideration is to establish the symmetries and the characteristic dimensions of the particles.

Finally it is necessary to recall that in the above analysis we have put $\Phi_{\nu=0} = \nu\varphi_0$ which supposes that the phenomenon φ_0 is the same for all the particles contained in the solution. This assumes implicitly that all the particles are identical (monodisperse solution).

Particular methods will be described in the following section which are actually used on the assumption of the following three conditions: (1) the solutions are infinitely dilute, (2) they contain particles of simple geometric shape (solids of revolution), and (3) they are monodisperse.

It has been explained above that the first two assumptions were not really restrictive and it has been shown that they do not present serious difficulty in their application to real solutions. The third assumption, on the contrary, is in general inadmissible. Monodisperse media are the exception among those of biological origin. A description and discussion of monodisperse media follows, principally to clarify this account and because methods applicable to polydisperse media rely on methods valid for monodisperse media to which they are not in principle dissimilar. The difficulties appear when actual values are interpreted and, as will be seen, these difficulties are still far from being overcome in a satisfactory manner. In fact, the determination of the distribution functions defined in the preceding pages is one of the pressing problems, to which the last section of this chapter will be devoted.

Naturally the methods in solution will be classified according to the nature of the phenomenon φ_0 of which the overall effect is observed and which depends on the sizes of the particles. There are two principal groups of methods. In the one, the elementary phenomenon consists of the viscous force exerted on the particle, moving relatively to the surrounding medium; in the other group, the elementary phenomenon consists of the effect of each particle on electromagnetic waves in the solvent (electromagnetic, or optical methods).

(b) Hydrodynamic methods (monodisperse solutions)

(i) Coefficient of laminar flow

General definitions. Consider a solid of any dimensions moving in a continuous fluid. The fluid, which is assumed to be initially at rest, is disturbed by the passage of the solid, so that to maintain the latter in motion an external agency must furnish certain work, in other words the fluid exerts a friction on the solid.

Hydrodynamics shows by theory and experiment that if the velocity of the solid relative to the liquid is less than a certain value, the disturbed layers of the fluid slide over each other like smooth skins, and without turbulent motion. In this case, known as laminar flow, the frictional forces exerted by the fluid on the solid are proportional to the coefficient of viscosity of the fluid, η_0, and to the velocity of the solid. The coefficient of proportionality depends on the shape of the solid.

Consider a sphere of radius R, and volume V, with a uniform velocity of translation, u. The resultant of the laminar forces, or viscosity, which it experiences, is a vector applied at its centre O, opposed to the direction of motion, and with magnitude:

$$F = uf\,, \quad \text{where } f = 6\pi\eta_0 R = 6\pi\left(\frac{3}{4\pi}\right)^{\frac{1}{3}}\eta_0 V^{\frac{1}{3}} \tag{2.1}$$

These two equations constitute Stokes' law. Similarly, if the sphere turns about a diameter with constant angular velocity ω, the viscous forces reduce to a resultant couple Γ which opposes the rotation. Hence:

$$\Gamma = \omega C\,, \quad \text{where } C = 8\pi\eta_0 R^3 = 6V\eta_0 \tag{2.2}$$

When the sphere possesses both translational and rotational motion it can be shown that the frictional forces reduce to those just given, with the same values for the coefficients f and C, augmented by terms of the second order

References p. 310

dependent on the velocity. Usually it is supposed, as in the case under consideration, that the velocities are sufficiently small for these terms to be negligible.

In the general case where the moving solid is no longer spherical, the general laws expressed by eqns. (2.1) and (2.2) are still valid, but the value of the coefficient (f) depends on the orientation of the solid with respect to its direction of translation, and similarly, the coefficient C depends on the axis about which rotation occurs.

For example, if the solid is an ellipsoid of revolution of which a is the semi-axis of revolution, b is the equatorial radius, $p = a/b$ is the axial ratio and $V = 4\pi b^2 a/3$ is the volume, then the coefficients of friction are functions of p and V for which an expression will be found in the appendix.

Under the above conditions, provided that the laws of hydrodynamics for continuous fluids are valid in the macromolecular region, measurement of one of the coefficients f or C for a sphere permits calculation of R, η_0 being known. For an ellipsoid of revolution, measurement of both f and C permits calculation of the two unknowns V and p (or a and b)[6].

Brownian movement. It is obvious that in the macromolecular region the assumption of the continuity of the dispersive liquid is not admissible *a priori* since the particle undergoes a Brownian movement, which adds a complication, and throws doubt upon the validity of the method just described. Briefly, the laws of Brownian movement are as follows.

(1) The first is strictly statistical and relies on the assumption that, at two instants t and τ, sufficiently separated, the directions of jumps of translation (or rotation) of the particle have independent probabilities.

That implies that the mean square $\bar{l}^2$ of the displacements of the centre of gravity of the particle, measured after equal intervals of time t, is exactly proportional to the time t. The same applies to the mean square $\bar{s}^2$, of the angles which a fixed axis in the particle makes with a fixed direction. The laws may be stated as:

$$\bar{l}^2 = 6\Delta t \tag{2.3}$$

$$\bar{s}^2 = 4Dt \tag{2.4}$$

The factors Δ and D which measure in some way the intensity of the Brownian movement are called respectively the translational and rotational diffusion constants of the particle in the liquid.

(2) The second is mechanical, relying on the theorem of the equipartition of energy, which shows that the constants Δ and D are given by the equations

$$\Delta = kT/f \tag{2.5}$$

$$D = kT/C \tag{2.6}$$

where T is the absolute temperature of the solution, k is Boltzmann's constant ($k = 1.38 \cdot 10^{-16}$ ergs), and f and C are respectively the coefficients of friction of translation and rotation experienced by the particle in the elementary jumps, the succession of which constitutes the Brownian movement.

(3) These general laws having been stated, consider for example a spherical particle in the solution to experience a force ϕ of constant magnitude and direction. In the absence of Brownian movement this particle will rapidly assume a uniform velocity u, which is reached when the force due to viscosity (uf) becomes equal to the motive force ϕ. Hence:

$$f = \phi/u \tag{2.7}$$

If Brownian movement is taken into consideration the velocity of the particle is no longer constant in magnitude and direction. It varies irregularly, but it can be shown to be purely and simply a superposition of Brownian movement on the movement of translation. The velocity $\vec{U}$ of the sphere is then equal to the sum of the velocities $\vec{u}$ which would have been observed if no Brownian movement had existed, and of the velocity $\vec{u}_s$, produced by the Brownian movement. At any instant therefore $\vec{U} = \vec{u} + \vec{u}_s$.

Hence if the velocity $\vec{U}$ is measured at different instants and the mean result is taken it is found, since the mean value of $\vec{u}_s$ is zero, that

$$\vec{U} = \phi/f$$

which is an analogous equation to (2.7). If the particle is not symmetrical, the preceding reasoning must be modified. In fact, the Brownian movement of rotation causes the particle to take different orientations according to the direction of translation and, consequently, the coefficient of viscosity which obtains is a mean of all the values assumed by the coefficient of viscosity for all the orientations of the particle. For that reason it is designated by the symbol $\bar{f}$.

It is the coefficient $\bar{f}$ which appears in eqn. (2.5) giving the translational diffusion constant. It is given by the following equation:

$$\bar{f} = \frac{6\pi}{(\frac{3}{4}\pi)^{\frac{1}{3}}} \eta_0 V^{\frac{1}{3}} \cdot 1/t(p) \tag{2.8}$$

where $t(p)$ is a function of axial ratio[7], given in the appendix. For $p = 1$, $t(p) = 1$, and $\bar{f}$ is equal to the coefficient of friction of a sphere of volume V.

References p. 310

It follows that $1/t(p)$ corresponds to what Svedberg called the factor of dissymmetry of the particle.

Finally, the Brownian movement of translation has not, after what has been said above, any influence on the Brownian movement of rotation. It is for this reason that the coefficient C of (2.6) is not a mean value.

It has already been stated that, for a sphere turning about one of its diameters, $C = 6\eta_0 V$. In the case of an ellipsoid of revolution turning about any equatorial diameter, C can be expressed in the same way as f, as follows:

$$C = 6\eta_0 V \cdot 1/r(p) \tag{2.9}$$

where $r(p)$ is a function of elongation[7] to be found in the appendix. $r(p) = 1$: for $p = 1$.

(4) It appears then that the existence of Brownian movement does not influence the definitions of the coefficients of friction for submicroscopic particles to any noticeable extent, any more than do their sizes. However, one question remains. Is it true, as has been assumed, that the expressions for the coefficients of friction are still given in this case by the laws of hydrodynamics for continuous fluids?

The answer to this question is not simple and categoric. It is evident that when the dimensions of the particles are very large by comparison with the molecular dimensions of the solvent, the latter can be considered as a continuous fluid and the corresponding laws should be valid. But it is equally probable that, as the particles become smaller and smaller, these laws become less and less exact. The idea of viscosity then becomes difficult to define in the molecular region, and the problem to be considered is one of the kinetics of liquids, which has not yet been given a satisfactory theoretical solution.

For the present it will be assumed that in the macromolecular region, the laws of hydrodynamics of continuous fluids are still valid in the mean, and that they give the correct expressions for the coefficients of viscosity.

Measurement of coefficients of friction. The methods of determining the radius of a sphere, or the dimensions of an ellipsoid (or a cylinder) of revolution from the coefficients of friction f and C are governed by the above considerations. It is now convenient to review the methods for measuring the coefficients. They fall into two groups according to the considerations just made.

The first group includes methods relying on Δ and D, and the application of eqns. (2.5) and (2.6).

The second includes those relying on the measurement of the mean velocity of displacement, u, of the particle in a uniform field of force g, and application of eqn. (2.7).

(ii) Measurement of the diffusion constants

The principle of these measurements is the following:

Constant of translational diffusion. The solution, of concentration ν_0, is placed in a vessel of sufficient depth in contact with the solvent. Under these conditions the macromolecules diffuse upwards and, after a certain time t, the concentration at a distance x from the surface of separation is $\nu(x, t)$. Now it can be shown from the laws of Brownian movement that the variation of the concentration obeys Fick's law, *viz.*:

$$\frac{\partial \nu}{\partial t} - \Delta \cdot \frac{\partial^2 \nu}{\partial x^2} = 0 \qquad (2.10)$$

By integration and from the experimental boundary conditions we have

$$\nu(x, t) = \tfrac{1}{2}\nu_0 \{1 - f(x/2\sqrt{\Delta t})\} \qquad (2.11)$$

where f is the Gauss function defined as:

$$f(y) = \frac{2}{\sqrt{\pi}} \int_0^y e^{-u^2} \, du$$

The value of Δ can be obtained by comparison of eqn. (2.10) with the experimentally determined function $\nu(x, t)$. Further it is necessary to note that, in keeping with what has already been said, eqns. (2.11) are only valid for infinitely small values of ν_0. It will therefore be necessary to repeat the experiment several times with decreasing initial concentrations of ν_0, and which give a different value of $\nu(x, t)$ each time. The value of $\nu(x, t)$ taken as being correct will then be the value for $\nu_0 = 0$, obtained by extrapolation.

Numerous techniques allow experimental realisation of the above scheme[8].

Diffusion constant of rotation (D). The method of measurement can be the same as for Δ, starting from a solution in which the particles are initially oriented, in the mean, in a definite direction. Neglecting the cause of the orientation, Brownian movement will progressively restore disorder. The law according to which the mean orientation decays can be established in spherical coordinates from Fick's law. By comparison with the experimental law the numerical value of D can be found. This is Benoit's method[9]. The orientation is obtained by the application of an electric field, and it is measured by the birefringence effect produced (Kerr effect). When the field is switched on suddenly, the birefringence grows gradually, and then decays when it is switched off (Fig. 3).

The value of D can be found from the curves of growth and decay of the

References p. 310

birefringence, which can be seen on the oscillograph screen. Experiment gives in addition the value of the permanent dipole of the particles. This method is not applicable to conducting solutions.

A second method, of very general interest, is based on the phenomenon of birefringence of flow. It can be shown that non-spherical particles (for

Fig. 3. Kerr effect. Upper trace: electrical pulse – Lower trace: photoelectric response.

example, rods or discs, elongated or flattened ellipsoids of revolution) tend to orient themselves parallel to a given direction when placed in a liquid undergoing streamline flow of constant velocity gradient. For example the solution can fill the interval between two coaxial cylinders. When one turns with an angular velocity Ω, and if R is the radius of the rotor, and d is the distance of separation between the two cylinders, then the velocity gradient G is practically constant throughout the liquid and is equal to R/d (Fig. 4a). If the particles contained by the solution have a mean orientation, the latter will be birefringent. Plane polarised light crossing the liquid parallel to the axis of the cylinders is elliptically polarised on emergence, except when the incident vibration is parallel with one or other of the two normal directions L_1 and L_2 between them, called the lines of isocline (Fig. 4b). In this case the vibration remains rectilinear but the corresponding indices of refraction n_1 and n_2 are different.

The orientation effect opposed to the Brownian diffusion of rotation increases with the velocity gradient, as does the observed birefringence, which becomes constant when the orientation is complete. What is remarkable about the phenomenon is that the position of the lines of isocline L_1 and L_2 depend on the rate of orientation. When the orientation is complete (G infinite) all the particles lie long the lines of flow of the liquid, and one of

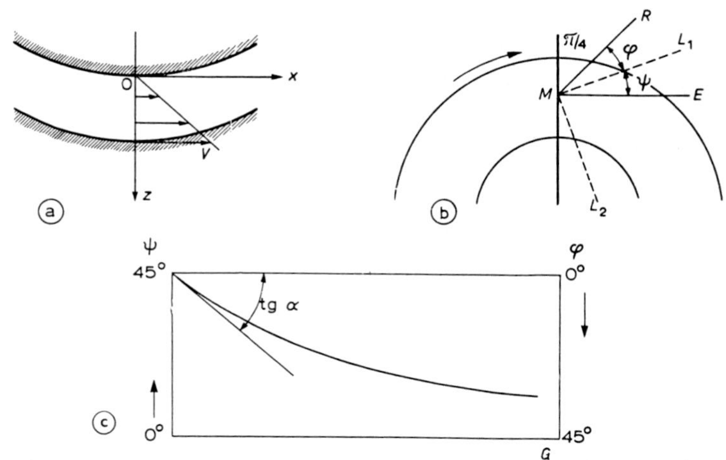

Fig. 4. (a). Velocity distribution between the two coaxial cylinders; (b) Lines of isocline and definition of the angles φ and ψ; (c) Variation of φ and ψ with G and determination of tg α.

the lines, L_1 for example, is parallel to the flow. When G diminishes, L_1 makes an angle Φ with the direction of flow, becoming larger and larger and approaches 45° as G approaches zero. The theory of the phenomenon[10] shows that tg α (Fig. 4C) is given by the relation:

$$\operatorname{tg} \alpha = \frac{1}{12} D \tag{2.12}$$

The variation of Φ as a function of G can easily be followed with suitable apparatus and the corresponding graph obtained. Then the value of tg α for $G = 0$ gives the value of D.

The method can obviously be applied to electrically conducting solutions. There is also a supplementary advantage; it shows in fact that if the particles can simulate ellipsoids of revolution of axial ratio p and of volume V, the value of the birefringence $\delta n = n_1 - n_2$ is given by the equation

$$\delta n = \frac{2}{15} \cdot \frac{e}{n_0} (g_1 - g_2) \frac{V}{M} c \cdot \frac{G}{D} \tag{2.13}$$

where e is $(p^2 - 1)/(p^2 + 1)$, c is the concentration in g/ml, M is the mass of the ellipsoid, and g_1 and g_2 are two factors given by the equation

$$g_i = (n_i^2 - n_0^2)/[4\pi + (n_i^2 - n_0^2)\, L_i/n_0^2]\,, \quad i = 1 \text{ or } 2$$

References p. 310

In this new expression n_0 is the index of refraction of the solvent, n_1 and n_2 are the principal indices of the ellipsoid, and L_1 and L_2 are the factors due to Maxwell, depending uniquely on the dimensions of the ellipsoid (see the appendix). When the latter is very elongated for example, the factors take the very simple values:

$$L_1 = 0\,, \quad L_2 = 2\pi$$

Therefore, knowing D (from tg α), and also M/V, the value of $\delta n/cG$, the Maxwell constant of the liquid, is a known function of n_1 and n_2. Further, the index n of the solution is also a known function of n_1 and n_2 given by:

$$n = n_0 + \frac{2\pi}{n_0}(g_1 + 2g_2)\frac{cV}{3M} \tag{2.14}$$

It is clear that n_1 and n_2 can be calculated from values of n and δn, *i.e.* the magnitudes related to the internal structure of the ellipsoid. In this manner the method gives not only the shapes and dimensions of the particles, but also the principal features of their construction.

(iii) The use of ultracentrifugation

The sedimentation constant. When one subjects a suspension of particles to an intense gravitational field, for example, in an ultracentrifuge, a force is exerted on each particle of magnitude

$$F = M\,(1 - V_{sp}\rho_0)g \tag{2.15}$$

In this equation g represents the intensity of the gravitational field, V_{sp}* represents the partial specific volume of the particle of the mass M, and ρ_0 represents the density of the solvent. By means of this force the particle moves in the solution with a speed which rapidly reaches its limit $\mu_s = F/\bar{f}$, where $\bar{f}$ is the coefficient of friction already defined above. The sedimentation constant s is defined by

$$s = \mu_s/g = \frac{M(1 - V_{sp}\rho_0)}{\bar{f}} \tag{2.16}$$

By a suitable device it is possible to measure s. If on the other hand one measures V_{sp}, and if one knows ρ_0, the value of s gives the value of the ratio $M/\bar{f}$. By combining the expressions (2.5 and 2.16), one obtains the well-known Svedberg equation

$$M = \frac{RTs}{\Delta(1 - V_{sp}\rho_0)} \tag{2.17}$$

* $V_{sp} = V^1/M$; V^1 is the volume of the dry particle.

which shows that the simultaneous measurement of s and Δ makes it possible to calculate the mass of the particle.

The sedimentation equilibrium. During the sedimentation, and when the factor $(1 - V_{sp}\rho_0)$ is positive, the particles tend to accumulate at the bottom of the diffusion cell. The higher the concentration becomes, the more Brownian diffusion opposes this effect and, if one waits long enough, a sedimentation equilibrium is attained.

At this moment, and always provided that (and always admitting that) g is uniform, the value of ν in a section of the solution at the distance x from the bottom of the vessel is given by the well-known equation:

$$M(1 - V_{sp}\rho_0)g - RT\frac{d \ln \nu}{dx} = 0 \tag{2.18}$$

The measurement of $\nu(x)$ thus makes possible the calculation of M. A disadvantage of the method is that it is necessary to wait a very long time (of the order of several days) before the equilibrium is attained. Much quicker methods have been devised[11].

Finally we point out that the direction of the sedimentation depends on the sign of the factor $(1 - V_{sp}\rho_0)$. If one creates, in the solvent inside the cell, a permanent density gradient caused by the centrifugation field, the suspended macromolecules will sediment in such a manner that they collect in the layer of the solvent in which the density is equal to about $1/V_{sp}$. One then observes a true sedimentation equilibrium around this layer, the position of which clearly depends on the value of V_{sp} for the macromolecules. This was the principle of the very beautiful experiments of Meselson *et al.*[12] (solvent: solution of caesium chloride in sedimentation equilibrium; macromolecule: deoxyribonucleic acid).

(iv) Viscosity of extended macromolecular solutions

While a liquid is maintained in streamline flow, it exerts forces on the walls of the containing vessel which are proportional to its coefficient of viscosity. The coefficient of viscosity can be determined from the measurement of these forces. For example, the determination of the pressure gradient necessary to make the liquid flow in a capillary of given radius for a given rate of flow, or that of the viscous couple exerted on one of the cylinders in Couette's vessel, are classical procedures of viscometry, of which the technique is too well known to be discussed at length here.

If η_0 is the viscosity of a pure liquid, and a solid particle is introduced into the liquid maintained in viscous flow, the flow is disturbed. Supplementary viscous forces act on the surface of the particle and because of this

References p. 310

the viscosity is increased. If η is the viscosity of a solution containing a single particle, then

$$(\eta - \eta_0)/\eta_0 = a$$

where a is a factor depending solely on the shape and the dimensions of the immersed particle. It represents the quantity φ_0 given in the introduction to this chapter. If now a solution containing ν particles per ml is considered, the disturbances produced by each particle will be additive, purely and simply, if ν is sufficiently small for there to be no interaction among particles. Hence

$$\eta_{sp} = a\nu$$

In general, however, interactions occur and

$$\eta_{sp} = a\nu + b\nu^2 + c\nu^3$$

If M be the mass of the particles and c the concentration in g/ml, $\nu = c/M$, and

$$\eta_{sp} = \frac{a}{M} \cdot c + \frac{b}{M^2} \cdot c^2 + \ldots$$

The limiting value of specific viscosity for $c = 0$ is called the intrinsic viscosity of the solution $[\eta]$. Then $[\eta] = a/M$. Now the value of a can be calculated from the laws of hydrodynamics for particles of simple geometrical shape*. For example, for spherical particles of volume V:

$$a = 2.5\ V \quad \text{or} \quad [\eta] = 2.5\ V/M \text{ (Einstein's formula)} \qquad (2.19)$$

For an ellipsoid of volume V and of axial ratio p $(= a/b)$:

$$[\eta] = \frac{V}{M} \Lambda(p) \qquad (2.20)$$

where $\Lambda(p)$ is an increasing function[13] of p, equal to 2.5 for $p = 1$ and for which the expression and values are to be found in the Appendix (p. 307). (*Note*: if M is the molar weight of the particle, the right hand side of the preceding equations has evidently to be multiplied by N_A, the Avogadro number.)

Here it is convenient to remark that, as already explained, in hydro-

* See Bibliography (p. 309).

dynamic flow elongated particles tend to orient themselves in the direction of flow of the liquid, doing so more easily as their constant of rotational diffusion is less. In these conditions the distribution of the orientation of the ellipsoids in the viscous flow depends on the velocity gradient of the flow. It will be the same for the hydrodynamic perturbation which they produce. Consequently the measured viscosity, η, will depend, in this case, on the velocity of viscous flow. The liquid is said to be non-Newtonian. It is necessary to take care, in this case, to make the measurements under conditions such that the velocity gradients in the viscometer may be sufficiently small for the orientation effect to be negligible. This is very easy in practice and it is only in exceptional cases that such effects give trouble. If the viscous flow has a uniform gradient, as in the case of the Couette cell, W. and H. Kuhn[14] have established that the intrinsic viscosity $[\eta]_G$ for a small gradient G is related to the viscosity $[\eta]$ for zero gradient, in the case of a very elongated ellipsoid, by the relation:

$$[\eta]_G = [\eta]\,[1 - 1.09\, G^2/32D^2] \qquad (2.21)$$

where D is, as is usual, the constant of rotational diffusion of the particle around an equatorial diameter.

(v) Principle of the measurements of dimensions by hydrodynamic methods

In conclusion, if it is supposed that the particles in solution resemble ellipsoids of revolution—very elongated or flattened—the following magnitudes, which are functions of their volume V and their axial ratio p, and also their mass M, can be determined from experiment:

(1) $\bar{f}(V, p) = kT/\Delta$ determined from the measurement of Δ.

(2) $C(V, p) = kT/D$ determined from the measurement of D (Kerr effect, birefringence of flow, viscosity of structure).

(3) $\frac{1}{f} M(1 - \frac{V^1}{M}\rho_0) = s$ determined by sedimentation, and $M(1 - \frac{V^1}{M}\rho_0)$ determined by equilibrium of sedimentation.

(4) $\frac{V}{M}\Lambda(p) = [\eta]$ determined by viscometry.

p and V can thus be calculated directly from the measurement of f and C, independently of M. The partial specific volume V^1/M can be obtained directly from the measurement of the density D.

References p. 310

The measurements of $\bar{f}$ or of C (preferably the former, for the constant of rotational diffusion is sometimes very difficult to measure) can be equated to that of the constant of sedimentation or to the intrinsic viscosity. If M is also known, the two measurements give V and p.

Finally, the measurement of three of the four expressions gives V, p and M. Thus, in principle, hydrodynamic methods alone can give the mass and the dimensions of the particles. Meanwhile it is necessary to add immediately that M can be measured directly by other methods, as for example by osmosis or the scattering of light, and that the specific partial volume $V_{sp} = V^1/M$ for the particles can be determined directly from a simple comparison of the densities of the solution and of the solvent.

In these conditions, in fact always, much that is available to solve the problem, is disregarded, and the experimenter can choose what may be easiest to determine for the particular case in question.

From this point of view, it might seem therefore that the problem of the determination of the masses and dimensions of particles in a monodisperse solution is largely resolved and all that remains is to perfect the technique of measurement. Unfortunately this is not so, as will be shown by the following remarks.

(a) Firstly, the functions $t(p)$ and $r(p)$ in the expressions for f and C are different according to whether the ellipsoid is flat or long. Determination of the dimensions of the particle which are based only on the measurement of f and C (whether or not involving M, or V/M from other methods) leads to ambiguity. This is often eliminated because it is known, from consideration of chemical structure, whether the particle is most probably simply a rod or a flat disc.

It can also be eliminated, quite rigorously, in the following way: f, C and M are measured on the one hand and $[\eta]$ on the other. The values of p, V and M given by the first set of measurements must, since they occur in the expression $(V/M)\Lambda(p)$, give the latter a numerical value comparable to that of the intrinsic viscosity. It is clear that this coincidence is unlikely if the model chosen for the ellipsoid is false.

(b) It has already been indicated in the general principles preceding this discussion that the particle might be supposed as an ellipsoid or cylinder of revolution. Hydrodynamic methods then only give the volume and the axial ratio of the ellipsoid which is equivalent to the real particle in the solution.

This is a difficulty inherent in these methods, but recognizing this, it is permissible to ask whether there is agreement among the values of V, p, M, M/V and V_{sp} measured by diverse techniques. First, it is evident that all of the above analyses are rigorously correct if the particle in suspension *is* a small ellipsoid around which the molecules of the solvent circulate freely. But this case is fictitious. The atoms or groups of atoms at the surface of the particle exert forces on the molecules of the solvent whose intensities depend on the chemical nature of both solute and solvent. Moreover, the fact of having replaced a volume of the solvent equal to that of the particle by a volume of different material, causes the molecules of the solvent in the neighbourhood of the particle to experience a field of force of the type producing surface tensions.

These effects give rise to a layer of variable thickness around the dissolved particle, where the molecules of the solvent are either fixed to the particle or partially connected to it, so that the viscosity of the solvent is no longer equal to η_0. Thus the situation is modified, as though the particle whose movement is being followed were surrounded by a solvate film which increased its volume and modified its axial ratio*.

It is quite evident that the coefficients $\bar{f}$ and C relate to this particular complex, which for this reason will be called the hydrodynamic particle. It is equally reasonable to admit that the values of V and of p occurring in the expression for the viscosity relate to the same hydrodynamic particle.

As for the mass M, which figures in the expression for the viscosity, this is introduced by equating the number of particles per ml to c/M. M is then the mass of the "dry" particle of matter dispersed in the liquid, and is not in fact the mass of the hydrodynamic particle. This value for the mass M will be given more directly, perhaps, by the measurement of osmotic pressure, or by the scattering of light.

Consequently the use of the values Δ, D and $[\eta]$, or the use of two of these values and a value for the mass (*e.g.* from osmotic pressure), leads to coherent results which give the dimensions of the hydrodynamic particle as well as the mass of the dry particle.

Besides, the pycnometric measurement of partial specific volume V/M gives the relationship between the volume of the dispersed matter and its mass (assuming the density of the enveloping dissolved film to be the same as that of the solvent, which it is not at all certain to be). V here is then the volume of the dry particle, to be denoted by V^1. If in addition the value of M has been obtained, pycnometry gives V^1. From values of V and V^1, the volume of the solvent $V - V^1$ associated with the dry particle may be deduced. Yet it is necessary to realize that the volume $V - V^1$ is not necessarily that of the molecules of the solvent actually attached by adsorption to the dry particle, since the particle may have a lacuna structure like a sponge. In this case the solvent molecules circulating in the hollows

* Another very important case is that of macromolecules carrying a large number of ionisable groups. In water solutions each of them is surrounded by a cloud of ions which it carries with it during its movement.

It is the total effect of the particle and of the cloud of ions which is measured by the various hydrodynamic methods. An actual analysis will not be given here, but we shall have occasion to return to this question below.

References p. 310

are incorporated in the general movement of the particle without adsorption as such occurring.

It is usual, particularly in biological work, not to use the sets of measurements which have just been discussed, but rather those including $\bar{f}$ obtained by sedimentation, Δ (often obtained in the course of the same experiment), and lastly that of V^1/M from pycnometry.

When no solvation occurs, the volume V of the particle is given by the relations: $V = V^1 = MV_{sp}$ and its axial ratio is obtained from the expression for $\bar{f}$, (2.8), which also gives the value of $t(p)$, V being known.

When solvation does occur, let the mass of solvent fixed to the particles be w per gram. Then the volume of the hydrodynamic particle in the expression for f is related to the volume V^1 of the dry particle by the relation*:

$$V = M\left(V_{sp} + \frac{w}{\rho}\right) \qquad (2.22a)$$

or

$$V = V^1\left(1 + \frac{w}{\rho V_{sp}}\right) \qquad (2.22b)$$

where ρ is the density of the solvated layer. Then according to (2.8):

$$\bar{f} = \frac{6\pi}{1.612} \cdot \left(1 + \frac{w}{\rho V_{sp}}\right)^{\frac{1}{3}} \cdot (V^1)^{\frac{1}{3}} \cdot \frac{1}{t(p)}$$

In this expression $\bar{f}$ is known, as is V^1 (from pycnometry). It follows that experiment gives the value of the product:

$$P = \left(1 + \frac{w}{\rho V_{sp}}\right)^{\frac{1}{3}} \frac{1}{t(p)} \qquad (2.23)$$

If the particle is spherical, $t(p) = 1$ and hence the value of either w/ρ or of V is obtained from eqn. (2.22). If the particle is ellipsoidal, the problem becomes indeterminate. However, if different values are given to w/ρ, eqn. (2.23) gives the corresponding value of p, and eqn. (2.22a) gives that of V. A new quantity may be introduced, *e.g.* the intrinsic viscosity which involves w/ρ in the equation:

$$[\eta] = \left(V_{sp} + \frac{w}{\rho}\right) \Lambda(p) \qquad (2.24)$$

* For discussion of the study of hydration see Edsall (Bibliography[20]).

The three unknowns V, p and w/ρ may be calculated from the three eqns. (2.22a) or (2.22b), and (2.23) and (2.24) and the value of M may then be obtained from the density*.

(c) All the above analysis is valid in the case where the dispersed particles are ellipsoids of revolution. It is evident that this is not always the case. When the particle does not have an ellipsoidal shape, the values of f, C and $[\eta]$ can still be defined and measured, but their theoretical expressions are no longer known as functions of the dimensions of the particle.

If the same expressions as above are applied, the three numbers p, V, M, which represent the dimensions and the mass of the fictitious ellipsoid, called the equivalent ellipsoid, can be calculated from these three values as has been shown. It is clear, however, that these dimensions and this mass can be totally different from those of the actual particle. In addition, there is an ambiguity, since it will be possible to define two equivalent ellipsoids, one long and the other flat. Comparison with the actual mass M, supposedly known from other methods, does not resolve the ambiguity since the observed deviation can be due to the fact that the particle is no longer ellipsoidal.

In particular if, from the measurement of V_{sp} and from the exact mass of the actual particle, the real (dry) volume is calculated $V^1 = V_{sp}M$, there is no reason why V^1 should equal V, even if the real particle is not spongelike (lacunar) and is not solvated. In these conditions, at least without previous knowledge of the shape of the particle, it is clearly impossible from these methods to obtain other than hypothetical data on the solvated layers. This criticism is of particular value in the study of proteins of small mass.

Instead of defining an equivalent ellipsoid, it is possible to define an equivalent cylinder of revolution by calculating p, V and M from the expressions for f, C and $[\eta]$ valid for such a cylinder. If it were known in advance that the particles were elongated, then for example, the actual mass could be compared with the two values calculated for M for the ellipsoidal and the cylindrical shapes. If for the actual particle that of the two shapes which gives the nearest mass to the actual mass is used, then a conclusion can be reached. In particular, if the particle is considerably elongated (p being some multiple of ten, for example) the expressions for f, C and $[\eta]$ as functions of a and of b are identical for ellipsoids and cylinders. Consequently from these three values, the exact values of a, b and M can be calculated, without knowing whether the particle is an ellipsoid or a cylinder.

On the contrary if, in this same case, f, C and $[\eta]$ are expressed as functions of p and V, two series of expressions are obtained which differ only in the factor which represents the ratio of the volumes of a cylinder and an ellipsoid having the same values of the dimensions a and b.

---

* See footnote on p. 286.

References p. 310

It is evident from what has just been said, that each particular case must be treated with circumspection, so as to include all possible data provided by other sources (chemical, biological, X-ray crystallography). It is equally true that any discussion as to precise values found for the dimensions, without prior accumulation of all possible reasons for the acceptance of a shape determined for the particle, is quite useless and there is a risk of its leading to considerable error. This opinion will be further reinforced when the large uncertainty of the data given by experiment has been indicated, notwithstanding the apparent accuracy of the measurements.

(c) Optical methods

These methods rely, as has already been stated, on the determination of the perturbation which the dissolved particles produce on the propagation of an electro-magnetic wave in the liquid solvent. Practically, this is confined to the case where the longest incident wavelengths are in the visible region, the shortest being in the X-ray region.

The case in which the particles themselves absorb the incident light will be neglected, and consequently it remains to consider how the dissolved particles influence (*1*) the velocity of propagation of the incident waves, and (*2*) the scattering of these waves in all directions.

The first of these problems, which is that of the influence of the particles on the refractive index of the solution, has not been treated to any extent from the point of view concerned here, *i.e.* the determination of the dimensions of particles, consequently no guiding principles have been established. The second problem, on the contrary, has been the object of a considerable amount of work, which has led to very interesting results.

The case in which the refractive indices of the substance of the particle and the solvent are not nearly equal will not be considered here; it has been treated by Mie[15] for the case of spherical particles. It will be admitted that for biological substances the indices may be practically identical, which leads to a field where a theoretical study of non-spherical particles can be commenced.

The molecule in solution is considered as an assembly of dipoles distributed throughout the whole volume which it occupies. Each dipole vibrates in phase with the incident ray and, in consequence, it radiates in turn electromagnetic waves of frequency equal to the incident frequency. Two cases are to be considered, (*a*) when the dimensions of the assembly are small compared with the incident wavelength and all the dipoles vibrate in phase and behave as one dipole, and (*b*) when the dimensions of the assembly are not small compared with the incident wavelength, and the phenomenon of interference occurs between the waves emitted by the different dipoles.

The energy diffused by the molecule, and consequently by the solution, is not expressed in the two cases by the same equation and, in particular, the shape and dimensions of the particle appear in the second one.

(i) The case of "small" particles

The theory shows that the particle may be considered as being small when its dimensions are less than a tenth or a twentieth of the incident wavelength. In this case the energy scattered by a ml of the solution* will be obtained by calculating the energy diffused by the ν particles, each of which behaves as a dipole. If the particles, supposed to be all identical, were disposed regularly with regard to each other, *e.g.* in a crystal lattice, then interference patterns would be produced and there would be no scattered rays. It is because these particles, undergoing Brownian movement, are distributed at random in the solution that the interference does not completely annul all the scattered intensity. The latter can be calculated by two different methods provided that the solution is very dilute. The result of the Einstein method** will be given below. This has the advantage of being valid for concentrations which are very small, but which are not zero.

Consider a wavefront of ordinary parallel light*** of intensity I_0 (Fig. 5) to pass through the solution, and consider the luminous energy scattered

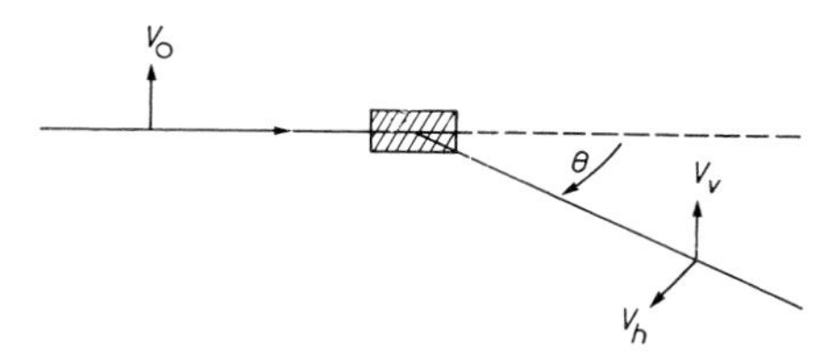

Fig. 5. Scattering of a vertically polarized light.

by a unit of volume of the solution, φ. It can be shown that the intensity I_θ of the light scattered by this unit of volume φ and observed at a distance r from the centre of the volume φ is given by the equation:

$$I_\theta = \mathscr{R}\varphi I_0\,(1 + \cos^2\theta)/r^2 \tag{2.28}$$

* Since the solvent scatters by itself a small amount of energy it will be understood that we are dealing here with the difference of the total energy scattered by the solutions and the energy scattered by the pure solvent.

** See Bibliography*I* (p. 309).

*** The study of the depolarisation by scattering of the plane polarised light will be omitted in order not to overburden this review.

References p. 310

From (2.28) we may immediately obtain

$$\mathscr{R}\varphi = I_{90^\circ} r^2 / I_0$$

$\mathscr{R}$ is the Rayleigh constant, which theory shows is related to the characteristics of the solution by the equation

$$Kc/\mathscr{R} = (1/M) + 2Bc \tag{2.29}$$

where:

$$K = 2\pi^2 n_0^2 \,(\mathrm{d}n/\mathrm{d}c)^2/N\lambda^4 \tag{2.30}$$

c is the concentration of the solution in g/ml; n_0 the refractive index of the pure solvent, n that of the solution; M the mass of the dissolved particles; N_A Avogadro's number; B the second virial coefficient, mentioned later, and λ the wavelength of the incident ray.

The total energy scattered in all directions by φ can also be calculated. This energy is obviously proportional to φ and to I_0. It is equal to $I_0\varphi\tau$, where τ is a factor smaller than unity called the turbidity of the solution* which is given by expressions comparable to the above *i.e.*:

$$Hc/\tau = \frac{1}{M} + 2Bc$$

with

$$H = 32\,\pi^3 n_0^2 \,(\mathrm{d}n/\mathrm{d}c)^2/3N\lambda^4 = \frac{16\,K\pi}{3}$$

This shows that the masses of the particles contained by a solution may be determined from the study of the light scattered by the solution.

Hence it suffices to measure the index increment $\mathrm{d}n/\mathrm{d}c$, which gives the value of K, and the Rayleigh constant for the same solution at different concentrations. Plotting the different values of $Kc/\mathscr{R}$ as ordinates and those of c as abscissae will give, at least in the region of small values of c, for which the theory is valid, a straight line, of which the slope gives B and the intercept on the vertical axis gives $1/M$.

This method is very elegant but provokes certain criticisms. Firstly, it is difficult to measure the Rayleigh constant directly. In general, such absolute

---

* It is evident that if I is the intensity of the wavefront after passing through the solution, then:

$$I = I_0 — \mathrm{e}^{-\tau\lambda}$$

Thus τ is also the coefficient of apparent absorption of the solution.

measurements are only made in the study of scattering of light by pure liquids, which scatter much less than the solutions. For the application to the determination of the masses of colloidal particles it is usually sufficient to measure the quantity $I_{90°}$ which is proportional to the Rayleigh constant and the proportionality factor can be determined by standardizing with a liquid of which the scattering has been determined absolutely, and for which the ratio I_{90}/I_0 is known.

(ii) The case of large particles

In this case each particle can be represented by a collection of dipoles which, because of their relative positions, do not vibrate in phase. The waves which they emit interfere, and theory shows that the energy scattered by a small volume of the solution is distributed dissymmetrically in space, being larger in the direction of propagation of the incident wavefront (θ small) than in the opposite direction (θ near to π).

In this case $\mathscr{R}$ is no longer a constant, as in (2.28), and it depends on θ. The theory shows that we have:

$$(I_\theta)_{c=0} = KcM \frac{I_0 \varphi}{r^2} P(\theta)\,(1 + \cos^2\theta) \tag{2.31}$$

or more generally,

$$\frac{Kc}{\mathscr{R}} = \frac{1}{MP(\theta)} \pm 2Bc \tag{2.32}$$

where $P(\theta)$ is a scalar with values extending from 0 to 1. The factor $P(\theta)$ can be calculated theoretically if the geometrical shape of the particle is known and if the index of refraction of the latter is very nearly equal to that of the solvent. Hence,

(a) for a sphere (radius L)

$$P(\theta) = \left[\frac{3}{h^3L^3}(\sin hL - hL\cos hL)\right]^2 \tag{2.33a}$$

(b) for a rod (length $2L$)

$$P(\theta) = (1/hL)\,S_i(2hL) - \left(\frac{\sin hL}{hL}\right)^2 \tag{2.33b}$$

(c) for a disk (radius L)

$$P(\theta) = \frac{2}{h^2L^2}\left[1 - (1/hL)J_1(2hL)\right] \tag{2.33c}$$

References p. 310

In these expressions:

$$h = \frac{4\pi n_0}{\lambda} \sin(\theta/2) \qquad (2.34)$$

$$S_i(2hL) = \int_0^{2hL} \frac{\sin x}{x} \, dx$$

J_1 is the Bessel function of the first order.

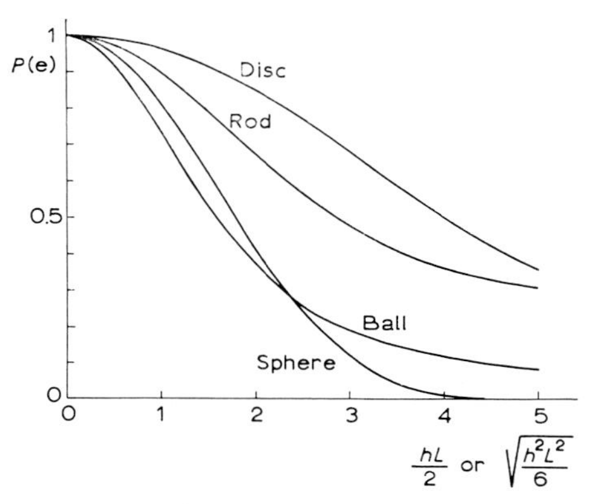

Fig. 6. $P(\theta)$ functions for different models.

It is of a great importance to give the limiting expressions for $P(\theta)$ in the two extreme cases: hL very small ($\theta \to 0$) and hL very large ($\theta \neq 0$ and $L \to \infty$).

(a) Light scattering at small angles ($h \to 0$). It may be shown that quite generally, and whatever could be the shape of the particles, the development of $P(\theta)$ is

$$\underset{\theta \to 0}{P(\theta)} = 1 - \frac{h^2 R^2}{3} \qquad (2.35)$$

where R is the radius of gyration of the particle. One knows that the radius of gyration of an assembly of n points A_i of same mass m_i is given by

$$R^2 = \frac{1}{n} \sum_i r_i^2 \qquad (2.36)$$

where r_i is the distance of A_i to the centre of mass of the assembly. Hence for an ellipsoid of revolution (length of the axis of symmetry $2L_1$, diameter $2L_2$)

$$R^2 = (2L_1^3 + L_2^3)/5L_1 \qquad (2.37a)$$

for a sphere (radius L)

$$R^2 = 3L^2/10 \tag{2.37b}$$

for a rod (length $2L$)

$$R^2 = L^2/3 \tag{2.37c}$$

As a consequence of (2.32) and (2.36) we see that

$$\left(\frac{Kc}{\mathscr{R}}\right)_{\theta=0} = \frac{1}{M} + 2Bc \tag{2.38}$$

and for $h \to 0$

$$\left(\frac{Kc}{\mathscr{R}}\right)_{c=0} = \frac{1}{M}\left(1 + \frac{h^2R^2}{3}\right) \tag{2.39}$$

With the use of proper extrapolations of the measurements we see that the determination of $(Kc/\mathscr{R})_{\theta=0}$ as a function of c allows the calculation of M and B, and that the determination of $(Kc/\mathscr{R})_{c=0}$ as a function of θ allows the determination of R.

Very often these operations are done according to a simple method which consists in plotting as ordinate the measured values of $Kc/\mathscr{R}$ for different values of c and θ, and as abscissae the values of $\sin^2(\theta/2) + nc$, where n is a numerical factor suitably chosen. One obtains a diagram such as illustrated in Fig. 7. Curves 1 ($c = 0$) and 2 ($\theta = 0$) correspond to the two extrapolations. Their common intercept gives the value of $1/M$, their initial slopes give respectively B and R.

(b) Large values of hL. In this case, which is realized when θ is near π,

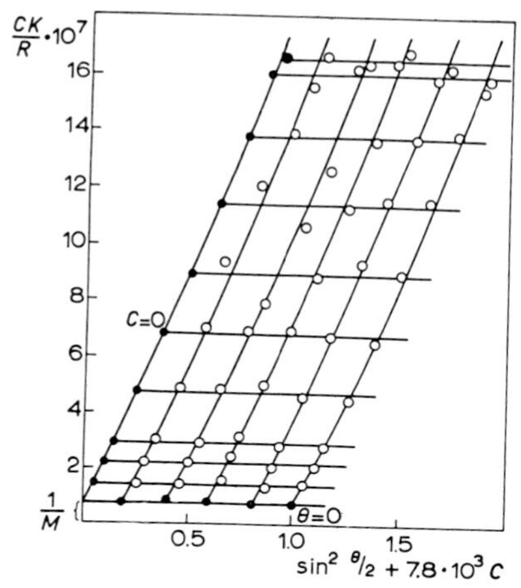

Fig. 7. Typical "Zimm-plot" for a sample of DNA.

References p. 310

and when L/λ is very large, one can give an asymptotic expression for $P(\theta)$ and hence for $(Kc/\mathscr{R})_{c=0} = 1/MP(\theta)$. One obtains the following expressions:

for a sphere
$$\left(\frac{Kc}{\mathscr{R}}\right)_{c=0} \cong \frac{2(hL)^4}{9M} \tag{2.40a}$$

for a rod
$$\left(\frac{Kc}{\mathscr{R}}\right)_{c=0} \cong \frac{2}{M\pi^2} + \frac{2hL}{\pi M} \tag{2.40b}$$

for a disk
$$\left(\frac{Kc}{\mathscr{R}}\right)_{c=0} \cong \frac{1}{2}\frac{(hL)^2}{M} \tag{2.40c}$$

These expressions show that the $(Kc/\mathscr{R})_{c=0, M\to\infty}$ values are proportional to $\sin^4 \theta/2$ in the case of spheres, proportional to $\sin^2 \theta/2$ in the case of disks, and to $\sin \theta/2$ in the case of rods.

(c) The dissymmetry factor. We see from (2.28) and (2.32) that

$$I_{45^\circ}/I_{135^\circ} = \mathscr{R}_{45}/\mathscr{R}_{135} = P(45^\circ)/P(135^\circ)$$

This ratio is called the dissymmetry factor Z and it can be readily measured with a simple experiment. It is evident from eqn. (2.33) that Z—which is equal to unity for "small" particles—depends of the shape and dimension of the "large" particle. It goes to a limiting value of 2.4 for an infinite rod and increases indefinitely for spheres or disks of increasing radius.

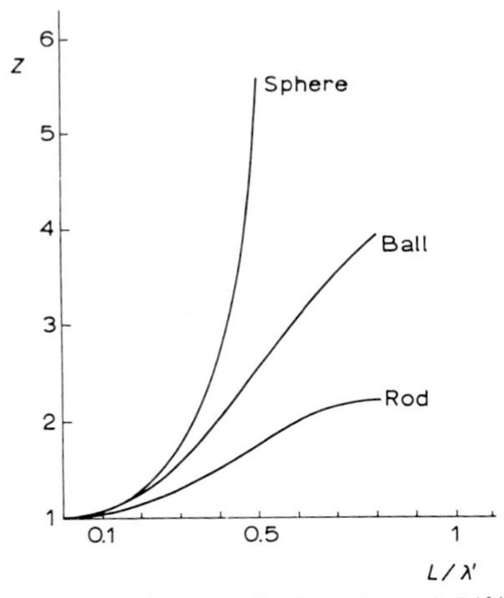

Fig. 8. Values of dissymmetry factor z in function of L/λ' and for different models.

(iii) Low-angle scattering of X-rays

The expression of the $P(\theta)$ function shows that the significant variable is hL, that is to say whether

$$\frac{4\pi n_0}{\lambda} L \sin \theta/2 \qquad \text{or} \qquad x = \frac{L}{\lambda} \sin \theta/2$$

When L/λ is very small, $P(\theta)$ is practically unity, even for values of θ, which are not small. In the present state of the precision of the measurements of $I(\theta)$, it is not possible to make any determination of $P(\theta)$ when L/λ is less than about 1/10. Hence in the case of visible light the particles of dimensions less than a few hundred ångstroms behave like "small" particles and the light-scattering experiments can give only the values of M and B.

The situation is different when one uses the scattering of X-rays at very low angles (much smaller than the angles of Bragg's reflexion). In this case it may be shown that the intensity scattered in the different directions is given by an equation very similar to (2.28).

$$I(\theta) = AcMP(\theta)\,(1 + \cos^2 \theta)$$

A is a factor depending on the repartition of the electron density and not, as K does, on the small heterogeneities in refractive index. However, since $P(\theta)$ expresses in both cases the effect of interferences between the waves emitted by the elementary oscillators, this function is quite the same for the same repartition of these oscillators, whatever their physical nature. For instance, the expressions given by eqn. (2.38) are still correct, on the condition that $n_0 = 1$ in the expression of h in (2.34).

Since the wavelength is about one thousand times smaller for X-rays than for visible light, it will be possible to measure the $P(\theta)$ function for much smaller particles. Moreover since large values of the parameter x here above defined, are available, it will be possible to obtain experimentally the asymptote to $P(\theta)$, to compare it with expressions (2.40). On the other hand, when $P(\theta)$ is very small, it is possible to use the development given in (2.35) and write

$$I(\theta) = A \exp\,(-\,4\pi^2 R^2 \theta^2/3\lambda^2)$$

or

$$\ln I(\theta) = C - 4\pi^2 R^2 \theta^2/3\lambda^2$$

Hence the possibility of measuring R by photography, or by counting photons. However, it is not easy to use this method directly for the determination of M.

References p. 310

(iv) Conclusions

The study of the scattering of the electromagnetic field by a solution of large particles permits, in principle, the calculation of their masses and an estimation of their shapes and dimensions. For this reason the method is of a considerable interest. Nevertheless there are certain practical difficulties.

First, as in the case of hydrodynamic methods, the theoretical expressions are only valid for infinitely small concentrations. It is therefore necessary, as noted, to extrapolate the results to zero concentration. Several practical complications follow.

Secondly, since the dissymmetry becomes more important as the size of the particles increases, it follows that the existence of dust in the solution, even to a small extent, involves considerable errors. It is therefore necessary to clarify the solutions completely, which is not always very easy.

Before ending this section it is necessary, as already stated, to discuss the significance of the dimensions measured by optical diffusion, as in the case of hydrodynamic methods. Here there are no subtle distinctions to be drawn. The diffusion which is measured is produced by the elements of the dissolved matter. Therefore the dimensions obtained are those of the space occupied by the matter of the dissolved particle. These dimensions are not necessarily those of the "dry" particle. For example the particle may be inflated, due to the penetration of the solvent into its interior. It is then the volume of the inflated particle which causes scattering of the light. On the contrary, in principle, the superficially adsorbed solvent plays no part in the scattering as long as its refractive index is the same as that of the free solvent.

In the case of a binary mixture of solvents of different refractive indices, the situation is quite different. It may well happen that the measurement of the intensity of the scattered light at $\theta = 0$ gives an apparent mass of the particle, which depends on the selective adsorption of one of the two solvents on the particle. The same situation occurs in the case of a large particle surrounded with a cloud of small ions. Here again we shall avoid a thorough discussion of this case and come back to this important question in our general conclusions.

3. Flexible chains

(a) Definitions

In this case we have to deal with a chain composed of atomic groups (the units) bound together by valence forces. A very simple example is that of a linear paraffin with the formula CH_3—$(CH_2)_n$—CH_3 where the elementary unit is —CH_2—. We have already given another example, that of the polypeptides in which the unit corresponds to the formula

—CH$_2$—CH—CO—NH—
|
R

In biological chemistry there exist a large number of other sorts of these high polymers with elementary units of very different kinds (polysaccharides, polynucleotides, etc.).

Because of the possible rotations around the covalent bonds and, in the absence of intramolecular forces (ester bonds, hydrogen bonds, sulphide bonds, etc.), the molecular chain is a long, flexible filament which takes, in solution, according to thermic movement an infinite number of sinuous configurations. If one can still attribute a mass to the particle, this no longer has either a form or simply defined dimensions. It is still possible, however, to define a certain number of structural characters. For example, a radius of gyration R (*cf.* eqn. 2.36) corresponds to each of the configurations. But, because the chain presents an infinite number of possible configurations, one will be led to consider the average $\overline{R^2}$ of R^2 for all these. Likewise one could define the root mean square $\overline{L_n^2}$ between the extremities of the chain comprising N units, or even between the extremities of a segment of it comprising a number n ($n \leqslant N$). It is in general possible to calculate their value if the number of the monomeres and the manner in which they are bound to each other are known.

It will be sufficient for us here to know that, in cases in which one can neglect the steric hindrance introduced by the elementary units, as well as the interactions (attractions or repulsions) operating between them in the solution, the average root mean square between the extremities of a segment of the chain including a sufficiently high number n of elementary links is given by the relation

$$\overline{L_n^2} = b^2 n \tag{3.1}$$

where b is a length depending on the dimensions of the unit as well as on the laws governing its articulation with units adjacent. In this case the probability dw_{nr} of finding one of the extremities of the chain at a distance from the other extremity situated between r and $r + \mathrm{d}r$ is given by the Gaussian law

$$\mathrm{d}w_{nr} = \left(\frac{3}{2\pi\overline{L_n^2}}\right)^{\frac{3}{2}} \exp\left(-3r^2/2\overline{L_n^2}\right) 4\pi r^2 \mathrm{d}r \tag{3.2}$$

A molecular chain whose extremities are distributed according to this law, or which, *a fortiori*, can be divided into segments of n elements each of which obeys Gaussian law, is called a Gaussian chain. As a general rule this

References p. 310

is not what is observed: steric hindrance and interactions exist and then the eqn. (3.1) is no longer valid and must be replacd by

$$L_n^2 = b^2 n^{1+\varepsilon} \tag{3.3}$$

where ε is a number between 0 and 1 which depends on the second virial coefficient of the solution. In this case the law of probability between the extremities of the chain is no longer a simple Gaussian law (*cf.* Flory, see Bibliography[21]).

(b) Hydrodynamic properties

(i) Brownian diffusion and sedimentation

One can, in a solution of coiled molecules, define a translational diffusion constant Δ and a sedimentation constant s, given by the eqns. (2.5) and (2.16). The elimination of $\bar{f}$ from these two equations still leads to (2.17) and the measurement of Δ and s makes it possible, as indicated above, to measure the mass of the particle. We must now relate the coefficient of friction $\bar{f}$ to the morphological features of the chain. It appears from all the theoretical and experimental considerations that this latter behaves as does a spherical particle whose radius R would be equal to $\frac{1}{2}(\overline{L_N^2})^{\frac{1}{2}}$ and whose volume is then $V = \pi/6\ (\overline{L_N^2})^{\frac{3}{2}}$. But, instead of f being given by the simple Stokes' law,

$$\bar{f} = 6\pi\eta_0 R = 3\pi\eta_0(\overline{L_N^2})^{\frac{1}{2}} \tag{3.4}$$

valid if the chain rigorously behaves like a rigid and full sphere, one observes that

$$\bar{f} = \psi\eta_0(\overline{L_N^2})^{\frac{1}{2}} \tag{3.5}$$

where ψ is a factor which does not depend very much on the nature of the solvent or on the solute, and is about equal to 5.1. Notwithstanding, one sees, according to (3.3) and (3.5), that the friction coefficient $\bar{f}$ for a series of homologous polymers is proportional to $M^{0.5+\varepsilon/2}$. Δ is then inversely proportional to this quantity.

(ii) Intrinsic viscosity and birefringence of flow

One can understand that, if a flexible chain is placed in a liquid which flows with a velocity gradient G, the forces of viscous drag exert on it tensions which tend to deform it. One could then, as has been done above, compare the chain to a spherical particle only to the extent in which G is so small that the deformations are negligible.

Negligible velocity gradient. In this case the expression of the intrinsic viscosity can still be put in a form comparable to (2.19), but with a proportionality factor different from 2.5. One suggests (M being supposed to represent the molecular weight of the particle)

$$[\eta] = \Phi N_A \frac{V}{M}$$

V still being the volume of the sphere having a diameter $(L_N^2)^{\frac{1}{2}}$; or even

$$[\eta] = \Phi N_A \frac{\pi}{6} (\overline{L_N^2})^{\frac{3}{2}}/M \tag{3.6}$$

One finds experimentally that the factor ΦN_A keeps the same order of magnitude whatever the solvent or solute may be. Its value lies between $4.0 \cdot 10^{23}$ and $5.2 \cdot 10^{23}$, whereas for a rigid particle of the same volume, it would be equal to $15 \cdot 10^{23}$. Nevertheless, one sees that, for a series of homologous polymers, $[\eta]$ varies like $(\overline{L_N^2})^{\frac{3}{2}}/M$ that is, according to (3.3) like $M^{0.5 + 3\varepsilon/2}$. In a general way one writes

$$[\eta] = KM^a \tag{3.7}$$

Non-negligible velocity gradients. In this case the higher the velocity gradient, the more the coil is deformed. Two main consequences result from this, on the one hand the value of $[\eta]$ depends on the gradient G; on the other hand the molecular coil, having no longer, on the average, a spherical symmetry, becomes optically anisotropic; the solution presents a birefringence of flow.

One then observes phenomena analogous to those produced by the orientation of rigid anisodiametric particles, but here, because the cause resides in a molecular deformation, the elementary laws are no longer the same.

We cannot here go into details[16] and we merely note that, contrary to what occurs in a solution of rigid particles, in which the value of tg α (*cf.* 2.12) is inversely proportional to that of the Brownian constant of rotation D (and therefore proportional to C/kT), in the case of coiled molecules tg α is related to η_0 by an equation of the type

$$\text{tg}\,\alpha = \frac{A}{kT} M[\eta]\eta_0 + \frac{B}{kT} \overline{L_N^2} \tag{3.8}$$

where A and B are two constants the values of which are given by the theory. It follows that although tg α varies linearly with η_0/kT it is no longer proportional to this last quantity (Fig. 9).

References p. 310

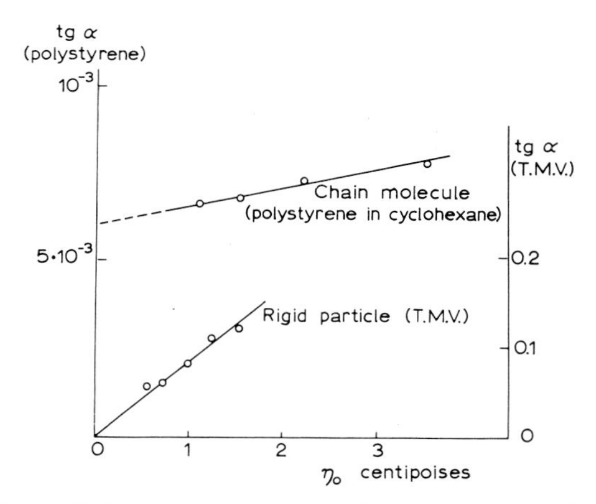

Fig. 9. Plot of tg α against η_0 in case of flexible chain and rigid particle (rigidity test)

(c) Light scattering

What has been said about rigid particles can, without difficulty, be transposed to flexible chains.

(a) When the dimensions of the coil are small, that is to say, smaller than about 1/20th of the wavelength of the incident light, all the elementary oscillators carried by the chain vibrate practically in phase and behave like a single oscillator. This is what happens in the case of 3 Å. There is no dissymmetry in the light-scattering distribution. The eqns. (2.29) and (2.30) are fully applicable and one measures M and B by determination of the ratio $I_{90°}/I_0$.

(b) When the dimensions of the coil become greater, the factor $P(\theta)$ is no longer equal to unity, except for $\theta = 0$, and dissymmetry appears (*cf.* section 2, p. 291). Then, however, in order to measure M one must extrapolate to $\theta = 0$ and, further, it is possible, just as in the case of rigid particles, to determine experimentally the function $P(\theta)$, which can be calculated, theoretically at least, for a Gaussian coil. One obtains

$$P(\theta) = \frac{2}{(h^2\overline{L_N^2}/6)^2}\left\{e^{-h^2\overline{L_N^2}/6} + \frac{h^2\overline{L_N^2}}{6} - 1\right\} \tag{3.9}$$

which completes the list of equations (2.33). Of course for small values of θ the development given by eqn. (2.35) or by (2.39) is still valid, and thus, as we have seen, it is possible to determine M and R^2. On the other hand, for high values of $h(\overline{L_N^2})^{\frac{1}{2}}$, one finds that $P(\theta)$ becomes proportional to $h^2L_N^2$.

Therefore in case of a very large coil and for values of θ near π, $P(\theta)$ varies as $\sin^2 \theta/2$.

(c) An interesting case, especially for the study of solutions of DNA[17], is that of a chain made up by the articulation of a series of small straight rods of length l, placed end to end which can take, one relative to another, all the orientations with the same probability. The behaviour of this kind of zig-zag has been recently studied[18]. If l is less than $\lambda/20$, each small rod behaves practically as a linear oscillator and the whole behaves as a Gaussian chain. But everything is different if l is greater than the limit indicated. In this case it can be shown that $P(\theta)$ is given by

$$P(\theta) = (1/N)P_l(\theta) + \left(\frac{1}{hl}\, si(hl)\right)^2 P_G(\theta)$$

In this equation N represents the number of rectilinear segments of the chain, $P_l(\theta)$ is the function $P(\theta)$ for a small rod of length l (*cf.* 2.33b) and $P_G(\theta)$ is the function $P(\theta)$ of a Gaussian chain with N elements. It is interesting to notice that the corresponding asymptotic form (*cf.* section 2bii, p. 277) is

$$\frac{Kc}{\mathscr{R}_{\begin{cases} c=0 \\ L\to\infty \end{cases}}} = \frac{hL}{M} + \frac{N}{\pi^2 M}\left\{2 - \frac{\pi^2}{2}\; \frac{N-1}{N}\right\} \tag{3.12}$$

One finds again, in fact, for the single small rod, ($N = l$ and $l = 2L$) the formula already given in (2.40b).

4. Polydispersity

If the solution contains particles which are not all identical, the conclusions reached in the preceding chapter must be modified. We will suppose that the polydispersity affects only one of the molecular parameters λ and that the distribution function is $f(\lambda)$ (*cf.* section 1c, p. 268).

(a) Mean values

(i) Definitions and examples

The size φ of the elementary phenomenon being a function of λ, the measurement gives a mean value $\bar{\Phi}$, taken on the whole of the elementary phenomenon. By applying the relations valid for a monodisperse system, $\bar{\Phi}$ corresponds now to a mean value $\bar{\lambda}$ of the parameter whose definition depends

References p. 310

on the method of observation used, but is always related to one, or to several, moments of the distribution function.

(a) Let us consider, as an example, measurements of osmotic pressure. At zero concentration, one has, for a monodisperse system:

$$\lim_{c=0} \left(\frac{\pi}{c}\right) = RT/M$$

In the presence of a distribution $f(M)$ of molecular weights, one will find:

$$\lim_{c=0} \left(\frac{\pi}{c}\right) = RT \int_{M_1}^{M_2} M^{-1} f(M) \, \mathrm{d}M$$

to which corresponds a mean molecular weight M_n in such a manner that $M_n = \langle M_{-1} \rangle^{-1}$. By sedimentation equilibrium, one can obtain, according to the method of observation, either the weight average $M_w = \langle M_1 \rangle$, or the "$z$" average $M_z = \langle M_2 \rangle / \langle M_1 \rangle$.

(b) The results of light-scattering measurements in the case of a mixture of Gaussian coils, can be represented by a diagram such as that shown in Fig. 10, in which figure the different mean values that are calculable.

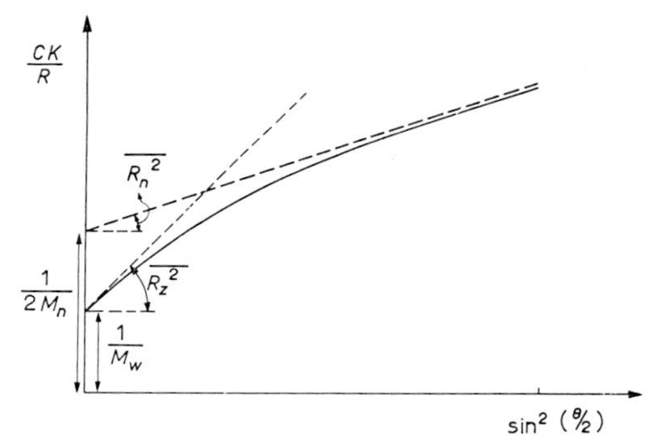

Fig. 10. Schematic diagram of the different averages obtained from light-scattering measurements on Gaussian coils.

(c) In a less direct manner the mean intrinsic viscosity $[\bar{\eta}]$ will correspond to an average M_η, by using the eqn. (3.9) in the form $[\bar{\eta}] = KM_\eta^a$. The position of M_η, by reference to the classical averages M_n, M_w, M_z depends on the value a.

(ii) Utilisation of mean values

The way in which the different moments of a distribution function $f(\lambda)$

are used depends, moreover, on the data one can obtain about its general behaviour. If the function $f(\lambda)$ is totally unknown, the comparison of these different averages can give nothing but a qualitative criterion of polydispersity. If on the contrary one knows *a priori* the form of $f(\lambda)$, it is possible, as a rule, to determine as many parameters of these functions as one has mean values. It is possible in this manner, for example, to make an analysis of mixtures of two or three components, within the limit of the precision in average determinations.

(b) Distribution curve

When certain methods are used, it can happen that φ depends, not only on λ, characteristic of molecular size, but also on a parameter α, which corresponds to experimental conditions. In the case of light-scattering, for example, the intensity diffused by a particle, the dimensions of which are not negligible compared to the wavelength, is a function at the same time of the mass (or the length) of the particle and of the angle of observation.

Likewise, in all phenomena related to translational Brownian movement (diffusion, sedimentation, electrophoresis) φ is a function not only of the size or the charge of the particle, but also of the abscissa and the time of observation. The measurable quantity Φ becomes a function of α, $\Phi(\alpha)$ being related to $f(\lambda)$ by an integral equation of the type:

$$\Phi(\alpha) = \int_{\alpha_1}^{\alpha_2} f(\lambda)\varphi(\lambda, \alpha)\, d\lambda \tag{4.1}$$

The resolution of this equation will solve the problem of polydispersity; setting aside the mathematical difficulties, this resolution is significant only if $\Phi(\alpha)$ is known with sufficient accuracy and in a range of values of α as widely extended as possible. We will not go into the details of the calculation of $f(\lambda)$. We will merely give some examples of its determination.

(a) When one sediments particles big enough to enable one to neglect their diffusion during the time of the experiment, there is then a one-to-one relation between the sedimentation constant and the abscissa X, that is to say between λ and α in the general notation used. Under these conditions (4.1) is directly integrable[19]. More precisely, one determines $f(\lambda)$ directly from $\Phi(\alpha)$, that is to say $f(s)$, from a concentration gradient dc/dx at each point of the cell (Fig. 11).

(b) When the diffusion is no longer negligible, it is necessary to develop an approximation method consisting of extrapolation to $t \to \infty$, the apparent distributions $f^*(s)$ being calculated at each time according to the method[20] *(a)*.

(c) From the measurement of Brownian diffusion one can determine $f(D)$

References p. 310

without any other assumptions by integration of (4.1) by means of the Fourier transformation[21].

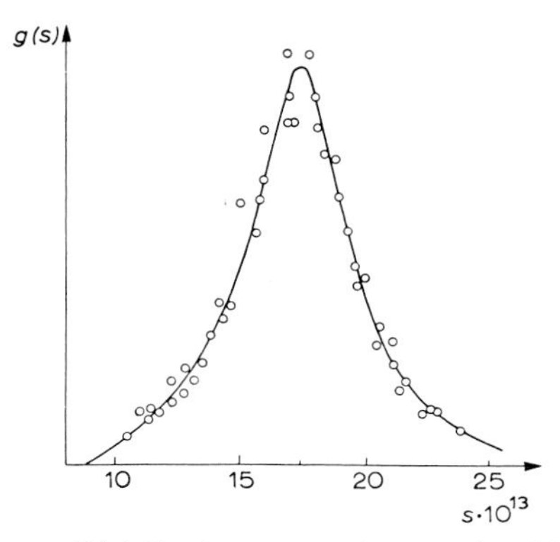

Fig. 11. s-Distribution curve of a sample of DNA.

This latter procedure can be extended to a large number of methods. Such calculations to determine $f(\lambda)$ may be applied to the measurements of light-scattered intensities as a function of the angle, or of intrinsic viscosities as a function of the shear rate, if in each case the parameter α varies in a sufficiently wide range of values[22,23].

5. Conclusions

It is a matter of fact that the statement above is superficial and incomplete; nevertheless it will enable the reader to understand the main point of methods leading to the determination of the mass and dimensions of macromolecules in solution.

One can now clearly see from what has been pointed out that this way of handling the problem can be extremely complicated, therefore it seems illusive to try to establish general rules which make it possible to proceed directly to the desired result.

We can, however, try to facilitate the systematic use of the methods which we have summarised, by making some complementary and simple remarks.

Remark 1

It is advisable, before all, to determine whether the given macromolecular solution is monodisperse or not, in relation to the mass and form.

(a) From a sedimentation diagram it is possible in general to obtain an answer. But it is necessary to point out that, because s is a function of the

mass and dimensions, the method does not, as a rule, permit one to determine whether the particles have the same mass and different dimensions or the same dimensions and different masses. In general, however, there is a simple relation between mass and dimensions and, in this case, there is only one type of polydispersity.

(b) One can also use as a test the comparison of the means M_n, M_w, M_z, obtained by the corresponding techniques. If, within experimental errors, these numbers are equal, the particles all have the same mass.

Remark 2

If the solution is not monodisperse, it is necessary to separate the various species that it contains. In multidisperse solutions this can be done completely. In polydisperse ones it can be done approximately, if one separates the mixture into thinner and thinner fractions containing macromolecules the masses of which (for example) are distributed between increasingly narrow limits. We have not studied here the "fractionation" procedures. It is known that the most commonly used methods are fractional precipitation and solubilization. Chromatography on a column is also more and more used.

Remark 3

Quite often one knows *a priori* whether the solution contains macromolecules of the rigid or flexible type. If, exceptionally, this is not so, one can apply the flow birefringence test (*cf.* section 3b, p. 298). Otherwise, if one changes the nature of the solvent, the interactions between the elements of the chain are modified and the chain swells up or shrivels. Then the value of $[\eta]$ changes, whereas, for a rigid particle it does not. The same effect is evidently observed in intermediate cases in which the macromolecule is a flexible chain wound on itself and maintained in this form by internal bonds.

Remark 4

Having established that a solution is monodisperse and that it contains macromolecules of a well-defined type, one may then use all the methods described in the preceding chapter.

Remark 5

Before concluding, one must not overlook a very important case, especially in biological substances, namely, macromolecules bearing ionisable groups. When these particles are dispersed in water, they are surrounded by a cloud of ions, the total charge of which is equal to the charge carried by the macro-ions.

Under these conditions high interactions occur between them and, for this reason, it is necessary to make measurements at extremely low concentrations if one wishes to extrapolate the results to zero concentration without making considerable errors.

Therefore it is recommended that experiments should be done with solutions containing a high concentration of small ions, by introducing, for example, sodium chloride into the solvent.

By this means, one considerably lowers the coulomb interactions and decreases at the same time the thickness of the double-layer of "counter-ions" and consequently the disturbances introduced by this cloud in the measurement of the hydrodynamic parameters. Likewise, under these conditions, one is in a better position to avoid certain troubles associated with interpretation of light-scattering measurements. It will always be useful to control these last by determining the value of the mass for various ionic strengths. If it remains constant, one will be certain that it has a significance beyond dispute.

Finally we note that, in the case of flexible molecules, although the mass measured should not depend on the ionic strength of the solution, this is not true of its dimensions. When the thread-like polyelectrolyte molecule is completely ionised, the charges it carries, by repelling each other, tend to separate the various elements of the chain from one another and the radius of gyration is thus increased. The introduction of electrolytes, such as NaCl, into the solution, weakens the repulsions and the gyration radius decreases considerably, which one perceives immediately from viscosimetry, light-scattering, sedimentation or Brownian diffusion.

We are well aware of the fact that, to make the contents of this paper as useful as possible, it would be necessary to add important further developments, which cannot be given in the space available. We hope, however, that we have at least been able to prepare the reader for a critical study of specialised books and for this reason we have tried to give, in the bibliography, a list of these which is as complete as possible.

Appendix A

FRICTIONAL COEFFICIENTS

(1) *t(p) for an ellipsoid*

$p > 1$ $$t(p) = \frac{p^{\frac{1}{3}}}{(p^2 - 1)^{\frac{1}{2}}} \ln p + (p^2 - 1)^{\frac{1}{2}}$$

$p < 1$ $$t(p) = \frac{p^{\frac{1}{3}}}{(1 - p^2)^{\frac{1}{2}}} \operatorname{arc\,tg} \frac{(1 - p^2)^{\frac{1}{2}}}{p}$$

(2) *r(p) for an ellipsoid*

$p > 1$ $$r(p) = \frac{3}{2} \frac{p^2}{p^4 - 1} \left[-1 + \frac{2p^2 - 1}{p(p^2 - 1)^{\frac{1}{2}}} \ln \frac{p + (p^2 - 1)^{\frac{1}{2}}}{p - (p^2 - 1)^{\frac{1}{2}}} \right]$$

$p < 1$ $$r(p) = \frac{3}{2} \frac{p^2}{1 - p^4} \left[1 + \frac{1 - 2p^2}{p(1 - p^2)^{\frac{1}{2}}} \operatorname{arc\,tg} \frac{(1 - p^2)^{\frac{1}{2}}}{p} \right]$$

(3) $\wedge (p)$

ellipsoïd $$\wedge (p) = \frac{p^2}{15} \frac{1}{\ln 2p - 1.5} + \frac{p^2}{5} \frac{1}{\ln 2p - 0.5} + \frac{14}{15}$$

cylinder $$\wedge (p) = \frac{p^2}{15} \frac{1}{\ln 2p - 1.8} + \frac{p^2}{5} \frac{1}{\log 2p - 0.8} + \frac{14}{15}$$

Appendix B

MAXWELL COEFFICIENTS

$$L_1 = \frac{4}{3} (1 - 2\alpha)$$

$$L_2 = \frac{4}{3} (1 + \alpha)$$

with

$$\alpha = \frac{1}{4(p^2 - 1)} \left[2p^2 + 4 \frac{3p}{\sqrt{p^2 - 1}} \ln \frac{p + \sqrt{p^2 - 1}}{p - \sqrt{p^2 - 1}} \right], \quad (p > 1)$$

$$\alpha = \frac{1}{2(1 - p^2)} \left[-p^2 - 2 + \frac{3p}{\sqrt{1 - p^2}} \operatorname{arc\,tg} \frac{\sqrt{1 - p^2}}{p} \right], \quad (p < 1)$$

Appendix C

NUMERICAL TABLES OF THE FUNCTIONS $t(p)$, $r(p)$, $\wedge(p)$ AND $\wedge t^3$ FOR AN ELLIPSOID OF REVOLUTION

(a) $p < 1$			(b) $p > 1$				
p	$t(p)$	$r(p)$	p	$t(p)$	$r(p)$	$\wedge(p)$	$\wedge t^3$
1	1.000	1.000	1	1.000	1	2.50	2.5
0.9	0.997	1.015	1.5	0.985	0.838	2.63	2.51
0.8	0.996	1.0156	2	0.958	0.664	2.91	2.56
0.7	0.989	0.998	3	0.900	0.428	3.68	2.68
0.6	0.977	0.996	4	0.846	0.294	4.66	2.82
0.5	0.960	0.883	5	0.802	0.216	5.81	3.0
0.4	0.932	0.776	6	0.761	0.169	7.10	3.13
0.3	0.889	0.530	8	0.698	0.106	10.10	3.43
0.2	0.817	0.444	10	0.648	0.0748	13.63	3.71
0.1	0.686	0.232	12	0.607	0.0608	17.76	3.98
0.05	0.561	0.117	15	0.559	0.0465	24.8	4.34
0.02	0.421	0.0471	20	0.501	0.02339	38.6	4.86
0.01	0.336	0.0235	25	0.458	0.0163	55.2	5.30
0.005	0.268	0.0118	30	0.424	0.0119	74.5	5.66
0.002	0.198	0.00471	40	0.375	0.00741	120.8	6.37
0.001	0.157	0.00235	50	0.339	0.00493	176.5	6.88
			60	0.312	0.00357	242.0	7.36
			80	0.273	0.00214	400.0	8.12
			100	0.246	0.00144	593.0	8.83
			125	0.221	0.000961	882	9.47
			150	0.202	0.000694	1222	10.07
			200	0.175	0.000412	2051	10.99
			300	0.143	0.000196	4278	12.49
			400	0.123	0.000116	7247	13.48
			500	0.109	0.0000765	10921	14.09
			600	0.0997	0.0000549	15216	
			700	0.0918	0.0000412	20250	
			800	0.0856	0.0000322	25880	
			900	0.0804	0.0000259	32200	
			1000	0.0760	0.0000213	39117	

BIBLIOGRAPHY

Measurements of particle dimensions in solution

[1] Ch. Sadron, *Progress in Biophysics*, Pergamon, London, 1953.
[2] H. A. Stuart, *Die Physik der Hochpolymeren*, Vol. 2, Springer, Berlin, 1953.
[3] A. Peterlin, Determination of Molecular Dimensions from Rheological Data, *Makromol. Chem.*, 34 (1959) 89.

Brownian movement and diffusion

[4] W. Jost, *Diffusion*, Academic Press, New York, 1952.
[5] J. Riseman and J. G. Kirkwood, *The Statistical Mechanical Theory of Irreversible Processes in Solutions of Macromolecules*, in F.A. Eirich, *Rheology*, Vol. I, Academic Press, New York, 1956.
[6] L. J. Gosting, *Adv. in Prot. Chem.*, 11 (1956) 429.
[7] S. de Groot, *J. chim. phys.*, 54 (1957) 851.

Flow birefringence

[8] A. Peterlin, *Streaming and Stress Birefringence*, in F.A. Eirich, (Ed.), *Rheology*, Vol. 1, Academic Press, New York, 1956.
[9] R. Cerf, La dynamique des solutions de macromolécules dans un champ de vitesses, *Adv. Polym. Sci.*, 1 (1959) 382.
[10] H. G. Jerrard, Theories of Streaming Double Refraction, *Chem. Rev.*, 59 (1959) 345.

Ultracentrifugation

[11] J. W. Williams *et al.*, The Theory of Sedimentation Analysis, *Chem. Rev.*, 58 (1958) 4, 715.
[12] H. K. Schachman, *Ultracentrifugation in Biochemistry*, Academic Press, New York, 1959.
[13] R. L. Baldwin and K. E. van Holde, Sedimentation of High Polymers, *Adv. in Polym. Sci.*, 1 (1960) 451.

Viscosity

[14] Ch. Sadron, *Dilute Solutions of Impenetrable Rigid Particles*, in *Flow Properties of Disperse Systems*, North Holland Publishing Company, Amsterdam, 1953.
[15] H. L. Frish and R. Simha, *The Viscosity of Colloidal Suspensions and Macromolecular Solutions*, in F.A. Eirich (Ed.), *Rheology*, Vol. 1, Academic Press, New York, 1956.

Light and X-rays scattering

[16] W. Heller, *Record of Chem. Progress*, 20 [4] (1959) 209.
[17] K. A. Stacey, *Light Scattering in Physical Chemistry*, Butterworth, London, 1956.
[18] A. Guinier and G. Fournet, *Small-Angle Scattering of X-rays*, Wiley, New York, 1955.

[19] W. W. BEEMAN *et al.*, *Size of Particles and Lattice Defects* in *Handbuch der Physik*, Vol. XXXII, Springer, Berlin, 1957.

See also

[20] J. T. EDSALL, *The Size, Shape and Hydration of Protein Molecules*, in *The Proteins*, Vol. 1B, Academic Press, New York, 1953.

[21] P. J. FLORY, *Principles of Polymer Chemistry*, Cornell University Press, Ithaca, 1953.

REFERENCES

[1] L. PAULING, R. C. COREY AND H. R. BRANSON, *Proc. Natl. Acad. Sci. U.S.*, 37 (1951) 205.
[2] P. DOTY, A. M. HOLTZER, J. H. BRADBURY AND E. R. BLOUT, *J. Am. Chem. Soc.*, 76 (1954) 4493; 78 (1956) 947.
[3] J. C. KENDREW, G. BODO, H. M. DINTZIS, R. G. PARRISH, H. WYCKOFF AND D. C. PHILLIPS, *Nature*, 181 (1958) 662.
[4] A. G. NASINI *et al.*, *Symp. Milan-Turin, La Ric. Scient. Suppl.*, (1955) 432.
[5] C. T. O. KONSKI AND A. J. HALTNER, *J. Am. Chem. Soc.*, 78 (1956) 3604;
B. BOEDTKER AND N. SIMMONS, *J. Am. Chem. Soc.*, 80 (1958) 2550.
[6] CH. SADRON, *Cahiers de Physique*, 12 (1942) 26.
[7] F. PERRIN, *J. Phys. Rad.*, 7 (1936) 1.
[8] L. G. LONGSWORTH, *J. Am. Chem. Soc.*, 69 (1947) 2510;
H. SVENSSON, *Acta Chem. Scand.*, 3 (1949) 1170;
M. DAUNE, L. FREUND AND G. SCHEIBLING, *J. chim. phys.*, 54 (1957) 924.
[9] H. BENOIT, *Ann. Phys.*, 6 (1951) 561.
[10] A. PETERLIN AND H. A. STUART, *Z. Phys.*, 112 (1939) 1.
[11] W. J. ARCHIBALD, *J. Phys. Coll. Chem.*, 51 (1947) 1204;
S. M. KLAINER AND G. KEGELES, *J. Phys. Chem.*, 59 (1955) 952.
[12] M. MESELSON, F. W. STAHL AND J. VINOGRAD, *Proc. Natl. Acad. Sci. U.S.*, 43 (1957) 581.
[13] R. SIMHA, *J. Phys. Chem.*, 44 (1940) 25.
[14] W. KUHN AND H. KUHN, *Helv. Chim. Acta*, 28 (1945) 97.
[15] P. MIE, *Ann. Phys.*, 25 [3] (1908) 771.
[16] R. CERF, *J. Polym. Sci.*, 12 (1954) 35; R. CERF, *J. chim. phys.*, 48 (1951) 59.
[17] CH. SADRON, *XIème Conseil de Chimie Solvay*, 1959.
[18] J. HERMANS AND J. J. HERMANS, *J. Phys. Chem.*, 62 (1958) 1543.
[19] R. SIGNER AND H. CROSS, *Helv. Chim. Acta*, 17 (1934) 726.
[20] J. W. WILLIAMS, R. L. BALDWIN, W. M. SAUNDERS AND P. G. SQUIRE, *J. Am. Chem. Soc.*, 74 (1952) 1542.
[21] M. DAUNE AND L. FREUND, *J. Polym. Sci.*, 23 (1957) 115;
L. FREUND AND M. DAUNE, *J. Polym. Sci.*, 29 (1958) 161.
[22] H. BENOIT AND G. WEILL, *Coll. Czech. Chem. Communs.*, 22 (1957) 35.
[23] V. LUZZATI, *Acta Cryst.*, 20 (1957) 33.

SUBJECT INDEX